Corrosion Inhibitors

J. I. Bregman

IIT RESEARCH INSTITUTE
ILLINOIS INSTITUTE OF TECHNOLOGY

Corrosion Inhibitors

THE MACMILLAN COMPANY, NEW YORK

COLLIER-MACMILLAN LIMITED, LONDON

First Printing

Library of Congress catalog card number: 63-18795

The Macmillan Company, New York
Collier-Macmillan Canada, Ltd., Toronto, Ontario

Printed in the United States of America

DESIGNED BY JOAN LAWS

Preface

For a long time now, it has been apparent that a need exists for a book on corrosion inhibitors used by industry for water and oil treatment. While a number of references to acid inhibitors can be found, a text to which plant engineers could turn for information on water and oil corrosion inhibitors has not been readily available. The substantial economic investment in these inhibitors by industry makes this text essential. This book is therefore being written to present both practical and theoretical information concerning corrosion inhibitors to those people who use them.

While a great deal of know-how exists on this subject, most of it is not available to the general public. The composition of inhibitors is a very jealously guarded trade secret. Many of the leading scientists in this field are affiliated with inhibitor suppliers, and thus the amount of information that they can publish is limited. I am in the unusual position of having considerable industrial inhibitor background, excellent contacts with inhibitor suppliers, and complete freedom of publication. These, then, are the factors that led to the decision to publish this book.

Corrosion problems are examined in this book as well as inhibitors for them. This method is used because the choice of an inhibitor is tied very closely to the particular corrosive condition. Inhibitors which are very satisfactory for one corrosion problem may be useless for another.

A large number of industrial concerns were kind enough to supply information concerning corrosion inhibitors. I am indebted to the following companies for supplying this information: Armour Industrial Chemical Company; Bradford Chemical Company; California Research Corporation; Dearborn Chemical Company; Dowell, Incorporated; E. F. Drew and Company, Incorporated; General Mills, Incorporated; Hagan Chemicals and Controls, Incorporated; Mutual Division, Allied Chemical and Dye Corporation; Nalco Chemical Company; Permutit Company, Pfaudler-Permutit, Incorporated; Philadelphia Quartz Company; Solvay Process Division, Allied Chemical and Dye Corporation; Tretolite Division, Petrolite Corporation; Universal Oil Products Company; and Visco Products, Nalco Chemical Company.

There are a number of pictures in this book illustrating various points, and for these I am indebted to the following contributors: Frank E. Clarke; Nalco Chemical Company; and Tretolite Division, Petrolite Corporation.

I am grateful to David B. Boies and Frank C. Martino for their reviews of the book and the many excellent suggestions they made for its improvement. I wish to thank Louise Busack Rokos for editing the rough copy. I am indebted to Armour Research Foundation for allowing me to publish this book and for supporting its preparation. Finally, I am deeply grateful to the large number of friends connected with various inhibitor suppliers who have given much encouragement and assistance in the preparation of this book. This attitude on their part truly represents a forward outlook and the industry is to be commended for it.

J. I. Bregman

Table of Contents

List of Figures and Tables   ix

List of Abbreviations   xi

1   Introduction   1

    Purpose of Book   1   *Selection of Inhibitors*   4   *Mechanisms*   6   *Method of Presentation*   16

2   Boiler-Water Treatment   19

    Literature   19   *Economics*   19   *The Problem*   20   *Inhibition*   35

3   Cooling Water—Cooling-Tower Systems   70

    Literature   71   *Economics*   72   *The Problem*   73   *Inhibition*   85

4   Cooling Water—Other Systems   126

    Internal Combustion Engines   126   Literature   127   Economics   128   The Problem   129   Inhibition   137   *Once-Through Systems*   153   Literature   153   Economics   154   The Problem   155   Inhibition   160   *Refrigerating Brines*   164   Economics and the Problem   164   Inhibition   166

5   Petroleum—Primary Production   175

    Literature   175   *Economics*   177   *The Problem*   180   *Inhibition*   191

6   Petroleum—Secondary Recovery   223

    Literature   224   *Economics*   225   *The Problem*   226   *Inhibition*   237

7   Petroleum—Refinery Product Problems   251

    Literature   252   *Economics*   253   *The Problem*   255   *Inhibition*   267

8   Petroleum—Storage and Transportation   285

    Literature   285   *Economics*   287   *The Problem*   289   *Inhibition*   298

Index of Authors   311

List of Figures and Tables

FIGURE

1-1	Polarization Diagram Where Anodic and Cathodic Polarizations Are Equal	11
1-2	Polarization Diagram Where Anodic Reaction Polarizes Slowly	12
1-3	Corrosion Process Under Cathodic Control	14
1-4	Corrosion Process Under Anodic Control	15
2-1	Oil Sludge Balls	23
2-2	Maximum $Ca(HCO_3)_2$ Concentration Which Can Be Maintained Without Deposition	43
2-3	Relationship Between pH and PO_4 Concentration in Terms of Prevention of Excess Caustic	51
3-1	Severe Localized Attack in a Refinery Heat Exchanger—Water Side	80
4-1	Corroded Diesel Cylinder Head	138
4-2	Diesel Locomotive Head Retainer After 793,000 Miles with Corrosion-Inhibitor Treatment	139
5-1	Damaged Equipment at an Illinois Producing Field	178
5-2	Corroded Tubing from an Illinois Producing Field	187
5-3	Oil Treater After Eight Years of Uninhibited Service at Rangely Field, Colorado	188
8-1	Corrosion in a Pipeline Ell Fitting	293

TABLE

2-1	Steam Purity	25
3-1	Cost Data for an Average Gulf Coast Cooling Tower	72
3-2	Cost Data for an Average Tower	73
3-3	A Comparison of Phenolic Compounds	90
4-1	Analysis of Domestic Waters	155
5-1	Relationship of Water Content to Corrosivity of Sweet Oil Wells	181
7-1	Yearly Chemical Cost	255

List of Abbreviations

Am. Chem. Soc. = American Chemical Society
Am. Inst. Mining Met. Engrs. Tech. Pub. = American Institute of Mining and Metallurgical Engineers Technical Publication
Am. Ry. Eng. Assoc. Bull. = American Railway Engineers Association Bulletin
Am. Soc. Refrig. Engr. = American Society of Refrigeration Engineers
Angenew. Chem. = Angenewandte Chemie
A.P.I. = American Petroleum Institute
Arch. Eisenhuettenw. = Archiv fuer das Eisenhuettenwesen
Arch. Metallk. = Archiv Metallkunde
A.S.M.E. = American Society of Mechanical Engineers
Automotive Inds. = Automotive Industry
Azerbaidzhan. Neft. Khoz. = Azerbaidzhanskol Neftyanoi Khozyaistvo
Belg. = Belgium
Bol. fac. ing. y agrimensure Montevideo = Boletin de la facultad de ingenieric y agrimensure Montevideo
Brit. Cast Iron Research Assoc. J. Research and Development = British Cast Iron Research Association Journal of Research and Development
British Pet. Magazine = British Petroleum Magazine
Bull. Assoc. Francaise Techniciens Petrole = Bulletin Association Francaise Techniciens Petrole
Bull. Centre Belge Etude Document. Eaux (Liege) = Bulletin du Centre Belge d'Etude et de Documentation des Eaux (Liege)
Calif. World Oil = California World Oil
Can. Chem. Processing = Canadian Chemical Processing
Can. J. Technol. = Canadian Journal of Technology
Chem. Absts. = Chemical Abstracts
Chem. and Ind. = Chemistry and Industry
Chem. Eng. = Chemical Engineering
Chem. Eng. News = Chemical and Engineering News
Chem. Listy = Chemicke Listy
Chem. Processing = Chemical Processing
Chem. Zentr. = Chemisches Zentralblatt
Chim. et Ind. (Paris) = Chimie et Industrie (Paris)
Civil Eng. = Civil Engineering
Corrosion and Matl. Prot. = Corrosion and Material Protection
Corrosion Eng. = Corrosion Engineer
Corrosion Prevent. and Control = Corrosion Prevention and Control
Corrosion Tech. = Corrosion Technology
Div. Petroleum Chem. = Division of Petroleum Chemistry
Doklady Akad. Nauk S.S.S.R. = Doklady Akademii Nauk S.S.S.R.
Elek. Stantsii = Elektricheskie Stantsii
Energietech. = Energietechnik
Eng. and Boiler House Rev. = Engineering and Boiler House Review
Fr. = France
Fuel Abstr. = Fuel Abstracts
Gas- u.Wasserfach = Das Gas und Wasserfach
Geol. Jahrb. = Geologisches Jahrbuch
Ger. = Germany
Gt. Brit. = Great Britain
Hydraulic Prob. = Hydraulic Problems
Ind. Eng. Chem. = Industrial and Engineering Chemistry
Ind. Refrig. = Industrial Refrigeration
Inds. Aliment. et Agr. (Paris) = Industries Alimentaires et Agricoles (Paris)
Ing. Ferroviaria = Ingegneria Ferroviaria
Inst. Heating Ventilating Engrs. = Institute of Heating and Ventilating Engineers
Izvest. Vysshikh Ucheb. Zavedenii = Izvestiya Vysshikh Uchebnykh Zavedenii

J. Am. Water Works Assoc. = *Journal of the American Water Works Association*
J. Appl. Chem. = *Journal of Applied Chemistry*
J. Australian Inst. Metals = *Journal of the Australian Institute of Metals*
J. Chem. Soc. = *Journal of the Chemical Society*
J. Coll. Sci. = *Journal of Colloid Science*
J. Electrochem. Soc. = *Journal of the Electrochemical Society*
Jernkontorets Ann. = *Jernkontorets Annales*
J. Gen. Chem. = *Journal of General Chemistry*
J. Inst. Fuel = *Journal of the Institute of Fuel*
J. Iron St. Inst. = *Journal of the Iron and Steel Institute*
J. Metals = *Journal of Metals*
J. New England Water Works Assoc. = *Journal of the New England Water Works Association*
J. Petrol. Tech. = *Journal of Petroleum Technology*
J. Phys. Chem. = *Journal of Physical Chemistry*
J. Proc. Am. Power Conf. = *Journal of the Proceedings of the American Power Conference*
J. Sci. Ind. Research = *Journal of Scientific and Industrial Research*
J. Tech. Phys. U.S.S.R. = *Journal of Technical Physics U.S.S.R.*
Khim. i Ind. = *Khimiya i Industriya*
Khim. i Khim. Tekhnol. = *Khimiya i Khimicheskaya Tekhnolojiya*
Khim. i Tekhn. Topliva i Masel = *Khimiya i Tekhnika Topliva i Masel*
Khim. Prom. = *Khimicheskaya Promishlennost'*
Korros. u. Metaleschutz = *Korrosion und Metaleschutz*
Latvijas PSR Zinatnu Akad. Vestis = *Latvijas PSR Zinatnu Akademijas Vestis*
Materialy po Geol. i Razrabotke Neft. Mestorozhdenii = *Materialy po Geologii i Razrabotke Neftyanykh*
                                                                    Mestorozhdenii Azerbaidzhana
Mech. Eng. = *Mechanical Engineering*
Metallurg. ital. = *Metallurgia italiana*
Mining Mag. = *Mining Magazine*
Mitt. Ver. Grosskesselbesitzer = *Mitteilungen Verein Grosskesselbesitzer*
Modern Power and Eng. = *Modern Power and Engineering*
Modern Railroads Ind. = *Modern Railroads Industry*
N.A.C.E. = National Association of Corrosion Engineers
Natl. Eng. = *National Engineer*
Oil Gas J. = *Oil and Gas Journal*
Oil in Can. = *Oil in Canada*
Paint Manuf. = *Paint Manufacturing*
Pet. Engr. = *Petroleum Engineering*
Petrochemical Ind. = *Petrochemical Industry*
Petroleum Engr. = *Petroleum Engineer*
Power Eng. = *Power Engineering*
Power Plant Eng. = *Power Plant Engineering*
Prace Inst. Naft. = *Prace Instytutu Naftowego*
Proc. Am. Pet. Inst. = *Proceedings of the American Petroleum Institute*
Proc. Am. Power Conf. = *Proceedings of the American Power Conference*
Proc. Am. Soc. for Testing Materials = *Proceedings of the American Society for Testing Materials*
Proc. Am. Water Conf. Engr. Soc. W. Pa. = *Proceedings of the American Water Conference, Engineering*
                                                        Society of Western Pennsylvania
Proc. A.S.T.M. = *Proceedings of the American Society for Testing Materials*
Proc. Midwest Power Conf. = *Proceedings of the Midwest Power Conference*
Proc. Natl. Conf. Instr. Methods Anal. = *Proceedings of the National Conference on Instrumental Methods*
                                                        of Analysis
Proc. Sixth Meeting Intern. Comm. Electrochem. Thermodynamics and Kinet. = *Proceedings of the Sixth*
                                                        Meeting of the Interna-
                                                        tional Committee on Elec-
                                                        trochemistry, Thermody-
                                                        namics and Kinetics

Product Eng. = *Product Engineering*
Public Health Repts. = *Public Health Reports*
Radioisotopes Sci. Research, Proc. Intl. Conf., Paris I = *Radioisotopes Scientific Research, Proceedings of the International Conference, Paris I*
Referat. Zhur. Khim. = *Referativnii Zhurnal Khimii*
Rev. Inst. Franc. Petrole et Ann. Combustibles Liquides = *Revue de l'Institut Francais du Petrole et Annales des Combustibles Liquides*
Rev. Met. = *Revue Metallurgie*
Ry. Age = *Railway Age*
Ry. Eng. and Maintenance = *Railway Engineering and Maintenance*
Ry. Eng. Assoc. Bull. = *Railway Engineers Association Bulletin*
Ry. Locomotives and Cars = *Railway Locomotives and Cars*
Ry. Track and Structures = *Railway Track and Structures*
S. African Ind. Chemist = *South African Industrial Chemist*
Sbornik, Komitet po Korrozii i Zashchite Metal, Vsesoyuz. Sovet. Nauch.—Tekh. Obshchestv = *Sbornik, Komitet po Korrozii i Zashchite Metal, Vsesoyuznyi Sovet. Nauchno—Tekhnicheskii Obshchestv*
Sbornik, Stud. Rabot Azerbaidzhan. Ind. Inst. = *Sbornik, Studentecheskikh Rabot Azerbaidzhanskojo Industrial'noso Instuta*
S.C.I. = Society of Chemical Industry
Soc. Chem. Ind. = Society of Chemical Industry
Southern Power and Ind. = *Southern Power and Industry*
Swed. = Sweden
Tech. Mitt. = *Technische Mitteilungen*
Tek. Tidskr. = *Teknisk Tidskrift*
Trans. Am. Inst. Mining Met. Engrs. = *Transactions of the American Institute of Mining and Metallurgical Engineers*
Trans. Am. Soc. Mech. Engrs. = *Transactions of the American Society of Mechanical Engineers*
Trans. A.S.M.E. = *Transactions of the American Society of Mechanical Engineers*
Trans. Electrochem. Soc. = *Transactions of the Electrochemical Society*
Trans. Faraday Soc. = *Transactions of the Faraday Society*
Trans. Inst. Chem. Engrs. (London) = *Transactions of the Institute of Chemical Engineers (London)*
Trans. Soc. Naval Architects and Marine Engrs. = *Transactions of the Society of Naval Architects and Marine Engineers*
Trudy Moskov. Energet. Inst. = *Trudy Moskovskogo Energeticheskogo Instituta*
Trudy Novocherkassk. Politekh. Inst. = *Trudy Novocherkasskogo Politekhnicheskogo Instituta im. Sergo Ordzhonikidze*
Trudy Ural. Politekh. Inst. im. S. M. Kirova = *Trudy Ural'skogo Politekhnicheskogo Instituta im. S. M. Kirova*
U.S. Bur. Mines, Inform. Circ. = *United States Bureau of Mines, Information Circular*
Vnutrikotlovye Fiz. -Khim. Protsessy, Akad. Nauk S.S.S.R., Energet. Inst. im. G. M. Krzhizhanovskogo = *Vnutrikotlovye Fiziko Khimicheskii Protsessy, Akademiya Nauk S.S.S.R., Energeticheskii Institut imeni G. M. Krzhizhanovskogo*
Vodosnabzhenie i Sanit. Tekh. = *Vodosnabzhenie i Sanitarnaya Tekhnika*
Werkstoffe u. Korr. = *Werkstoffe und Korrosion*
Zavodskaya Lab. = *Zavodskaya Laboratoriya*
Z. Elektrochem. = *Zeitschrift Elektrochemie*
Zhur. Fiz. Khim. = *Zhurnal Fizicheskoi Khimii*
Zhur. Priklad. Khim. = *Zhurnal Prikladnoi Khimii*

1

Introduction

PURPOSE OF BOOK

Considerable use is made today of corrosion inhibitors, and plant operations of vast magnitudes are dependent upon their successful application. Nevertheless, the compositions of most inhibitors are hidden under trade names, and their methods of application as well as the mechanisms by which they function are not clear. This book has been written for the purpose of bringing information concerning these aspects of corrosion inhibitors to their users. There exists a strong need for an explanation so that plant engineers who are faced with the responsibility of selecting and using inhibitors will have background knowledge. Although this book has been written primarily for these plant engineers, it may be of value to chemical engineers who are interested in corrosion inhibition as a process and to chemists charged with the task of developing new and better inhibitors. Detailed references are included as an aid to the reader.

There are a number of other methods used on large scales for combatting corrosion. These include cathodic protection, coatings, equipment design, changes in metallurgy, and so on. In many situations the use of one or more of these measures is preferable to the use of inhibitors. The economics, the nature and use of the liquid to be inhibited, and the design of the system all must be considered in making a decision as to which type of protective approach to take. Many of the noninhibitor approaches are mentioned throughout this book in the cases of specific corrosive situations where such approaches may be used either as alternate or supplementary measures.

The extent of corrosion-inhibitor usage has increased manifoldly during the past ten years. The field of inhibitors for corrosion by water in aqueous and oil systems is the one covered in this book. That field alone has grown from a few known chemicals for use in cooling and boiler waters to a large number of complex and highly effective formulations for the solution of multimetal corrosion problems in a vast new area of applications. In addition, these formulations have been developed to embrace the solution of a number of other difficulties such as scaling or microbiological problems which go hand in hand with corrosion problems and increase their intensities.

While the dollar volume of corrosion inhibitors sold by individual suppliers is a closely guarded secret, a reasonable estimate of the total amount of money spent annually in the United States for inhibitors for the applications described in this book would be $50 million. The magnitude of industrial corrosion problems that still need solution by inhibitors is so great that this dollar figure could easily double or triple in the next decade. Another interesting figure to consider is the amount of money spent on corrosion inhibitors by individual plants. Here again, the figures are closely guarded, but it is generally acknowledged that certain of the largest oil refineries and government atomic energy installations may expend as much as $100,000 apiece annually. It thus becomes apparent that in the case of the largest users, at the very least, a better knowledge of what these materials are and how they function could result in considerable dollar savings.

The fact that so little is known about corrosion inhibitors by their average user is due to a peculiar use condition. Corrosion inhibition is never a process in itself, but rather is always incidental to some other process. For example, in a refinery a series of heat exchangers may be part of a specific conversion process. In these exchangers hot oil on one side is cooled by water on the other. The use of inhibitors generally does not come into the picture until severe corrosion begins to show on either side. At this point it becomes urgent that inhibitors be promptly applied so as to prevent failure and shutdown. The plant engineer concerned with the particular unit process generally has little or no background in corrosion inhibition and must call in a reputable inhibitor supplier to help him out of the immediate crisis. This book is in no way intended to supplant the outside consultant. It is designed, however, to give the engineer sufficient background in corrosion inhibition so that he may recognize the problem earlier, understand it better, and make more efficient use of the inhibitors. Most inhibitor suppliers will verify the fact that a large percentage of the problems which occur when inhibitors are used come about because of the failure of plant personnel to follow proper application procedures. A better working knowledge of corrosion inhibitors would go a long way toward minimizing this difficulty.

The utility of this book for chemists seeking to develop new inhibitors was mentioned earlier. A large number of laboratories are devoted to the development of effective corrosion inhibitors for specific problems, and a number of others are seeking possible corrosion-inhibition applications for specific chemicals. One of the objectives of this book is to ease the lot of these laboratories by presenting a detailed picture of inhibitors used for specific problems with a thorough bibliography for each of these problems. This bibliography may be of considerable background and reference value to researchers in these laboratories and may serve to stimulate new ideas for further progress in these areas.

Finally, we hope that the information presented in this book may prove to be of value to those students and professors in universities who are interested in the mechanism of corrosion inhibition and who are seeking to increase our knowledge of this phenomenon.

Because of the variety of corrosion-inhibitor applications in use today, the scope of this book was necessarily limited to a specific area. Such large-scale uses as inhibitors for acids or vapor-phase corrosion inhibitors have been bypassed because there already exists a considerable body of knowledge concerning them. Instead, the field of corrosion inhibitors for problems caused by water in certain aqueous and petroleum systems has been selected. These specific systems form a cohesive whole and have many common conditions. In addition, many industrial plants will be plagued by more than one of these corrosion problems at the same time. Further, related problems such as scaling, foaming, and bacterial attack have been discussed wherever they contribute to the corrosion problems or interfere with their solutions. In practice, corrosion-inhibitor formulations are carefully made to solve these problems also and cannot be ignored in a study of inhibitors.

SELECTION OF INHIBITORS

The proper selection of corrosion inhibitors for specific problems is based on a common-sense approach. Nevertheless, improper selection procedures are frequently employed with the result that inhibitors which are eminently satisfactory for certain applications are utilized for others where they are relatively valueless. For this reason, a brief discussion of factors which must be considered follows.

First of all, it must be clearly understood that no universal corrosion inhibitor exists. Each inhibitor must be tailored to the specific corrosion problem that needs solution. Inhibitors that are valuable for some cooling-water corrosion problems, for example, can actually be harmful to other cooling waters under certain circumstances. While the use of inhibitors for some types of corrosion can be similar to others, this similarity must be treated as a coincidence. Even within one category of corrosion problem, a change in some of the factors affecting the system, such as pH and hardness content of the water, can result in the need for a new inhibitor or else for a new method of using the old inhibitor. Considerable economic damage has been done to many industrial systems by careless extrapolation from one system to another.

The first step in the development of a corrosion inhibitor for a specific system is a close study of the system itself. This study will initially involve a field examination of the problem at first hand. When possible, several units having the same problem should be examined rather than just one. The nature of the corrosion, the amount, and the location must be examined. All factors in the system which could have a bearing on it must be studied. This investigation includes such things as the flow diagram of the system, the materials of construction and their juxtaposition with regard to each other, the composition and physical properties of the fluid and any gaseous or solid particles that may be present with it, the temperature conditions, the time the system operated, the composition of the corrosion product, the presence of any other concomitant problems such as scaling or bacteria, the flow conditions, the type of operation (intermittent, hot-cold), the heat transfer surfaces, and the presence of corrosion inhibitors or additives for other purposes. The peculiarities associated with the particular type of corrosion encountered can be directly related to any one or more of these factors. The corrosion should further be examined as a function of time rather than just at one particular occasion. Generally, the corrosion engineer who has examined a corroded system in detail will have a good impression of the causes and, incidentally, a detailed understanding of the operation of the system.

The next step in the inhibitor development is to bring the corrosion problem into the laboratory. It is frequently difficult or impossible to create a small laboratory model of the field problem, and certain of the field conditions may not lend themselves to duplication. Nevertheless, by the use of a good deal of ingenuity laboratory conditions can usually be set up wherein most or all of the corrosive conditions are established in the same relationship to each other that they have in the field problem. A failure at this point to bring the critical corrosive conditions into the experiment will negate the value of all subsequent work. The success or failure of this part becomes apparent when the "blank" is run. The corrosion must be like that encountered in the field problem. The nature (i.e., general *vs.* pitting), the location, and the corrosion-product composition should correspond very closely. The intensity must generally be considerably greater in the laboratory test, since it is desired to establish the corrosion in as short a period of time as a day or two, whereas in the field weeks or months may be required for an appreciable amount to develop. At this point, some of the corrosive factors may be carefully varied so as to produce the desired intensity, while maintaining the same basic type of corrosion. Finally, the blank must be reproducible and the test itself must be fairly simple to conduct so that it may lend itself to routine evaluation of inhibitors. At this point, the problem has been brought into the laboratory and, in many cases, the most difficult part has been solved.

The next step is the development of an inhibitor. This procedure will vary considerably depending upon the background of the investigator. A novice may start by setting up an elaborate series of screening tests to evaluate various classes of inhibitors in the hope of finding some which will show promise. A skilled investigator will apply his knowledge of the mechanism by which inhibitors function and, perhaps more important, his practical background and experience as to which types of inhibitors are known to function under related corrosive conditions. In the case of both investigators, not only will established inhibitors be screened but also new materials which might be expected to be interesting on a theoretical basis. Eventually certain classes of materials will emerge as the favored ones. At this point more elaborate and intensive tests will be conducted within those classes to determine which are the preferred chemicals. The testing can become much complicated by the need for a combination of inhibitors to protect the various types of metals present.

After developing an effective combination, there are still other factors that must be evaluated. What are the conditions of pH and concentration at which these materials function? How can they be suitably solubilized or made compatible with each other? Does one affect another? What about the other detrimental factors such as scaling or foaming—must other materials be added to combat these? Are the inhibitors dangerous; i.e., do they lose their effectiveness and become aggressive below certain concentrations? How are they affected by drastic changes in the corrosive components? All these questions and many more must be answered before the inhibitor development proceeds to the next stage.

It is necessary to evaluate certain other factors which may have little or nothing to do with the inhibitor performance. First and foremost is the cost. An inhibitor that has more than a certain unit cost or else a cost $\times$ dosage figure may be unusable in the system. It may have to meet and pass certain government specifications. It must lend itself to certain feeding techniques. A rapid test for inhibitor concentration may necessarily be developed. It must not promote foaming and may require a certain color. All these specifications and many others may have to be passed before the inhibitor is considered usable, regardless of its corrosion-inhibiting abilities.

The inhibitor formulation is then ready for field testing. A series of field tests that are typical of the problem should be set up. Close control of inhibitor application and a good evaluation of field performance must be carried out. Whenever possible, the inhibitor should be evaluated side by side with competitive products. A careful study of the results of these field tests will determine whether the inhibitor is ready for general use or whether it must be returned to the laboratory for additional work.

This lengthy procedure which is required for the development and the use of a good corrosion inhibitor explains why most inhibitors are developed and sold by specialists in that field. Unless an industrial concern uses inhibitors on a very large scale, it will generally prefer to deal with inhibitor suppliers rather than develop its own materials.

MECHANISMS

It is obviously impossible to discuss corrosion and corrosion inhibition without some consideration of the basic mechanisms involved in each.

There is no general theory of corrosion or of inhibition which is applicable to all situations. The corrosion mechanism can vary considerably depending on the corrosive factors that are present. Similarly, the mechanism of inhibition will vary depending on the chemical nature of the inhibitor and the factors causing corrosion. For this reason, we have chosen to discuss theoretical concepts of corrosion and inhibition in each of the chapters on specific types of corrosion. In this way mechanisms can be directly related to specific situations and a more realistic picture can be obtained.

There are certain generalities concerning corrosion and inhibition mechanisms which can, however, be mentioned at this time. A few basic concepts will be introduced so that as the reader comes across references to them or to specific terms connected with them he will at least have a sense of familiarity.

Let us first consider some of the generally accepted basic facts concerning the mechanism of corrosion in water. Corrosion in this case is generally agreed to be an electrochemical process. The theory states that the corrosion occurs at anodic points on the surface where iron goes into solution as follows:

$$Fe \rightarrow Fe^{++} + 2e^- . \qquad [1\text{-}1]$$

In order to balance this reaction and use the electrons which are left in the metal, a reaction occurs at the nearest cathodic point as follows:

$$2H^+ + 2e^- \rightarrow 2H^0 , \qquad [1\text{-}2]$$

and

$$H^0 + H^0 \rightarrow H_2 . \qquad [1\text{-}3]$$

Hydrogen ions from water are converted into hydrogen atoms by utilization of the electrons left behind by the anodic reaction. The hydrogen atoms then combine into a hydrogen molecule at the surface.

These cathodic reactions are all predicated upon the reduction of hydrogen ions. This reduction will occur in acidic solutions. As the solution becomes neutral, however, the concentration of hydrogen ions decreases sharply and the predominant cathodic reaction then becomes one of the conversion of oxygen to hydroxyl ions:

$$\tfrac{1}{2}O_2 + H_2O + 2e^- \rightarrow 2OH^- . \qquad [1\text{-}4]$$

In addition to these basic reactions, certain other reactions can develop. Thus, if the water is neutral or alkaline, the ferrous ions that were dissolved at the anode will react with the hydroxyl ions to precipitate ferrous hydroxide either at the surface or near it in solution:

$$Fe^{++} + 2OH^- \rightarrow Fe(OH)_2 . \qquad [1\text{-}5]$$

In most cases there is sufficient oxygen in the water to oxidize the ferrous hydroxide to ferric hydroxide:

$$2Fe(OH)_2 + \tfrac{1}{2}O_2 + H_2O \rightarrow 2Fe(OH)_3 . \qquad [1\text{-}6]$$

Ferric hydroxide is actually a hydrated ferric oxide. This oxide is the brownish material found at or near the surface of iron that is corroding in water. Upon air drying it is converted to ferric oxide or what is commonly called rust.

When chloride ions are present in the water, the total corrosion process can be pictured in terms of ferrous chloride being formed at the anode and sodium hydroxide at the cathode. These two products will then meet and react to form ferrous hydroxide and sodium chloride. The ferrous hydroxide is then oxidized.

A very interesting phenomenon can occur at the cathode which will tend to stifle the cathodic reaction and consequently force the anodic reaction to slow down and stop. This phenomenon is the formation of a protective layer of hydrogen atoms over the cathode, preventing hydrogen ions from reaching the electrons that are at the metal surface. It is also known as *polarization*. Occurrence at the cathode is termed *cathodic polarization,* while a corrosion-stifling occurrence at the anode would be *anodic polarization.* In actual practice, however, the hydrogen atoms may either react with each other to form hydrogen gas molecules (as in Equation 1-3) and depart from the surface, or else the protective film will be destroyed by the dissolved oxygen to form water:

$$2H^0 + \tfrac{1}{2}O_2 \rightarrow H_2O . \qquad [1\text{-}7]$$

In the latter case the oxygen is said to have *depolarizing* action.

The discussion thus far has been limited to corrosion where only one metal is present. Frequently two or more different metals will be found in a corroding system. If they are isolated from each other, their only effect on each other will be that of corrosion products of one that come in contact with the other. If the metals are in mechanical contact an electrochemical corrosion system is set up. The more electropositive metal, i.e., the one that dissolves the most readily, becomes the anode and the other one becomes the cathode. One metal is thus corroded while the other, the more noble metal, remains intact. An example of this process would be an iron-copper couple where the iron corrodes at the area of contact while the copper remains essentially untouched.

The discussion of corrosion thus far has been confined to general corrosion. Localized or pitting corrosion is an extremely dangerous form of attack that can lead to severe failures in a short period of time. A number of examples of this corrosion will be discussed in great detail in various sections of this book. For many reasons, specific points on a metal surface may be especially prone to attack. In this case the anodic corrosion is concentrated in one small area instead of a wider and more shallow area and will penetrate through the metal very rapidly in the form of a small pit.

For the present, it suffices to consider pitting in terms of the cathodic and anodic mechanisms already discussed. If the anodic area is large, the corrosion will be spread all over it and a low-corrosion rate, general type of attack will ensue. However when the anodic area is very small and the cathodic area is very large, a considerable amount of attack will be concentrated on the small anodic area. This attack will result in rapid deep penetration of the metal leading to the formation of pits. There are many circumstances which can bring about this type of attack, e.g., galvanic corrosion, deposits, mill scale, stresses, and local concentration cells. All these areas will be explored in more detail later in this book.

Many of the factors that constitute the chemical and physical environment of the system will have a profound effect upon the nature of the corrosion and its intensity. For example, in the case of steel, the more acidic the solution is, the more intense the corrosion will become. As the solution becomes slightly alkaline, the corrosion continues to drop and a natural inhibition sets in. Continuation of the pH increase, however, will lead to a situation where another phenomenon known as *caustic cracking* sets in with catastrophic results.

Generally, an increase in dissolved solids content of water will mean an increase in corrosion rate. Water is the electrolyte in an electrolytic cell envisioned by the electrochemical theory of corrosion. As the dissolved solids content increases, the conductivity of the electrolyte will increase, thus favoring a speedup of the electrode reactions. In addition, the dissolved ions can penetrate the protective coating formed by corrosion product or inhibitor on the metal and cause it to be loose and nonadhering. The chloride anion is especially prone to this penetration probably because of its small size and great mobility.

Rates of corrosion reactions will increase rapidly with temperature in a manner similar to that of other chemical reactions. In addition, the diffusion of oxygen and the conductivity of the solution both will be increased. Each of these factors will cause more rapid corrosion. On the other hand, as the temperature approaches the boiling point of water, the rapid decrease in oxygen solubility will be a mitigating factor. When scale builds up on a heat transfer surface, thus causing local overheating of the metal, the chance of localized failures at the points of overheating will increase.

The water velocity will have an effect. Generally, stagnant conditions are bad in that they lead to formation of local cells. A slow flow rate seems to be the most desirable from a protective point of view. As the flow rate increases, however, corrosion usually increases with it. This increase occurs because a fresh supply of oxygen is continually being fed to the metal surface, while at the same time protective films are being swept or torn away.

Many other factors, such as the presence of certain gases in the water, localized deposits or scales, and bacterial growth can contribute to accelerated corrosion. The facts cited in these last few paragraphs make clear the reasons that all details concerning a specific corrosive system must be known if the corrosion in that system is to be brought into the laboratory and successfully overcome.

The term *corrosion inhibitors* as used in this book denotes chemicals that are added to the liquid phase in order to bring about corrosion inhibition. While the mechanism of inhibition by specific chemicals in specific corrosive systems will be discussed later in appropriate locations in this book, there are a few generalized terms that will be explained here.

Anodic inhibitors are those chemicals that function by stifling the reaction at the anode. The term *anodic polarization* is frequently used to describe their action. Generally, they function by reacting with the initially formed corrosion product such as the ferrous ions from Equation 1-1 and by forming an extremely insoluble, tightly adhering film right on the metal surface. This precipitate prevents any more of the corrosive solution from coming into contact with the metal surface and thus ends the dissolution of the metal.

Cathodic inhibitors, by contrast, stifle the cathodic reaction. A discussion was given earlier of cathodic polarization by a film of hydrogen atoms. Divalent cations such as zinc or calcium are cathodic inhibitors since they can react with the hydroxyl anions from Equation 1-4 and

form precipitates which cover the cathodic areas and prevent the cathodic reaction from continuing. These cathodic inhibitors are generally much less effective than anodic inhibitors. The precipitate formed
is not as insoluble and it does not bond to the metal surface as tightly.
In addition, the mechanism of corrosion prevention is indirect, whereas
the anodic inhibitors directly prevented the metal from corroding.

   The term *polarization* has been used and the current-potential relationships in corrosion cells have been suggested. It would be worth while
at this point to pursue the subject further. In the case of the coupling of
dissimilar metals there is a difference in electrochemical potential between the two. This difference is the driving force for the corrosion

FIGURE 1-1. Polarization Diagram Where Anodic and Cathodic Polar-
izations Are Equal

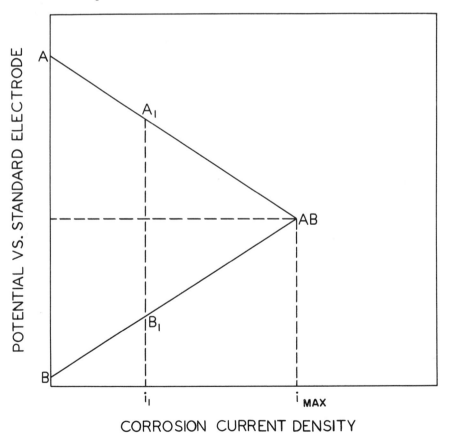

reaction. In a similar manner, a difference in potential exists between the anodic and cathodic areas on the same metal when it is the only one in the system. This potential difference is termed *corrosion potential*. The current that flows between the anode and the cathode during corrosion is termed *corrosion current*.

Figure 1-1 serves to illustrate idealized current-potential relationships. On the vertical axis, which denotes the potential with relation to a standard electrode, A is the potential of the cathode, while B is the potential of the anode. The distance from A to B is the total potential difference. No current flows at this value. As current begins to flow, the potential difference decreases, so that at a corrosion current density of i_1, for example, the actual potential difference between the cathode and

FIGURE 1-2.   Polarization Diagram Where Anodic Reaction Polarizes Slowly

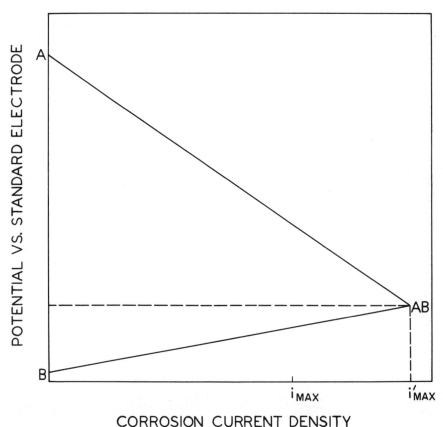

CORROSION CURRENT DENSITY

the anode is presented by the distance A_1 to B_1. The corrosion current value of i_{max} is the current at the maximum rate of attack, a point at which the potential difference has effectively vanished. This potential value is indicated by the term AB. The curves $A–AB$ and $B–AB$ are termed the *cathodic polarization curve* and the *anodic polarization curve,* respectively.

Several interesting things become apparent from the idealized polarization diagram shown in Figure 1-1. In that diagram, the cathodic and anodic polarization curves proceeded at the same rate. If one of them was to proceed at a slower rate, due to rapid removal of the corrosion product by a high liquid velocity, then the point AB would come at a higher corrosion current density. The result is that the corrosion rate increases to a degree proportional to the increased current density. Figure 1-2 illustrates a relationship of this type. The distance from i'_{max} to i_{max} is the increase in corrosion current. It is also apparent that another polarization diagram variation of Figure 1-1 could have been drawn where the cathodic polarization slope would have been less and the corrosion would have increased for that reason.

Another variation that becomes readily apparent from a study of polarization diagrams is that a rapid polarization of the anode or of the cathode will slow down the corrosion rate and cut down the corrosion current. Examples of this effect are given in Figures 1-3 and 1-4. In Figure 1-3 there is a rapid cathodic polarization leading to the small corrosion current i''_{max}. This corrosion reaction is said to be under cathodic control; i.e., a rapid polarization of the cathode cuts down the corrosion rate. Figure 1-4 shows anodic control; i.e., a rapid polarization at the anode is the factor that reduces the corrosion.

A logical question at this point is one regarding the mechanisms by which corrosion inhibitors can function as anodic or cathodic inhibitors. Some discussion has already been presented. In the ensuing chapters, specific types of inhibitors will be examined for the manner in which they function. It will become apparent that inorganic inhibitors in aqueous systems will function mainly by stifling the reaction at either the anode or the cathode. This method of inhibition or polarization of the electrode reaction lends itself to explanation by using polarization curves.

The discussion thus far has dealt with inorganic inhibitors in aqueous solutions. Classification of these materials as anodic or cathodic inhibitors becomes simplified by the fact that they will enter into some reaction which will be primarily directed toward either the anode or the

FIGURE 1-3. Corrosion Process Under Cathodic Control

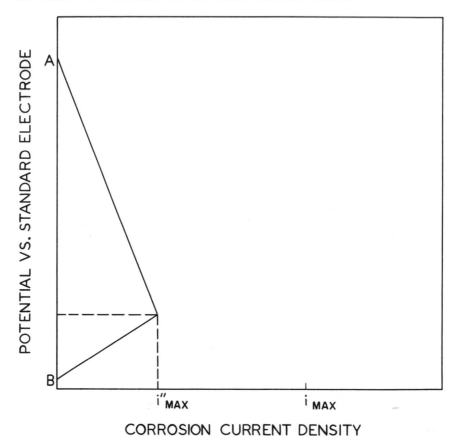

cathode and will halt the reaction there. The situation is quite different
with a number of organic high-molecular-weight inhibitors, especially
in systems containing hydrocarbons. Later a theory of inhibition for
these materials will be developed that will depend upon a "film-
forming," multilayer effect. The theory will postulate that there is some
chemical bond between the polar group of the organic inhibitor and the
metal surface, which is formed at either the cathode or the anode. The
balance of the organic inhibitor lies down on the metal surface and
covers it with a protective film. Attached to the oleophillic end of the
organic molecule is a layer of oil which is deposited on top of the organic
film. The corrosive materials in the aqueous phase are thus prevented

from getting to the metal surface by two layers: one of inhibitor and one of oil. With this mechanism the terms "anodic" or "cathodic polarization" mean very little. The protective film is the key to the inhibition.

The method of corrosion-rate measurement is worth noting. The primary concern in corrosion is not necessarily the weight of corrosion product developed. This amount can vary widely depending upon the nature and the size of the system. It is, instead, the thickness of metal that has disappeared, since this depth is a measure of how close the metal has come to penetration by the liquid; i.e., the development of holes, or failure. For this reason corrosion rates are usually described in terms of thickness per unit time. For example, *inches per year* (ipy) or *mils* (0.001 in.) *per year* (mpy) are the most commonly used American terms.

FIGURE 1-4. Corrosion Process Under Anodic Control

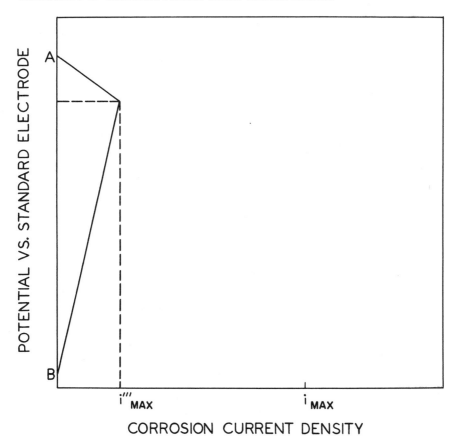

The values of mpy or ipy are average figures calculated for the entire metal under observation. They make no allowance for localized attack. Here the over-all corrosion rate can be very low, but the attack at a specific point can be highly concentrated and lead to a very rapid failure. For this reason the location, the number, and the depth of pits becomes very important.

METHOD OF PRESENTATION

A great deal of thought has been given to the contents and layout of this book. In the past, treatises on inhibitors have followed certain basic patterns. The majority have been restricted to acid corrosion with emphasis on possible theories of inhibition. Other books have been simply a collection of papers published in a specific area. In still others, selected authors have discussed specific topics. None of these approaches fits the purpose of this book, which is essentially to teach plant engineers what they should know about the inhibitors that they must use. Questions which need answering are

"What causes the corrosion in my system?"
"What types of inhibitors should I use and why?"
"How should I use them?"
"What is their mechanism of inhibition?"
"Where can I find more information on my particular problem?"

This book attempts to provide answers to these questions for the majority of water-treatment applications in use in industry today.

We have decided to have a series of chapters, each of which would deal with a specific phase of commercial industrial inhibitor usage. To make the book of the most possible value to plant engineers, the areas chosen have been water-treatment areas where considerable volumes of inhibitors are used today. A large amount of space is devoted to the petroleum industry, since the corrosion problems that lend themselves to prevention by inhibitors are invariably caused by the presence of water in the oil. Using these principles as a guide, the chapters that follow will be devoted to the following subjects:

Chapter 2: Boiler-water treatment
Chapter 3: Cooling water—cooling-tower systems
Chapter 4: Cooling water—other systems
Chapter 5: Petroleum—primary production
Chapter 6: Petroleum—secondary recovery
Chapter 7: Petroleum—refinery product problems
Chapter 8: Petroleum—storage and transportation

Boiler-water treatment, the classical and best known use of aqueous corrosion inhibitors, is reviewed first. The next two chapters are devoted to cooling waters. A variety of applications comes to mind here. The first of these chapters is devoted completely to cooling tower systems in view of the magnitude of inhibitor use for this application. The second one deals with a number of other systems. The first of these is internal combustion engines which covers diesel engines, automotive cooling systems, and antifreeze, which is primarily used in those systems. "Once-through" systems are then discussed, in connection with both municipal distribution systems and home hot-water heaters.

Finally, a brief discussion of refrigerating brines is presented. This topic really does not belong in the chapter on cooling water but it is given there as a matter of convenience. We feel that the system is interesting enough and of sufficient practical value to warrant its inclusion at that point.

The chapters on petroleum follow the course of the substance from the initial production point to its transportation to the ultimate consumer. The producing oil well is discussed first, followed by a chapter on secondary recovery. This latter procedure has become of considerable importance in oil recovery and for all practical purposes cannot be carried out for very long without the use of chemical additives. The next chapter deals with a variety of problems encountered during the refining operation. Finally, the problems encountered during the storage and transportation of both crude and finished petroleum products are reviewed.

A systematic presentation has been adopted for each corrosion-inhibitor usage. After a brief introduction, a review of literature dealing with the subject in a general manner is presented. The economics connected with the particular corrosion problem are then reviewed. This review gives an appreciation of the magnitude of the problem and also sets base lines that limit types and amounts of inhibitors that can be used for the solution. The corrosion problem itself is then discussed in considerable detail with other related problems. Before one can determine how to prevent corrosion, it is necessary to obtain a good grasp of the problem itself. This understanding includes both the specific corrosive conditions involved and the theory of the corrosion mechanism. Inhibition is then discussed in terms of mechanisms, chemicals used, and application procedures. Finally, references used in preceding sections are given. Liberal use has been made of literature, which enables readers to obtain more detailed discussions of various aspects.

2

Boiler-Water
Treatment

LITERATURE

The prevention of corrosion in boilers and in feed water and return lines associated with them has been a major problem for several decades. The literature is replete with hundreds of papers on this subject. A few general review articles are listed in references 1 through 12. Recent reviews on specific topics include packaged boilers,[13] low-pressure heating boilers,[14, 15] high-pressure boilers,[16-20] and nuclear power-plant experience.[21, 22]

ECONOMICS

The economic loss due to corrosion of boilers must be broken down into two categories: (1) direct replacement and repair costs and (2) indirect losses due to "down time." The former costs have been estimated to run from 50 to 100 million dollars per year in the United States alone, while the latter costs are incalculable but are probably more costly because of loss of production.

THE PROBLEM

Corrosion in boiler systems cannot be isolated from a number of other concomitant problems which have a direct effect on the type, the amount, and the location of corrosion and the functioning of the boiler. These problems will be considered with the corrosion problems since they are all interrelated and since the corrosion inhibitors used are generally a part of a "package water treatment" containing additives for the solution of other problems. For simplicity, these additional problems can be defined as scale, sludge, and carryover.

Another complication arises in that there are a number of locations in a boiler system where various types and amounts of corrosion can occur. In this discussion, the boiler system will be investigated in three generalized locations—preboiler, boiler, and postboiler—and the problems associated with each will be considered separately.

Preboiler

The preboiler system is defined here as the feedwater pumps and the lines entering the system. If not restricted, one could include a vast variety of units in which the make-up water is conditioned but which in themselves are essentially not part of the boiler system.

Using this definition, one finds both corrosion and deposit problems in the preboiler system. The corrosion can manifest itself as general corrosion, pitting, or erosion-corrosion. The deposit problems can be either the precipitation of suspended solids which should have been removed in earlier clarifier units or else it may be the formation of adherent calcium, magnesium, or iron scales.

CORROSION. The corrosion can be of iron, copper, or nickel, depending upon the materials of construction. General corrosion or pitting may occur for conventional reasons, e.g., dissolved oxygen, low pH, presence of deposits, stagnant areas, stresses in the metal, defects in metal composition, and surface conditions. Dissolved oxygen will often cause pitting attack when coupled with certain other conditions such as deposits on the metal surfaces or metal defects. The oxygen will oxidize ferrous hydroxide film to magnetite (Fe_3O_4) or to hydrated ferric oxide. This oxidation will occur at a finite distance from the metal allowing more iron to dissolve at the surface under the loose corrosion product. Acidic *p*H values will lead to general corrosion. The other factors will generally favor localized attack. Cavitation-erosion can be encountered in the pumps or else in other locations where turbulent or high-velocity flow may occur.[23]

The composition of water going through feedlines may vary from distilled water to softened water to tap water with either acidic or alkaline *p*H values. Contaminants can include corrosion products, dissolved gases, or oil. Temperatures can vary from ambient to close to boiler temperatures.

DEPOSITS. There are two major sources of deposits in the preboiler system. One source results from improper clarification of the water before it enters this system. The standard coagulation process is generally a lime-soda softening which removes most of the hardness and changes the alkalinity balance of the water. In addition, suspended turbidity, such as clay particles, is removed from the system. Additional coagulants, such as high-molecular-weight polymeric materials, are frequently used, as are alum, iron salts, or sodium aluminate. Frequently the residence time in the clarifiers is not sufficient or else the filters used do not function properly. Therefore fine floc particles are carried through to the preboiler system and some grow, settle out there, and cover the lines with a deposit. The particles which do not settle out in the lines go to the boiler system and cause trouble there.

The other major source of deposits—the formation of calcium, magnesium, or iron scales—is common to practically all aqueous systems. Tightly adherent calcium carbonate or phosphate, magnesium hydroxide, or iron-compound films are laid down on the metal surface, impede water flow, interfere with heat transfer, and set the stage for localized pitting. The composition of the deposits varies widely and is a function of the water analysis and temperature. Calcium carbonate can result from failure to remove sufficient calcium in the lime-soda softening and from bicarbonate breakdown at elevated temperatures. The presence of an excess of alkalinity in the water also contributes to carbonate formation. Magnesium hydroxide formation can be attributed to the same basic reasons—i.e., an excess of magnesium and the creation of a highly alkaline system. The various iron compounds, such as oxides, phosphates, or carbonates, can be the result of either too much iron in the makeup water or else the incorporation of corrosion products in the deposits. The presence of phosphate deposits represents a real anomaly. On the one hand, polyphosphates are deliberately added (as will be shown later) to prevent adherent deposits, and on the other hand, their reversion product, orthophosphate, causes undesirable deposits. For this reason, temperature and pH conditions which accelerate reversion of polyphosphates must be considered carefully. Green[24] discusses these factors in some detail.

Boiler

There has probably been more literature written and more man-hours expended on the solution of boiler-water problems than on any other single water-treatment area. The problem is very significant historically, and one phase, embrittlement, was the subject of an excellent treatise by Straub[25] in 1930. The growth in variety and pressure ranges of boilers is such that new problems arise as rapidly as old ones are solved. This discussion makes no effort to treat specific boiler systems in any great detail, but instead it concentrates on the general problems of deposits, carryover, and corrosion, which are common to most or all systems.

DEPOSITS. Deposits in boilers can be broken down to two major categories: sludge and scale. The general method of distinguishing between the two is by the nature of their adherence. Scale is generally thought of as being tightly adherent to metal, while sludge can be dispersed in the boiler water, can be spread on the metal surface but is easily removable, or else can possibly serve as a bonding agent for the scale.

Sludge is often created deliberately. For example, orthophosphate is added to boilers in the "internal treatment" with the objective of precipitating all of the calcium and the magnesium in the form of easily removable sludge. An example of sludges which are not desirable, on the other hand, is given by Andrews[26] who found that some failures in steam locomotive boilers in Ontario were caused by organic compounds, such as terpenes, which resulted from contamination of feedwater during passage through areas planted with conifers.

The presence of oil due to feedwater contamination causes a sludge which adheres to the walls and is difficult to remove. The formation of sludge balls can be encountered where the binder is a corrosion inhibitor, a paint residue, a fuel oil, or a lubricant.[27] These sludge balls can become very large under specific turbulent conditions. Figure 2-1 shows a number of such sludge balls.

FIGURE 2-1. Oil Sludge Balls[27]

Photograph Courtesy of F. E. Clarke and INDUSTRIAL AND ENGINEERING CHEMISTRY

An interesting study has recently been reported[28] of the corrosion effects of a sludge accumulation on various pressurized water nuclear powerplant tubing alloys. Under the specific test conditions, severe attack was obtained on carbon steel and even on Monel.

Analyses of the components of sludges vary widely depending on the particular system involved.[23, 27, 29, 30] An excellent discussion of this subject is presented in the "Symposium on Boiler Water Chemistry."[9] It shows that almost any component of the feedwater or its contaminants can be found in the sludge with the ratios varying according to the peculiarities of the particular system involved. Zenekevich and Karasik[29] found that chemical analyses of a large number of sludges in boilers at 185 atm indicated that they were mixtures of crystalline hematite, magnetite, cupric oxide, and phosphorite. The compositions of slimes taken from different sections of the boilers were similar, which indicated that they were all formed under identical thermodynamic conditions. Deev *et al.*[30] found that calcium phosphates and serpentine are sludge formers, although phosphorite, hematite, magnetite, and metallic copper might also be present. Clarke and Hopkins[27] give detailed analyses of various sludges which clearly relate their compositions to the peculiarities of the particular systems.

Scales in low-pressure boilers commonly consist primarily of very adherent deposits of calcium carbonate, sulfate, or silicate, magnesium hydroxide, or analcite (sodium aluminosilicate). Calcium carbonate generally is formed when heat in the boiler decomposes the soluble calcium bicarbonate, driving off carbon dioxide, and leaving insoluble calcium carbonate behind. Calcium sulfate is quite soluble at room temperatures, but drops off sharply to about 84 ppm at 360° F.[31] Calcium silicate will form a very adherent glassy scale which has high-heat insulating properties. Magnesium hydroxide is formed by decomposition of magnesium bicarbonate. Analcite is formed between 350 and 800° F and has strong insulating properties. In high-pressure boilers, iron compounds are prevalent,[23] and complex silicon compounds are frequently found with the "hardness" (calcium and magnesium) compounds.

It is difficult to arbitrarily assign specific compounds to scale or sludge since many of these compounds may deposit in either form, depending on operating conditions. For example, Clarke and Hopkins[27] point out that silica may enter the boiler as dirt and then deposit as sand sludge or it may enter as soluble silicate and deposit as silicate scale.

A study of the formation of scale in boilers and its adhesive properties leads to many interesting observations. Scale forms directly in place on heated metal surfaces and generally consists of columnar crystals[27] growing at right angles to the surface, whereas sludge lacks crystallinity. Analcite, magnetite, and magnesium phosphate deposits are among the densest[32] and show the greatest reduction in heat transfer. Samilov and Smirnov[33] show that there appears to be a critical temperature of about 470° F where calcium hydroxide is converted to calcium oxide regardless of pressure. At this temperature, the amount of calcium which is carried away in generated steam drops markedly in accordance with the creation of its new state.

Gerke and Tebenikhin[34] studied scale formation on boiler plate samples in solutions of $Ca(HCO_3)_2$, $Mg(HCO_3)_2$, and $CaSO_4$. They found that scale formed preferentially on roughened surfaces, that it varied according to the material of composition of the substrate, and that it was directly related to the potential of the metal. More scale formed on zinc and aluminum than on boiler plate, while less formed on nickel, copper, brass, and glass. Peters and Engell[35] were able to relate the adhesion of scale on steel to the thickness of the scale, the steel composition, and the oxidation temperature.

CARRYOVER. Carryover from boilers can be defined as the presence of water in the steam leaving the boiler. The water contains solids which cause deposit and corrosion problems in the postboiler system. The most serious of these problems is the rapid build-up of silica deposits on the turbine blades. The silica concentrations are so critical that Kot[36, 37] states that saturated steam is not safe for turbine vanes unless it contains less than 0.010 to 0.015 mg $SiO_3^=$/kg. The problem of silica deposits on turbine blades is primarily present under high-pressure conditions, whereas at lower pressures, a considerable amount of SiO_2 can be tolerated in the boiler water. The problem of silica deposits on turbine blades is primarily present under high-pressure conditions, whereas at lower pressures a considerable amount of SiO_2 can be tolerated in the boiler water.

If salt mixtures like NaCl, Na_2SO_4, or NaOH are carried over and form deposits, then corrosion occurs, especially if the melting point of the mixture is lower than the steam temperature.[38] Copper and its oxides, if deposited, can also cause corrosion. Wickert[38] showed that H_2S can be formed from Na_2SO_4 and Fe in the presence of water vapor at temperatures over 300° C, while at 440° C NaCl reacts with the vapor to form HCl and NaOH. The NaOH is retained by the NaCl, while the HCl lowers the pH of the condensate in which it gathers. Catalysts of the reaction are SiO_2, Cu, and especially $CuCl_2$. Table 2-1 gives the allowable tolerances for total solids as presented by Ulmer.[23]

TABLE 2-1. Steam Purity[23]

OPERATING BOILER PRESSURE ($lb/in.^2$)	TOTAL SOLIDS (ppm)
0–300	3,500
301–450	3,000
451–600	2,500
601–750	2,000
751–900	1,500
901–1,000	1,250
1,001–1,500	1,000

The carryover can occur as a result of foaming and priming, mechanical carryover, and solubility of solids or entrainment in the steam. The foaming problem is the most difficult to control and can be caused by a number of factors. Some of the major ones follow:

1. *Oil contamination.*
2. *Other organic or colloidal contamination.*
3. *High total dissolved solids content.*
4. *Suspended solids.*
5. *Boiler design, primarily the volume load of the surface of evaporation.*

Schudlich[39] *et al.* have established maximum limits for oil in boilers of 7 ppm or less than 1 per cent of the suspended solids. Tatarinov[40] showed that at constant loading of a boiler the height of the foam rises with the salt content of the boiler water. The nature of the salt is important; Na_2CO_3 has a greater effect than $NaCl$ or Na_2SO_4. Villar[41] showed that foam can be caused by solid carbonates which are present due to evaporation of feedwater or dislodged incrustants.

Styrikovich[42] presented a detailed mathematical analysis of contamination of saturated vapor by impurities which are present in the boiler water in high-pressure cylindrical boilers due to both mechanical carryover and steam solubility. He showed that a stable deposit is formed only when there is a significant mechanical transfer, so that the contamination of the steam by any substance exceeds the solvation capacity of the steam.

CORROSION. The electrochemical corrosion reaction for iron boiler metal surfaces is generally acknowledged[12, 43] to be

$$3Fe + 4H_2O \rightarrow Fe_3O_4 + 4H_2, \qquad [2\text{-}1]$$

where H_2O may be liquid or gas. The protective film is magnetic iron oxide, Fe_3O_4, and the major inhibitor approach is to maintain it as a continuous, very adherent, very thin film. For a properly treated boiler, this isolation of steel from boiler water can be maintained for many years of service. Conversely, rupture of the film by either mechanical or chemical means will promote the solution of iron.

The corrosive factors in a boiler vary, but in a broad sense they can include dissolved oxygen, high temperatures and pressures, high salt concentrations, high-heat transfer conditions, stresses, localized concentrations of caustic (boilers are purposely operated at high pH values), erosion, peculiar localized flow conditions, carbon dioxide, deposits of salts, metals and metallic oxides, and scales and sludges with localized overheating. The materials of construction are invariably carbon steel or low-alloy iron and steel. Various types of corrosion which can be encountered include pitting, concentration corrosion, caustic embrittlement, stress corrosion, and erosion-corrosion.

From this list it becomes apparent that the major corrosion problems in the boiler are local in nature. General corrosion of boiler tubes does not present much concern. Failures occur at specific sites and are associated with unique factors, such as deposits, crevices, and stagnation. A brief survey of some of the more common types follows.

Pitting. Pitting is frequently associated with attack by dissolved oxygen and is manifested throughout the boiler system. The oxygen causes the formation of Fe_2O_3 instead of the desired Fe_3O_4 and causes rapid tube failure. Conditions in the boiler are such that the development of oxygen concentration cells under scale or sludge deposits is favored. The last traces of oxygen must be removed to prevent this type of attack. Even then the oxygen in water can react with steel to cause pitting, especially in localized concentrated NaOH.[44]

Deposits, such as those caused by scale, sludge, or mill scale, promote the formation of pitting beneath them. The deposits are cathodic to iron and intensify local attack, while at the same time they assist overheating at that point.

Metal precipitation, especially copper, is generally considered to accelerate pitting. The origin of the copper is uncertain, but it is suspected[45] that copper oxide which comes into the system through feedline corrosion reacts with the metal surface to form iron oxide and spongy copper. More copper oxide is then entrapped by the resulting deposit, and gradually a large deposit builds up. A strong galvanic cell is set up at this point. In addition, the pH of the water near the tube wall drops, loses part of its ability to maintain the desired Fe_3O_4 film, and contributes further to the action of the corrosion cell.

The presence of stresses or solid impurities in the steel promotes pitting.[12] Anodic areas are formed and the pits are found to be aligned with the stress, such as in fin tubes at the point where the fin has cracked and in the expanded area of boiler tubes.

Concentration Corrosion. A number of forms of localized corrosion problems can be grouped under the general term *concentration corrosion*. This corrosion is essentially the result of high concentrations of chemicals in specific locations, brought about by deposits and/or stagnant flow conditions, crevices, and localized overheating. The most common causative agent is a high sodium hydroxide concentration.

Partridge and Hall[12] showed how the attack on steel at 310° C is a function of pH and that the maximum protection is obtained at pH 11 to 12. As the concentration of NaOH rises, the attack becomes rapidly aggravated by the formation of soluble Na_2FeO_2 instead of the protective Fe_3O_4. Corrosion rates also increase as the pH drops below 11, but the NaOH attack is by far the more common occurrence. Attack by concentrated NaOH proceeds more intensively in high-pressure boilers than in medium-pressure boilers.[46]

Corrosion due to local concentrations as a result of stagnant conditions, deposits, or overheating manifests itself in the form of isolated zones which can be either in the shape of saucers or in the form of elongated bands. The point of attack is frequently related to minor mechanical irregularities in the tube wall and is frequently found on the downstream side of a weld zone. The corroded area is generally covered with a voluminous corrosion product which is primarily Fe_2O_3, although considerable quantities of copper may also be present.

Excess NaOH is caused primarily by concentration of boiler water. Hall[47] points out that the formation of bubbles of steam at the surface of a boiler tube results in a localized temperature increase, which, in turn, concentrates the boiler water at the interface between the bubble and the heat transfer surface. The result is a rapid increase in caustic content at that point.

Caustic Embrittlement. Caustic embrittlement can be considered as a special case of the caustic-concentration problem. The major corrosive factor here is the presence of an abnormally high concentration of caustic in contact with steel under relatively high tensile-stress. Crevices in the system, especially at rivet holes, present an ideal set of conditions for embrittlement, and the bulk of cracking of this type has been associated with the presence of rivets.

It is of interest to note that the cracking tendency of steel is not necessarily related to its corrosion resistance. Tseitlin *et al.*[48] showed that corrosion-resistant Cr-Ni and Cr-Ni-Mo steels have a strong tendency to crack under stress in the presence of hot alkali solutions, while carbon steel, which is more easily corroded, has a lower tendency to crack under these conditions.

Podgornyi[49] subjected steel samples to a pressure of 40 atm and a temperature of 225° F in a solution containing 20 per cent NaOH, 20 per cent NaCl, and a trace of Na_2SiO_3. He found that the resultant caustic embrittlement could be directly related to the cathodic polarization. He further found that correct mechanical and thermal pretreatment of metals minimized cathodic potential and cracking. Embrittlement was found to be related to the strain produced by the curvature of the metal, to the chemical composition of the steel, and to the concentration of the alkali solution. The caustic embrittlement increased with increasing boiler-water concentration. Hydrogen atoms were formed in localized areas and migrated through the intercrystalline interstices.

The mechanism of embrittlement cracking is generally believed to be dependent on happenings at grain boundary atoms. Parkins[50] states that it is based on the distorted nature of ferrite in the region of grain boundaries. Hecht, Partridge, Schroeder, and Whirl in their section in Uhlig's *Corrosion Handbook*[12] state that grain boundary atoms are attached to crystals of different orientation and can be maintained in position by atomic force lines distorted from their normal position. Removal of such atoms from their strained position is therefore much easier than from the body of a crystal. Concentrated alkaline solutions can cause these intercrystalline cracks. A number of other theories including hydrogen,[50, 51] precipitation,[50] oxide film,[50] colloidal phenomena,[52] and mechanical and boundary distortion theories[50] have also been suggested. Oxides are usually found in the cracks, and precipitated salts may also be present. The presence of silicate is reported to accelerate cracking. Akimov[53] postulates that alkali acts upon iron to form sodium ferrate, Na_2FeO_2, and hydrogen. The corrosion then proceeds along the grain boundaries and is accelerated by the internal stresses which separate the grains along the weakened boundaries. A crack forms, water penetrates into the weakened metal, and intercrystalline corrosion spreads still further. In addition, the absorption of the evolving hydrogen by the metal can aid deterioration.

Nitrate cracking can also cause localized corrosion problems. Parkins[50] compared nitrate cracking with caustic cracking and stated that nitrate cracks are intergranular, while caustic cracks are intercrystalline, although a certain amount of transcrystalline cracks can also be present.

Stress Corrosion. Caustic embrittlement is actually only one type of stress-corrosion cracking. It is the one most frequently found in boilers and for that reason merits special consideration. A theory of the more general phenomenon of stress-corrosion cracking was advanced by Dix[54] and extended by Waber, McDonald, and Longtin.[55] This theory states that the metal must have an inherent susceptibility to selective corrosion along a continuous path, such as a grain boundary. This corrosion will occur when the structure is microscopically heterogeneous and the continuous phase is anodic to the rest of the metal in the particular corrosive medium under consideration. There must also be a high tensile-stress along this continuous phase. The corrosion will then proceed along the anodic path. A self-accelerating reaction is initiated in which the corrosion produces more stresses which in turn open up easier paths for the corrosion. The development of protective films is thus minimized and fresh anodic material is continually being exposed to the corrosive medium. In addition, precipitation of materials, such as iron nitride (in the case of mild steel), is hastened by high local stresses. They in turn cause the development of galvanic cells and dissolve to form cracks. The picture of stress corrosion thus presented is one of a catastrophic chain reaction in which the physical stresses and the electrochemical corrosive reactions are mutually accelerating.

Concern has become quite prevalent during recent years over the stress cracking of steels by chlorides. This interest has come about because of the increasing work in pressurized water nuclear power plants. The United States Navy has been especially interested in connection with the Submarine Thermal Reactor Boiler[56] and nuclear propulsion systems, nonmagnetic auxiliary boilers for mine sweepers, and superheaters in general.[57, 58]

Identification of chloride as a major causative agent has been made by Williams[57] who reviewed a number of published reports of cracking of stainless steel in high-temperature water or steam and in each case found high concentrations of chloride in the region where the cracking occurred. Both mild steel and austenitic stainless steel are involved, with primary interest centering around the latter. Recent literature on this subject includes articles by Clarke and Ristaino,[56] Phillips and Singley,[59] and Edeleanu and Snowden.[60]

The most likely place for cracking to occur is in the stainless steel tubed steam generator where high chloride concentrations develop, as well as steam-blanketed areas.[59] In addition, considerable free oxygen is present. The adverse effect of oxygen on chloride stress corrosion is pointed out by Williams[57] who shows that oxygen and chloride must both be present for stress corrosion to occur.

Temperature and time are both important factors here. Cracking can occur at the boiling point of water,[57] but it will be accelerated by temperature increase. Time is important because of the possible need for an inductive period, although failure can be very rapid under highly conducive conditions.

The problem of stress-corrosion cracking becomes especially severe for those stainless steel parts which are intermittently exposed to boiler water. Both Clarke and Ristaino[56] and Williams[57] point out that this exposure represents a much more severe condition for inhibition than in the case of the parts that are submerged in water continually. The cracking in the parts that are in the vapor phase does not occur if the water which contains chloride does not come in contact with them by splashing or some other mechanism.

Erosion-Corrosion. On occasion, failures occur in boiler tubes which can be attributed to an erosion mechanism. They generally occur at areas in the tubes where the normal direction of flow has been altered abruptly, a condition of turbulence created, and a new flow path followed. The resultant corrosion is similar to that found in some feedline systems. Here again a situation exists where the primary cause of the failure is a physical one, i.e., the flow pattern, but the resultant chemical corrosion causes the damage.

An example of this type of attack is cited by Schoofs[61] who describes the erosion-corrosion of brass tubes in a reheater of a power-station boiler. The attack took place where the direction of flow changed. Overheating and local boiling took place with a disruptive effect on the protective film, particularly at the exit and the entry where turbulence was the greatest.

Another example of the relation of corrosion to turbulence is the situation where copper pitting may be the causative effect but the corrosion is found downstream of a weld zone. The mixture of spongy, deposited copper and iron oxide acts as a barrier to flow of boiler water and entraps more copper oxide. The water reaching the tube walls is no longer agitated vigorously, and a peculiar localized corrosive condition is created.[45]

Postboiler

The postboiler system is broken down into two areas—(1) the superheater and (2) the condensation and return system. Each will be considered separately.

SUPERHEATER. The allocation of the superheater to the postboiler group rather than to the boiler itself is purely arbitrary. The problems in the superheater are similar to both those of the boiler and those of the return and condensate system. For that reason it serves as an effective transition problem between the two.

The attack on superheater tubes can be attributed to three corrosive

factors—(1) the reaction between steam and metal at high temperatures, (2) the carryover by steam of salts which are then deposited on
the metal surfaces, and (3) condensation that occurs when the system
is banked or is temporarily out of service. The *corrosion of metal by steam*
at very high temperatures is a serious problem, but it will not be treated
here since it is not amenable to solution by use of corrosion inhibitors.
It must be minimized by the choice of suitable alloying materials. The
reader is referred to reviews by Kovacs[62] and Grobner and Bret[63] and
to excellent detailed discussions in Uhlig's *Corrosion Handbook.*[12]

Carryover by steam of salts which deposit on the metal surface and
cause corrosion is a very serious problem in superheaters. Wickert[38]
showed that deposited NaCl could react with steam at 440° C to form
NaOH which would be retained by the NaCl. The direct reaction between deposited NaCl and the metal is the subject of much controversy,
but there is little doubt that the presence of NaOH, whether it be from
the reaction postulated above or whether it is present due to entrainment in the steam, will lead to severe local attack under the deposits.
Wickert points out that this is especially true if the melting point of
the deposited salt mixture is lower than the steam temperature. He
also states that copper and its oxides, if deposited, can also be corrosive
if electron acceptors like oxygen or hydrogen ions are present.

Hass[64] showed that deposited calcium salts, especially $CaCl_2$, can
also decompose to form the hydroxides at boiler temperatures. It was
shown that the conversion of $CaCl_2$ with water vapor was accelerated
by the presence of silica. Styrikovich[65] studied phase diagrams for water
with SiO_2, NaCl, Na_2SO_4, and $CaSO_4$, respectively, at both subcritical
and supercritical pressures, and he detected the hydrolysis of salts by
superheated steam at temperatures as low as 550 to 600° F. He also
studied the distribution of a number of substances between water and
steam phases and found most carryover for weak acids (silicic, boric),
less for chlorides and hydroxides, and least for sulfates, silicates, carbonates, and phosphates.

Condensation of steam in superheaters occurs readily when the boiler is
banked or shut down. The corrosive system becomes analogous to that
for steam condensate systems. The condensed water has oxygen and carbon dioxide in it, which results in an aggressive solution. The dissolved
oxygen is an active depolarizer, and if oxygen concentration cells
develop under corrosion or salt deposits it promotes rapid pitting. The
dissolved carbon dioxide renders the water weakly acidic and promotes
both general and localized attack.

STEAM CONDENSATE AND RETURN SYSTEMS. Corrosion of steam condensate and return systems presents a twofold problem to power-generating and steam-heating plants. Equipment damage and frequent replacement of lines, valves, and taps result in a serious maintenance problem. In addition, the corrosion products frequently formed are carried back into the steam-generating equipment and deposit there. The result is plugging of lines, localized overheating, and promotion of corrosion in the boiler system itself. Examples of these failures are cited by Ulmer and Wood[66] and Straub.[67] Since preventive treatments for condensate systems frequently are inserted into the boiler itself, these combinations prove the need for an over-all approach to the boiler-water problem rather than its isolation by sections.

The corrosion in the condensate system manifests itself in certain typical forms, depending upon the corrosive factors involved. These factors arc basically oxygen, carbon dioxide, and condensed water. The attack due to dissolved oxygen is characterized by tuberculation, pitting, and build-up of iron oxide deposits. The mechanism involved is thought to be one of depolarization of the cathodic areas on the metal surface. Collins and Henderson[68] made a detailed study of oxygen attack and arrived at the following conclusions:

1. Oxygen concentrations below 0.5 ppm cause negligible corrosion when the temperature is less than 70° C and the pH of the condensate is 6 or higher.

2. In the pH range 6 to 8 and at oxygen concentrations of 0.5 to 4 ppm, the rate of attack for general corrosion is given by the equation

$$R = 24(C - 0.4)^{0.9}, \qquad\qquad [2\text{-}2]$$

where R is the average rate of penetration in mdd and C is the oxygen concentration in ppm.[68]

They state that this equation is not valid for pitting corrosion and does not take into account the accelerating effect of temperature.

Skaperdas and Uhlig[69] showed that an increase in temperature from 60 to 90° C will double the rate of oxygen corrosion. Normally, one would expect a dual effect due to oxygen as a function of increasing temperature. On the one hand, the corrosion reaction rate should increase rapidly with temperature in accordance with normal kinetic considerations. On the other hand, the decreasing solubility of oxygen with temperature should decrease the attack. In this particular *closed* system, however, the oxygen cannot escape and consequently the normal increase in reaction rate with temperature is to be expected and does in fact occur.

Carbon dioxide attack manifests itself by thinning and grooving the metal walls with failure occurring most readily at the threaded connections. The walls are relatively clean and shiny, in contrast to the masses of corrosion products which cover the areas of oxygen attack. Collins[70] also studied the corrosion rate of carbon dioxide attack and developed the equation

$$R = 5.7W^{0.6},$$ [2-3]

where R is the rate in mdd and W is the concentration of carbon dioxide in condensate in ppm multiplied by the weight of condensate flowing in lb/hr multiplied by 0.1. Here again the temperature effect is not considered. Skaperdas and Uhlig[69] found that an increase in temperature from 60 to 90° C raised the rate of attack of carbonic acid on low carbon steel by a factor of 2.6. The absolute magnitude of the corrosion will, of course, vary from system to system. Osmond and Welder[71] describe a system where the corrosion rate of steel panels in the desuperheating condensate system was 1,285 mdd prior to treatment.

It is interesting to note that the steam which would normally be thought of as being pure distilled water and relatively inoffensive is instead highly corrosive and contains considerable CO_2 and O_2. The principal source of these two gases is the boiler feedwater, although some gases may enter as a result of leaks or return-tank breathing. Efforts are generally made to eliminate the oxygen in the boiler water as will be discussed later, but these efforts are not always successful. The carbon dioxide results mainly from decomposition of bicarbonates and carbonates in the boiler with the resultant liberation of free CO_2.

Collins *et al.*[12, 70, 72] point out that a peculiar equilibrium exists between the gases in the vapor and those in the condensate. Normally, the amounts of O_2 and CO_2 in the condensate could be readily predicted from their partial vapor pressures, which decrease with increasing condensate temperature. When steam consumption of pressure equipment is very high, however, great concentrations of noncondensable gases accumulate in the vapor space of the unit. A gradient mixture of steam and noncondensable gases occurs with the highest concentration of gas present at the vapor condensate interface. This partial pressure at the interface determines the amount of gas dissolved in the condensate, and the result is that higher quantities are dissolved than would normally be expected. Collins[12] also explains the decrease in the corrosion as one proceeds downstream in the system as due to the progressive increase in the iron content, which raises the pH and makes the system less corrosive.

The nature of the condensed water also affects the type and amount of corrosion. The presence of droplets leads to localized pitting attack. A uniform film, on the other hand, causes more general corrosion. Rozenfeld and Zhigalova[73] report this phenomenon in some detail.

INHIBITION

Discussion of chemical inhibition of the corrosion problems previously mentioned will be given in the same order as were the problems. Solutions of scale, sludge, and carryover problems will also be discussed because these problems were shown to be intimately linked to the corrosion problems and also because the corrosion inhibitors are rarely used alone in boiler systems.

Preboiler

The addition of chemicals or the use of other treatment techniques as applied to feedwater is generally known as "external treatment," i.e., external to the boiler. This external treatment generally is intended to solve both corrosion and scale problems in preboiler and boiler systems.

PRETREATMENT. *Pretreatment* of feedwater is designed to render it as noncorrosive or nonscale-forming as possible. Corrosion-control methods include various *ion-exchange techniques* designed to remove dissolved ionized solids from raw water which is blended with the condensate makeup to compose the feedwater. The ion-exchange materials most commonly used for this purpose are the synthetic organic exchangers, rather than the naturally occurring zeolites or their synthetic analogues which at one time were in wide use.

An ion-exchange resin can be considered to be a solid polyelectrolyte with a fixed charge and a movable (in water) countercharge or "gegenion." Cation-exchange resins have fixed anionic groups and exchangeable cations. The fixed anionic group can be sulfonic, carboxylic, phenolic, or phosphonic. "Strong base" anion-exchange resins have fixed positive quarternary ammonium cations and exchangeable anions. "Weak base" anion-exchange resins have fixed primary, secondary, or tertiary amines and can take up acid molecules from water. The exchange reactions for these resins can be written as follows:

1. Cation exchange:

$$RSO_3^- H^+ + Na^+ Cl^- \rightleftharpoons RSO_3^- Na^+ + H^+ Cl^-. \qquad [2\text{-}4]$$

2. Strong base anion exchange:

$$R_4N^+ OH^- + Na^+ Cl^- \rightleftharpoons R_4N^+ Cl^- + Na^+ OH^-. \qquad [2\text{-}5]$$

3. Weak base anion exchange:

$$RNH_2 + HCl \rightarrow RNH_2 \cdot HCl. \qquad [2\text{-}6]$$

In all cases R represents all of the resins except the functional group. Most of the resins commercially available are polystyrene-divinylbenzene copolymers which have been treated to possess the desired functional group.

As can be seen from these equations, an equilibrium is set up between the competing ions. This equilibrium can be driven in one direction by passing a solution containing one ion through a fixed bed of resin in another ionic form. Each resin particle acts as an equilibrating system, and by the time the solution comes out of the bottom of the column all of the unwanted ion originally present in the solution has been replaced by the exchangeable ion of similar charge on the resin. Thus, for instance, an NaCl solution can be completely converted to HCl or vice versa.

It is apparent that resins can be used to soften water by removing the hardness ions, i.e., Ca^{++} or Mg^{++}, and replacing them with sodium. Similarly, use of a cation resin in the hydrogen form produces an acid. Passage of the produced acid through an anion-resin bed in the hydroxide form results in pure demineralized water. This process can be done either by having one resin bed immediately after the other or by mixing the two resin types in one column. Similarly, alkalinity content and type of feedwater can be controlled by a suitable exchange of ions.

Deaeration to remove oxygen from feedwater is frequently practiced. A number of different mechanical systems, wherein water is heated to drive out dissolved gases, have been devised for this purpose. A detailed discussion of their use is beyond the scope of this book. Contact of feedwater with scrap iron is also employed occasionally for deaerating purposes. Mamet and Glushenko[74] made a detailed study of the effectiveness of steel shavings for oxygen removal and found that high temperatures, sufficient contact time, and low hardness are required.

CORROSION. The prevention of general corrosion is most frequently practiced by use of p*H control* measures. The maintenance of a *p*H value of 9.0 reduces general corrosion appreciably.[75, 76] There have been two approaches to the raising of the feedwater *p*H to this value.[43] The earlier one consisted of either adding NaOH or recirculating alkaline boiler water; it applied to the protection of all metals generally found in these systems.[77, 78] Evans[4] postulates that the mechanism of inhibition is as follows. As the (OH^-) activity is raised, the solubility of all oxides and hydroxides is reduced, and the degree of supersaturation set up in the liquid very close to the metal is raised. This situation favors production of closely spaced nuclei of ferrous hydroxide, ferrous oxide, or magnetite and promotes the formation of a protective film. Ferrous oxide or hydroxide are formed initially, and the transformation to magnetite can take place readily if nickel or copper are present as catalysts. There are some inherent disadvantages to this approach, however.[43] Sufficient recirculation of the alkaline boiler water may be impractical or may lead to deposit problems as precipitate formation proceeds with the lowering of temperature. Use of NaOH can cause increased blowdown requirements in the boiler system. Two interesting points in this regard are made by Potter.[19] He noted that (1) alkalinity arising from dissolution of massive iron is no replacement for the addition of alkali, and (2) in view of the temperature involved, measurement of *p*OH would be of more value than measurement of *p*H since the former is much less temperature-dependent.

A more recent and quite popular approach to *p*H control in preboiler systems is the use of ammonia or other amines.[43, 77, 78] These weak bases permit a more closely controlled regulation of *p*H. Andres[43] gives the following values in ppm for the amount of material necessary to give pure water a *p*H of 9.0:

1. *Ammonia—less than 0.5.*
2. *Cyclohexylamine—2.0.*
3. *Morpholine—4.0.*

One obvious concern relating to this approach is the effect of amines on the inhibition of nonferrous metals and especially copper. Decker and Marsh[78] evaluated the above amines and NaOH for control of erosion-corrosion on a number of ferrous and nonferrous alloys. They found that cyclohexylamine and ammonia were effective for ferrous metals but not for nonferrous. Sodium hydroxide was effective for all metals, and morpholine was ineffective for all metals. Tash and Klein,[22] on the other hand, found morpholine to be an effective inhibitor, provided hydrazine was also used. Grabowski[77] found that the volatile amines can be effective and claimed that NH_3 in the pH range of 8.5 to 9.5 reduced the corrosion of copper. He states that to keep the copper and iron surfaces from corroding, the O_2, CO_2, and SO_2 gases must be kept at a low value while the proper pH is being maintained. Homig and Richter[76] found that morpholine was superior to ammonia or cyclohexylamine for iron inhibition, but here again it was essential that the O_2 and CO_2 content be kept at a minimum. The primary problem appears to be oxygen, and it is generally believed that use of ammonia or amines for pH control is satisfactory provided that the oxygen content is also carefully controlled.

Control of dissolved oxygen in the boiler water is accomplished chemically by the use of either sodium sulfite or hydrazine. The sodium sulfite or preferably catalyzed sodium sulfite has been used for many years, while hydrazine has become prominent for this purpose only during the past decade.

The level to which it is necessary to remove the dissolved oxygen to prevent corrosion varies as a function of temperature. Speller, in Uhlig's *Corrosion Handbook,*[12] gives figures of 0.30 ppm of oxygen in cold water, 0.10 ppm in hot water (70° C), 0.03 ppm in low-pressure boilers under 250 psi without economizers, and less than 0.005 ppm in high-pressure boilers or when economizers are used. In practice, it is generally attempted to keep the oxygen concentration down to zero regardless of what the system is.

Sodium sulfite is used alone, as a catalyzed formulation, or with activated carbon. The catalysts generally employed are very small amounts of copper or cobalt. The sulfite alone is effective in removing oxygen from water rapidly. Varying amounts are recommended. Speller[12] states that about 8 lb of sodium sulfite are required to remove 1 lb of oxygen and recommends that an excess of about 30 ppm be maintained to insure complete oxygen removal. Deev[79] describes cases which point out this need for an excess of sulfite and describes how even at an excess of 2.6 ppm of Na_2SO_3 there is still some oxygen left dissolved in water. Typical dosage values recommended by suppliers for scavenging oxygen are 20 to 40 ppm. Tash and Klein[22] used 25 to 100 ppm of sodium sulfite in their boiler water at the Shippingport nuclear power station, while Arthurs et al.[16] specified 100 to 140 ppm of Na_2SO_3 for their high-pressure boiler-water composition. In the case of a 1,700-lb/in.² boiler, they used both vacuum and pressure deaeration to reduce the dissolved oxygen content of the feedwater to 0.005 ppm.

Catalyzed sulfite is used in the same range as uncatalyzed sulfite but is more rapid and more effective. Activated carbon, as an additive to sulfite, functions by adsorption and concentration of the oxygen. An increase in temperature is advantageous. A detailed description of the use of activated carbon is given in a German patent by Oertel.[80]

There are certain disadvantages implicit in the use of sodium sulfite. One disadvantage is that it can decompose to form SO_2 or H_2S in high-pressure, steam-generating equipment, thus appreciably increasing corrosion rates in the steam-fed water cycle.[81] Fiss[82] found that above a limiting concentration of 10 ppm for 900-lb/in.² boilers, sulfite decomposition occurred. Another disadvantage is the increase in the total dissolved solids in the boiler water which will require more blowdown. The catalysts can plate out in boiler tubes and promote pitting. For these reasons, there has been a considerable amount of interest displayed in the use of another chemical additive for deoxygenation-hydrazine.

There is much recent literature on the use of hydrazine. For some of the more thorough studies the reader is referred to papers by Woodward,[83-86] Zanchi,[87, 88] Zimmerman,[89] and Hartmann and Resch.[90]

The reaction between hydrazine and oxygen has been stated to be the following:[85, 87, 88]

$$N_2H_4 + O_2 \rightarrow N_2 + 2H_2O, \qquad [2\text{-}7]$$

with further hydrazine then reducing metal oxides. However, Nissen[91] said that hydrazine will not attack the protective FeO layer. Dickinson *et al.*[92] state that the reaction rate increases rapidly with temperature to the extent that substantially all the oxygen can be completely removed at 400° F with reasonable values of reaction times and N_2H_4 concentration. Leicester,[93] on the other hand, feels that the mechanism of the N_2H_4–O_2 reaction has not yet been fully established, but that it is a surface reaction, is heterogeneous, and does not always involve quantitative reaction with the dissolved O_2.

Zimmerman and Brinkman in their patent[94] show that Ag, Cu, or activated carbon are catalysts for the N_2H_4–O_2 reaction. Oertel[80] also shows the advantages of using activated carbon.

A competing reaction which can cause the formation of undesirable products is the catalytic or thermal decomposition of hydrazine. The resulting ammonia may attack nonferrous metals. Dickinson *et al.*[92] believe the reaction is as follows:

$$2N_2H_4 \rightarrow H_2 + N_2 + 2NH_3.$$ [2-8]

Hartmann and Resch[90] say that at pH 8 the reaction is the following:

$$3N_2H_4 \rightarrow 4NH_3 + N_2.$$ [2-9]

They made a very thorough study of the decomposition of hydrazine hydrate under conditions of high-pressure boiler application. It was found that when the log of the ratio of the concentration of N_2H_4 after a given time to the initial concentration, C, is plotted against time, t, a straight line results. The half-period (50 per cent decomposition) is given by the following equation:

$$t_{1/2} = \frac{0.301t}{[-\log(C/C_o)]}.$$ [2-10]

Equation 2-10 was found to decrease with increasing pH, presumably owing to the formation of NH_4OH and its ionization at the higher pH values.

The nature of the contact surface will have an effect on the decomposition. Thus Hartmann and Resch[90] found that when the surface was quartz, the decomposition rate was exceedingly slow with only a slight amount of thermal decomposition occurring. On the other hand, metallic copper or else Fe_3O_4 accelerated the reaction and copper brought about the production of N_2O.

In a quantitative measurement of the decomposition reaction, Leicester[93] found that if the residual hydrazine content of the boiler is kept below 0.2 ppm, the NH_3 content of the steam will not be greater than 0.3 to 0.5 ppm. In actual plant operation[83] it was shown that feeding hydrazine at three to five times the theoretical amount required to react with the dissolved oxygen left a residue in the boiler water and produced an NH_3 content in the feedwater of 0.05 to 0.15 ppm. Stones[95] found that the addition of hydrazine 100 per cent in excess of the oxygen figures resulted in a rapid rise in NH_3 and pH values with a resultant corrosion of his copper-nickel and brass tubes.

If the concentration of N_2H_4 is regulated carefully to prevent breakdown of the excess to NH_3, the use of hydrazine instead of sodium sulfite has a number of advantages. The salt content does not increase as is the case when sulfite is added. Another advantage is that the alkalinity can be controlled by use of proper excess of hydrazine. Maintenance of a hydrazine residual in the water protects the boiler against occasional increases in dissolved oxygen content which occur with variations in operating conditions. Finally, the cost is relatively low, the removal of oxygen is more efficient than by use of sodium sulfite, and much smaller dosage levels are required.

A number of comparisons of the use of Na_2SO_3 and N_2H_4 have been published. Massart and Missa[96] compared Na_2SO_3 with N_2H_4. They found that although Na_2SO_3 was more reactive than N_2H_4, the latter was advantageous when air was accidentally admitted. The vapor pH was less than 7 with Na_2SO_3 compared to a desirable value of 9 for N_2H_4. The amount of dissolved Fe decreased with the use of N_2H_4, but the amount of Cu in solution was unaffected. Economically, the use of N_2H_4 was superior despite a higher initial chemical cost. Woodward[85, 86] also showed hydrazine to be more efficient than Na_2SO_3, while Fiss[83] substituted hydrazine for sulfite in a 1,500-lb/in.^{2} boiler that had experienced a series of tube failures. The hydrazine stopped tube failures. It was also effective in 1,850-lb/in.^{2} boilers.

Hydrazine is now being used in boilers with a wide spectrum of pressures ranging from 400 to 2,500 lb/in.^{2}.[83] It is easy to apply and can be controlled readily. There is a toxicity possibility, and due care must be exercised in handling the material.

Some variations of hydrazine are now being examined. Dihydrazine phosphate is now being used in England to treat idle boilers.[83, 93] A new salt of dinaphthylmethanedisulfonic acid containing 11 to 15 per cent hydrazine is stated to have promise.[93] In addition to corrosion inhibition, this latter material is a good dispersant and assists in fluidizing solids in the boiler.

DEPOSITS. As indicated earlier, deposit problems in preboiler systems can be divided into two categories based on their origin. The first is the deposition of floc which has carried over from the coagulation process, while the second is the formation of Ca, Mg, or Fe scales.

The *first* problem, the *carryover of floc,* is attacked by *improvement of the coagulation process.* Generally, this involves either (1) redesigning the clarification system so that more residence time is provided for the floc to settle out, (2) cleaning out the filters or increasing their capacities, or (3) changing the chemical coagulation procedure.

Efficient operation of the softening or coagulating processes is essential for proper feedwater maintenance. The details of the lime-soda softening procedure and other clarification procedures will not be discussed here since they are beyond the scope of this book. Recently there have been several exciting developments in the discovery of high-molecular-weight polymeric materials which improve clarification procedures markedly. This approach is expected to produce much better water for boiler feed purposes. As an example of this, a case is cited[97] where river water was being treated for high-pressure boiler feed in a high-rate solids contact reactor with extremely poor results. At times, chemical loadings as high as 120 ppm alum and 20 ppm activated silica were utilized, but still they did not provide proper clarification. The use of 0.5 ppm of new polymeric coagulant which is a high-molecular-weight polyacrylamide, possibly very slightly hydrolyzed, during a period of extremely difficult operation enabled this plant to cut the alum loading in half, eliminate activated silica, and achieve the desired clarity. It also improved the operation of the ion-exchange beds used for water softening.

Schwarz[98] has made the interesting observation that degasification of water in a vacuum chamber with turbulent water circulation is not only carried out for the purpose of removing corrosive gases. It also serves to convert $Ca(HCO_3)_2$ into suspended $CaCO_3$ which will go on into the boiler sludge rather than having adherent $CaCO_3$ deposited on the hot feedline surfaces.

The most commonly used procedure for the *prevention of deposits* in the *feedlines* is the "threshold treatment" with molecularly dehydrated phosphates (polyphosphates). The process is based on the fact that very low concentrations of the polyphosphates will prevent the deposition of calcium carbonate upon moderate application of alkali or heat to hard bicarbonate water. There are many excellent discussions of this subject in literature, and the reader is especially referred to articles by Rice *et al.*[99, 100] for specific application to the boiler feedline problem.

An interesting aspect of the threshold treatment approach is that it appears to function in a twofold manner by preventing the build-up of scale deposits and also by minimizing corrosion. In the boiler-feed application, it is used primarily for the former purpose, but in many other applications corrosion inhibition is the major benefit sought. In view of this unusual behavior, this treatment will be examined in some detail.

The concentration of polyphosphate needed for the inhibition of calcium carbonate deposition is about 2 ppm. This figure has been verified for Calgon, which is one of a series of glassy phosphates and has a P_2O_5 content of 67 per cent.[99] Other polyphosphates behave in a similar manner with slightly varying dosages. Higher concentrations are generally necessary only when the water is held at high temperatures for such a long period that reversion (i.e., addition of H_2O and a resultant break-down to orthophosphate) becomes appreciable, or else when foreign solids are present which will adsorb considerable amounts of the poly-phosphate.

Hatch and Rice[99] carried out an interesting study on the effect of temperature on the maximum amount of calcium bicarbonate that can be stabilized. Results in Figure 2-2 show the rapid drop in stabilization

FIGURE 2-2. Maximum $Ca(HCO_3)_2$ Concentration Which Can Be Maintained Without Deposition[99]

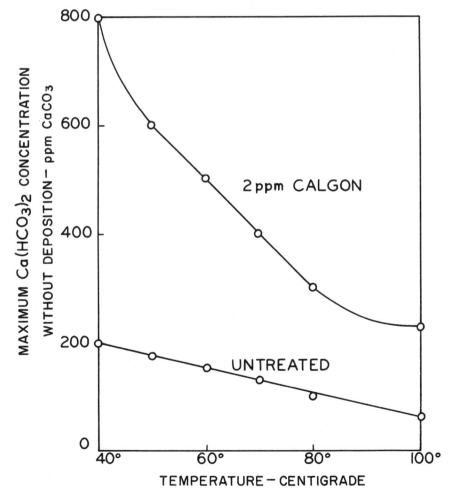

with increasing temperature and the effectiveness of Calgon in overcoming it. Fitzpatrick[31] stated that hot water free from CO_2 holds 13 ppm $CaCO_3$, while cold water containing CO_2 dissolves 906 ppm of $CaCO_3$ which becomes calcium bicarbonate.

It was suggested[99, 100] that the prevention of calcium carbonate deposition by the molecularly dehydrated phosphates apparently results from the stabilization of a condition of supersaturation with respect to $CaCO_3$. Adsorption of the phosphate upon initially present or subsequently formed nuclei for crystallization appears to prevent $CaCO_3$ deposition; in the case of foreign materials which do not adsorb the phosphate but which can act as nuclei for the crystallization, adsorption will occur as soon as $CaCO_3$ is deposited, with a subsequent inactivation of the surface as a nucleus for crystallization. As an example of the effect on foreign solids, Hatch and Rice[99] studied an incrusted sand filter which was serving as a source of carbonate incrustation when a lime-soda softener effluent was passed through it. Introduction of a polyphosphate into the water gradually eliminated further $CaCO_3$ precipitation on the sand filter.

A possible explanation of the effect of molecularly dehydrated polyphosphates on calcium carbonate was given by Buehrer and Reitemeier.[101] They show that adsorption of phosphates results in gross deformation of calcium carbonate crystals formed when phosphates were present in quantities insufficient to inhibit deposition completely by complexing the calcium.

Reference was made earlier to the reversion of molecularly dehydrated phosphates to produce orthophosphates. While this reversion is desirable in the boiler itself, it is very undesirable in the feedlines because of the build-up of calcium phosphate deposits. Users of polyphosphates in the preboiler system must consider this problem.

The most thorough study of the problem was made by Green.[24] He found that the stability of the phosphates decreased with decreasing pH. Sodium tripolyphosphate and sodium pyrophosphate behaved similarly, while sodium hexametaphosphate was exceptionally stable under all test conditions. The rate of reversion increased with increasing calcium content of the water, but it was either unaltered or decreased with increasing magnesium content. Increasing the temperature caused rapid increases in reversion rates.

The polyphosphate which is added to feedlines for deposit control also functions as a corrosion inhibitor. The mechanism of protection is described elsewhere in this book in connection with cooling-water corrosion control. The polyphosphate can also prevent the precipitation of hydrous ferric oxide if the water contains soluble iron.

Boiler

DEPOSITS. The term *internal treatment* is used for the direct addition of chemicals to the boiler, in contrast to *external treatment* which can involve mechanical processes or chemicals added to the feedline system. Internal treatment for preventing deposits can be divided into two techniques —*phosphate control* and *carbonate control*. These two procedures involve the formation of calcium phosphate or carbonate sludges, their dispersion (frequently aided by various organic chemicals), and finally their removal by blowdown. Each control method will be reviewed separately.

Phosphate control has become standard practice in boilers working above 200 psi and has also found use at much lower pressures.[102] It involves tying up all the calcium in the boiler in the form of a calcium phosphate sludge. Calcium phosphate readily forms a finely divided sludge in contrast to other calcium salts which form scales. Both poly- and orthophosphates can be used since the polyphosphates will revert to the ortho form very rapidly under boiler conditions, and it is the ortho form which reacts with the calcium. In practice, the choice of phosphate generally lies between Na_3PO_4 and Na_2HPO_4.

The actual choice of Na_3PO_4 or Na_2HPO_4 depends on two factors— economics and boiler-water alkalinity.[31] It will be shown that for corrosion-control purposes the boiler-water alkalinity must be kept at a certain level since a certain ratio of $NaOH$ to Na_3PO_4 is desirable to minimize cracking. In choosing the type of phosphate, therefore, the question of whether more alkalinity should be added to the water by use of Na_3HPO_4, or whether the less expensive and less alkaline Na_2HPO_4 can be used must be answered.

Another reason for the use of sufficient alkalinity with phosphate control is that at low alkalinity values calcium phosphate becomes more soluble and tends to form a sticky adherent sludge. Adequate alkalinity for complete reaction with calcium requires a minimum pH of 9.6 in a steaming boiler,[31] a figure comparable to 10.5 at room temperature. The "phenolphthalein alkalinity" must be greater than one half of the "methyl orange alkalinity," and the latter value should be at least 200 ppm. Brooke[2] favors a pH of 11.0 to 11.5 for scale prevention and advocates its maintenance by use of NaOH or Na_3PO_4. In practice, a blend of Na_3PO_4 and Na_2HPO_4 is used. The conventional commercial treatment for use up to 2,200 psi has a phosphate content of 54 per cent and a 5 per cent solution averages 8.0 to 8.2 pH.[31]

Since the mechanism involved here is one of actually reacting with the calcium on a mole for mole basis, it is apparent that an excess of phosphate must be maintained. This excess will vary from 10 to 100 ppm of phosphate, depending on the plant operating conditions and the efficiency of the feedwater hardness control. The upper limit of 100 ppm is used because above this value magnesium phosphate can begin to precipitate instead of the more desirable hydroxide which is obtained by use of sufficient alkalinity.

Carbonate control is not practiced as widely as phosphate control. Not only is the calcium carbonate precipitate more difficult to control (i.e., remove from boiler) but an excessive amount of soda ash must be fed to the boiler to maintain an adequate amount of carbonate.

Gray,[103] in an empirical survey of 101 low-pressure boilers, found that successful sludge and scale control could be maintained by observing only two conditions: (1) the Mg hardness of the feedwater must be kept above a certain minimum value which is a function of the Ca hardness and the SiO_2 content and (2) the total carbonate alkalinity in the boiler should be between 200 and 300 ppm as $CaCO_3$ (i.e., sufficient to restrict the total hardness in the boiler water to 5 ppm). Gerard[104] disagrees with Gray's suggestion because of the difficulty in maintaining the 200 to 300 ppm of carbonate alkalinity. He points out that the decomposition of Na_2CO_3 to form NaOH would lead to caustic cracking; the added CO_2 would increase condensate corrosion. In addition the $MgSO_4$ and Na_2SO_4 can lead to more deposits in the feedlines. Anchev[105] describes the successful use of both the NaOH plus Na_2CO_3 and the Na_3PO_4 plus Na_2HPO_4 approaches to combat boiler scale in an electric power plant.

After the phosphate or carbonate precipitates are formed in the boiler, they must be conditioned so that they remain suspended in the boiler water as a free-flowing sludge. Unconditioned or improperly conditioned sludges tend to collect in locations where circulation rates are low and form packed layers of deposit on metal surfaces which can interfere with circulation and heat transfer.[106] A variety of *organic dispersants* have therefore been developed which will keep this sludge in the free-flowing state.

The range of organic materials used for this purpose prior to 1951[107] included tannins, lignins, sulfite liquors, alginates, glucosates, and starches. Some of the materials which have been patented since that time include alkaline tannin extracts,[108] vegetable derivatives,[109] polymeric compounds containing adjacent carboxy groups such as a methylstyrene-maleic anhydride copolymer,[110] *o*-nitrophenol dimers,[111] colloidal peat,[112] and a wood-fat-molasses-coal mixture.[113]

In choosing a material for this purpose it is important to remember that not only must it keep sludge suspended, but also that it should be able to flake off old scale and sludge which have accumulated on the boiler surfaces. In addition, the organic compound used should not promote foaming or be corrosive.

On occasion, it may be necessary to remove SiO_2 from boiler water or deposits. It has been found[114] that the use of basic magnesium carbonate, magnesium oxide, or sodium aluminate in an amount equal to the sum of SiO_2 and MgO contained in the boiler water decreases the SiO_2 one half to one third and makes the deposits small and fragile. Conversely, if magnesium deposits are troublesome, addition of silicates to boiler water can prevent the formation of adherent magnesium phosphate.[115] Control of magnetic iron oxide deposits has been obtained by use of sodium nitrite[116] or an organic nitrite derivative[20] to convert it to ferric oxide. Kahler[117] has claimed that water-soluble lignins are more efficient at preventing Fe precipitation from water supplies than are molecularly dehydrated phosphates.

CARRYOVER. Carryover from boilers is often minimized by proper design of equipment and frequent blowdown. Silicon dioxide can be removed by washing in a three-step evaporation unit,[36] and the amount removed depends on the alkalinity of the water. The major approach to be discussed here, however, will be the use of *antifoams*.

Denman[118] used high-speed photography to illustrate his theory of the mechanism by which antifoams function. The photographs of a foaming boiler show that numerous small steam bubbles are present and that they remain in intimate contact without coalescing. The photographs show that after a polyamide antifoam agent is added the small steam bubbles rapidly coalesce into large steam bubbles. This coalescing occurs both at the heating surface and in the body of the boiling water. The large steam bubbles are irregular in shape because of distortion during movement in the boiling water, and in many cases the nonspherical bubbles formed by coalescence do not have time to round out.

An excellent review of antifoam development is also given by Denman, and the reader is referred to his paper for details. Early antifoams were based upon crudely refined mineral oils such as castor oil. These materials were not very effective and were prone to rapid hydrolysis in the hot alkaline boiler water to form soaps which promoted foaming. The result was an intensive search for more effective synthetic products. From this search has come the two major classes of antifoams used in boiler waters today—polyamides and polyoxy antifoams.

Polyamides are made from polyamines and carboxylic acids. There are a number of excellent materials in this class. For any given amine there will be a limited range of carbon atoms in the carboxylic acid for maximum effectiveness. Similarly, for a given acid the range of amines is limited. Denman gives examples of the most effective diamides that can be made from ethylenediamine or diethylenetriamine, the most effective triamides from diethylenetriamine, and the distearoyl amides of dibasic acids and of alkylenediamines.

Polyoxy antifoams are polyoxyalkyleneglycols and derivatives. They are made by taking a hydrophobic material and increasing its water solubility by ethoxylating it. One member of the more important groups in this series is the high-molecular-weight diether of polyoxyalkyleneglycol.

Some typical patents on antifoams for boiler water include the following:

1. *Johnson: Diether of a polyoxyalkyleneglycol.*[119]
2. *Denman: "Pluronics"—polypropyleneglycol-ethylene oxide.*[120]
3. *Ryznar: Amine-ethylene oxide addition product.*[121]
4. *Johnson: Trihydroxypolyoxyalkylene ethers of alkylenetriols and their reaction products with propylene or ethylene oxides.*[122]
5. *Bird and Jacoby: Symmetrically unsaturated diacylated polyamines.*[123]
6. *French Railroad: Formaldehyde—amide condensation product.*[124]
7. *Villar: Wetting agents plus isoamyl alcohol.*[41]

Certain waters appear to require particular types of antifoams. The polyoxy antifoams work well with low-solids water and the polyamide materials function well with high-solids water.[118] Hardness affects antifoams adversely.

Most commercial antifoams sold today are blends of several materails. The addition of other materials, such as powdered tannin, desulfonated lignin, Na_2CO_3, polyphosphates,[121] humates, or starches,[118] appears to improve the over-all performance. It is likely that these other materials act as dispersants for the antifoams.

CORROSION. It has been stated many times that the way to prevent corrosion in boilers is to *keep oxygen out of the system, maintain proper alkalinity,* and *keep the surfaces clean.* While this method is obviously an exaggeration of the ease of inhibiting corrosion, the basic principles are sound and their utility becomes apparent in this chapter.

The problem of pitting was shown to be directly associated with the presence of dissolved oxygen and the development of deposits. The use of hydrazine or sodium sulfite together with the prevention of scaling serve as the optimum means of minimizing this type of attack. The other corrosive agent, copper deposition, must be prevented by proper treatment of the feedlines. It should be noted that oxygen can enter the system by leakage, and consequently it is essential to insure that an excess of hydrazine or sodium sulfite is present in the boiler. One method of insuring this excess is to add some of the oxygen scavenger directly to the boiler on a continuous basis.

The problem of corrosion, because of high localized NaOH concentrations, is generally attacked by one of a number of methods, all of which rely on proper ratios of various salts and alkalinity in the boiler water. Thus, the need for close control of boiler-water composition and its frequent analysis becomes apparent.

The pH control situation is very complicated since the hydroxyl ion will passivate the surface, but too much will cause cracking. As Evans[4] points out, an adequate hydroxyl reserve is not necessarily the same thing as a high pH value, since a good buffer system can maintain a supply of hydroxyl ions, replenishing those used up in film formation without giving a high pH. The problem then is to use a system which substitutes something else for most or all of the NaOH as a source of alkalinity. The *coordinated pH approach* rests upon the premise that the alkaline pH should come from trisodium phosphate as much as possible rather than from NaOH. The amount of phosphate which may be present should be compatible, however, with the need for a boiler-water content of low dissolved solids.

The exact figures on the amount of alkalinity necessary to minimize corrosion, the maximum permissible hydroxide content, and the phosphate levels vary from boiler to boiler. A few typical examples are cited here.

Pincus[15] found that corrosion and scale formation in low-pressure boilers could be held to a minimum by maintaining the boiler water at a hydroxide alkalinity of 100 to 350 ppm and a total alkalinity of 300 to 500 ppm, both expressed as $CaCO_3$. He used silicates, carbonates, phosphates, and chromates to make up his nonhydroxide alkalinities. Alkalinities up to 1,000 ppm did not harm. Hamer[6] controlled corrosion of boilers operating below 200 lb/in.[2] by keeping the total alkalinity at 10 to 15 per cent of the total dissolved solids. When the boilers went over this pressure he also deoxygenated the water. Clarke and Ristaino[56] used the coordinated phosphate-pH control for the Submarine Thermal Reactor Boiler with considerable success when the metal surfaces were immersed in water. Rath [125] found that alkaline phosphates protected boiler steels subjected to a substantial amount of stress and the combined action of caustic soda and silica. A ratio of Na_3PO_4 to NaOH equal to or greater than one was necessary to prevent caustic cracking. Akolzin, Kagan, and Kot,[126] in a study of drum-type boilers without stages of evaporation, found that the excess PO_4 concentration should be maintained at below 40 ppm and a minimum NaOH alkalinity at 9 ppm. For boilers with stages of evaporation, the last stage should show a maximum of 100 ppm PO_4 and a minimum in the boiler of 5 to 7 ppm with the water tinged by phenolphthalein.

Schroeder, Berk, and Partridge[127] said that a ratio of Na_3PO_4 to NaOH equal to or greater than one was necessary to prevent cracking. They postulated that the protective mechanism was the precipitation of phosphate in capillary crevices before NaOH therein would attain the dangerous concentration of about 4 per cent. Data developed by a number of water-treatment companies over a period of many years have shown that phosphated waters which produced cracking invariably had more NaOH than PO_4. Brooke,[2] on the other hand, presented data which he interprets as meaning that the use of an Na_3PO_4 to NaOH ratio is without merit, and that Na_3PO_4 functions well only in the absence of hydroxide ion, a situation which occurs only infrequently in boilers.

Evans[4] states that if the water contains sodium phosphate with a ratio of Na_2O to P_2O_5 slightly lower than that corresponding to a solution of pure Na_3PO_4, then a concentration of hydroxide ion can be maintained by hydrolysis in the body of the water which is sufficient to prevent ordinary corrosion, but not to cause an excessive hydroxide-ion concentration in seams or recesses. Once the concentration has reached the level at which solid Na_3PO_4 is thrown out, the concentration of hydroxide ion cannot rise further. He further states that Na_3PO_4 generally need not be added, but that if the water is already alkaline, Na_2HPO_4 or $(NaPO_3)_n$ (i.e., Calgon) which reverts in the boiler can be used.

Whirl and Purcell[128] plotted the curve shown in Figure 2-3. This curve, which has frequently been used by proponents of the phosphate approach, gives the relationship between pH and phosphate concentration and shows the areas in which caustic or phosphate will occur on evaporating surfaces. When pH and phosphate values intersect below the curve, the residue will be phosphate. Above the curve, free caustic will be present.[57] Boiler water conditioned according to the

FIGURE 2-3. Relationship Between pH and PO_4 Concentration in Terms of Prevention of Excess Caustic[128]

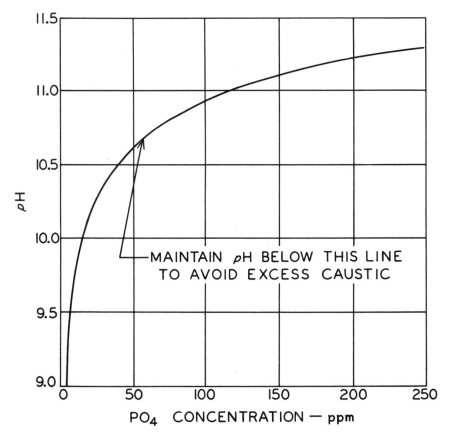

Figure Courtesy of T. E. Purcell, S. F. Whirl, and TRANSACTIONS OF THE AMERICAN SOCIETY OF MECHANICAL ENGINEERS (1942)

area below the curve can be concentrated without raising the hydroxyl-ion concentration appreciably.[12]

Another approach to the prevention of caustic cracking involves the maintenance of the *ratio of sodium sulfate to alkalinity* in the boiler water above a certain value. This method is subject to considerable dispute, and there are two schools of thought as to its value. Akimov[53] says that this approach is satisfactory. He states that the mechanism functions when the concentration of the alkali in the joints and seams becomes dangerous and sulfate precipitates and protects the metal from the action of alkali. In an examination of the basic soundness of the sulfate treatment Weir and Hamer[129] state that the mechanism is either the deposition of solid Na_2SO_4 or $CaSO_4$ on the highly stressed parts of the boiler plate or the plugging of a seam. Stanisavlievici[130] and Hamer[6] in more recent publications state that Na_2SO_4 has an inhibitive action. The American Society of Mechanical Engineers Boiler Code of 1940 recommended maintenance of a high sulfate to hydroxide ratio for prevention of embrittlement, although more recently the American Railway Engineers Association[131] recommended that this procedure be disregarded on the basis that operating experience showed it to be without merit.

Evans[4] makes a detailed analysis of the sulfate-ratio controversy. He points out that any beneficial effects might be attributed to keeping the hydroxyl-ion concentration low, rather than to keeping the sulfate-ion concentration high. The former can be defended on sound theoretical grounds, whereas the latter is a matter of conjecture. He studies results of this treatment in England and concludes that the value of the sulfate is doubtful. Hecht, Partridge, Schroeder, and Whirl in their chapter on boiler corrosion in Uhlig's *Corrosion Handbook*[12] go even further and make the flat statement that "sodium sulfate does not prevent cracking of embrittlement detector specimens."

Kagan *et al.*[18, 126] state that if chemically treated water is used along with condensate as the feedwater, then the ratio of (Cl^-) plus $(SO_4^=)$ to NaOH should be no less than 5. Akolzin and Ratner[46, 132] recommend that excessive alkalinity be reduced by neutralizing with H_2SO_4, and then using an ion-exchange resin to free the water of excess alkalinity by replacing Na ion with H ion. Both of these approaches appear to indicate that the SO_4 ion itself is not an inhibitor.

The *neutral salt* approach is suggested by Hall.[47] It suggests maintaining a high concentration of neutral salt, such as sodium sulfate, in the boiler water relative to the amount of hydroxyl ion present. This approach is similar to the method proposed by Kagan and his co-workers. Straub[133] also recommends this approach, which reduces the effect of the caustic through the dilution effect of added salt as the boiler-water concentrates.

The most widely accepted chemicals for the prevention of caustic embrittlement are the *nitrate ion* and *quebracho extract.* Andres,[43] Brooke,[2] Podgornyi,[49] Akolzin,[134] and many others show that nitrate is very effective for this purpose, while Parkins,[50] Hecht *et al.,*[12] Andres,[43] and others describe the successful use of the quebracho extract.

The amount of nitrate used is critical, and Brooke[2] states that this must be 40 per cent of the total alkalinity calculated as NaOH. Podgornyi[49] found that 35 per cent gave the best results. Hecht *et al.*[12] say that sodium nitrate has been used at pressures up to 750 psi and that concentrations should be maintained at about 20 or 30 per cent of the NaOH alkalinity. Potassium nitrate functions as well as the sodium salt,[130] and waste sulfite liquors containing $NaNO_3$ are also effective.[41, 134] Tannins[130] and butyric acid (in the amounts of 0.5 per cent of the amount of alkali present)[49] are also effective in preventing caustic embrittlement.

Phillips and Singley[59] present a very interesting study of methods of preventing chloride stress-corrosion attack of austenitic stainless-steel-tubed steam generators in nuclear power plants. They used an alkaline-phosphate boiler water containing up to 500 ppm chloride and found that sodium nitrate and sodium sulfite were effective inhibitors. The combination of the two was superior to either inhibitor alone or to any other inhibitor or combination.

The *erosion-corrosion problem* in boiler tubes is attacked by (1) redesigning the system to avoid turbulent flow, (2) eliminating deposits and keeping the tubes clean, (3) preventing corrosion of the copper in the preboiler system, and (4) maintaining proper dosages of the corrosion inhibitors previously mentioned, especially the oxygen scavengers. The solution thus becomes a combination physical and chemical approach.

Postboiler

SUPERHEATER. It was pointed out earlier that the *corrosion of metal by steam* at very high temperatures is not readily prevented by the use of corrosion inhibitors. The most satisfactory preventive technique is the choice of suitable alloys, a procedure whose discussion is beyond the scope of this book.

Carryover of salts by steam is best attacked by prevention of the carry-over. This process is normally accomplished in the boiler by use of properly designed steam separators. When such separation is not effective, *antifoams* are used. *Prevention of silica carryover* is especially important, and this problem is generally attacked by external treatment of feedwater with strong base anion-exchange resins so as to remove the silica before it ever enters the boiler.

Corrosion due to *condensation of steam in superheaters* is treated in the same manner as corrosion of steam condensate and return systems. This subject will be discussed in detail in the following section.

STEAM CONDENSATE AND RETURN SYSTEMS. The earlier discussion of the causes of corrosion in the steam condensate and return systems indicates that the corrosive agents are oxygen and carbon dioxide. The development of corrosion inhibitors for these systems should therefore bear these two factors in mind. The first problem, the corrosion due to oxygen, is generally attacked by techniques described for *eliminating the oxygen content* of boiler water. This method is usually sufficient to reduce the oxygen content so that the oxygen present in the condensate will essentially be derived from leaks in the return systems. When leakage of oxygen into the return system becomes sufficient to promote corrosion, then the preferred solution is the mechanical one eliminating the leaks or else using proper alloys. Sodium sulfite can be added to the condensate system in those cases where the oxygen cannot be eliminated in any other manner. A preferred approach is the increase in condensate pH by volatile amines. Raising the pH of the condensate will minimize oxygen attack.

A very successful approach to the problem of acidic corrosion caused by CO_2 is by the use of *volatile amines*. These materials are added to the boiler water, volatilize along with the steam, condense with it, neutralize the CO_2, and produce a condensate having a neutral or alkaline pH. Alternately, they can be added to the steam lines. In either event, they stay with the steam and condense with it, thus providing the alkaline material at the points where it is needed.

A number of amines have been examined for this purpose. The most obvious one and the first studied was ammonia. Some of the earliest demonstrations of the effectiveness of ammonia were reported by

Straub[67] and Leick.[135] The material is generally added in the form of ammonium hydroxide or ammonium sulfate to the boiler feedwater with the resultant liberation of ammonia in the boiler. The major use of ammonia is in central stations with low percentage make-up and low CO_2 concentrations in the steam.[136] When the CO_2 concentrations are quite high, as they tend to be in industrial plants, the required ammonia level for neutralization becomes high, and this treatment runs into the disadvantage of the serious corrosion of copper- and zinc-bearing metals.[136, 137] For this reason, other neutralizing amines have been developed which will not be corrosive to copper at the dosages required for CO_2 neutralization. A case of the lack of effectiveness of ammonia is described by Sperry[138] who was attempting to protect turbines in generating stations from corrosion. He found that when ammonium compounds were added to the boilers, the resulting NH_3 was largely lost in the steam and resulted in a low-condensate pH and serious corrosion of condensate pumps.

The two neutralizing amines used most frequently today are morpholine (C_4H_9NO) and cyclohexylamine ($C_6H_{11}NH_2$). Both of these chemicals are being sold in considerable quantities under different trade names by inhibitor manufacturers. Jacklin[139] states that the vapor pressure of morpholine is such that even at low concentrations in boiler water it vaporizes and the proper proportion condenses with the first droplets of condensate which form in the system. Most other amines have vapor pressures which are too high or too low and consequently do not condense in the first-formed droplets, leaving a critically important part of the cycle unprotected. Maguire[136] also points out that this feature of prevention of acidic corrosion at the point of initial condensation is of value in large central-station turbines, and that this prevention is an example of a case in which morpholine provides better control of the corrosion problem than is possible with ammonia.

Patzelt[140] calculated that at 25° C the pH at which carbonic acid is completely converted to morpholine bicarbonate is 7.3. He found that in actual experimental work, a slightly higher pH value was desirable because of the slower inhibition at the lower pH value. He also found that contamination of the condensate by 1 per cent of a synthetic boiler water raised the pH from 7.3 to 8.0 and lowered the untreated corrosion rate. This latter phenomenon was stated to agree with field observations that plants having trouble with boiler-water carryover in the steam generally do not have condensate-corrosion problems as serious as in the absence of carryover. Sperry,[138] in the case of volatile amines for turbine protection cited previously, found that morpholine was much more effective than ammonia. It is stable at high temperatures and pressures and is evenly distributed. For effective corrosion control, a pH of 8.8 to 9.0 and a morpholine residual of 3 to 4 ppm are maintained. Mondoux[141] and Jacklin[142] state that morpholine is stable up to a boiler pressure of 2,500 psi and to a temperature of 1,200° F in super-heated steam.

A number of articles have appeared in the literature[143, 144, 145] reviewing the advantages of cyclohexylamine and dicyclohexylamine as inhibitors for the prevention of the corrosion of iron by steam condensate containing oxygen and carbon dioxide. One commercial brand of cyclohexylamine sold under the trade name Hagamin is stated to require 2.25 lb of amine to neutralize 1 lb of carbon dioxide to the phenolphthalein end point. The pH of the condensate is maintained at 8.3 to 9.0 for complete protection.[146] The cyclohexylamine has been used without significant harmful degradation to ammonia at temperatures up to 1,050° F and pressures up to 2,700 psi.

Several other volatile amines have been evaluated for this purpose. Some of them include benzylamine,[147] 2-diethylamineothanol,[142] ethylene diamine,[12] and amine alcohols.[147] None of these amines has been shown to be as effective as morpholine or cyclohexylamine, either because they lacked good neutralizing ability, were insufficiently volatile, or else were unstable under boiler conditions.

Obviously, the volatile amines can be introduced to the steam condensate system either by addition to the feedwater, boiler, or return lines. Ulmer and Wood[66] discuss the advantages and disadvantages of each approach in some detail. They prefer direct addition to the boiler or else the feedwater. Hanlon[148] points out one objection to this method in that it becomes necessary to treat the entire system to obtain adequate protection in a desired localized section. In the latter case, the preferred method is direct injection of the inhibitor into the steam or condensate lines by means of a chemical feedpump.[66]

Another approach to the prevention of corrosion of steam condensate and return lines is that of using "film-forming" chemicals to lay down a protective film on surfaces subject to corrosion. This approach has come into widespread use during the past six or seven years with the development of suitable long-chain nitrogenous materials for this purpose. It is especially effective in those systems where high concentrations of CO_2 make the use of neutralizing amines uneconomical.

Early unsuccessful attempts to accomplish inhibition by this technique involved materials such as sodium silicate, oils, or polyphosphates. The use of sodium silicate[12] decreased corrosive action but could not prevent it entirely. It was postulated[12] that the protective mechanism might involve the formation of an SiO_2 film on the metal surface, the neutralization of the CO_2 by the alkali, or both. Addition of oil to condensate showed that inadequate quantities might accelerate rather than decelerate corrosion on those surfaces not covered by the oil.[68] Polyphosphate treatments have been added to return lines in a number of steam-generating plants with some degree of success.[140] Laboratory experiments by Patzelt[140] showed, however, that a lengthy period of time is necessary to allow the development of a protective film on the metal surface. This development time presents a considerable disadvantage since during that period corrosion may have proceeded to a point where it no longer can be treated. Hanlon[148] notes the impermanence of such phosphate films, and Ulmer and Wood[66] point out that it is necessary to maintain the dosages of these materials at the original value to prevent dissolution of the films.

The use of long-chain nitrogenous compounds as film-formers for condensate and return lines has been very successful. While a number of materials are now being employed, octadecylamine $(C_{18}H_{37}NH_2)$ and its salts are in most frequent use and typify this class. The following discussion as to the possible protective mechanism will therefore revolve around octadecylamine.

Octadecylamine does not function by neutralizing CO_2 in the system. There is generally too much CO_2 present in relation to the amount of amine for any stoichiometric reaction to occur. In addition, the amine is not volatile and adheres to the metal surface. Consequently, it is spread over the entire metal surface, not just the spots at which condensation occurs, and thus even less amine would be available as a neutralizing agent. The inhibitor is fixed to the metal surface, and thus the amine portion is not sufficiently mobile for neutralization purposes. It is obvious, then, that another mechanism, most likely that of a protective-film formation, must be involved.

An observation of the physical appearance of a metal surface treated with octadecylamine gives a clue to the inhibitory mechanism. Water condenses on such a surface in the form of droplets rather than as a uniform film. The surface wetting is kept to a minimum since the protective hydrophobic organic film which is already present repels the water and acts as a barrier between the metal and the corrosive condensate, thus protecting it against both oxygen and carbon dioxide attack. The result is a much better transfer of heat from the steam through the metal and a minimum formation of heat-insulating corrosion product. This drop-wise condensation effect has been shown by a number of authors, including Cannon[149] and Maguire.[136]

The adsorbed film on the metal surface is believed to be substantially of monomolecular thickness and does not increase in depth with continued treatment.[136] No study has been reported in the literature on the mechanism by which the long-chain amine is bound to the metal surface in this specific system. A review of general theories which were developed for film-formers, with the particular conditions involved here, however, can serve a worthwhile purpose.

There is no accepted theory for the exact mechanism by which long-chain organic nitrogenous inhibitors function. The division of materials into cathodic and anodic inhibitors which serves for many inorganic materials cannot be employed here, although many believe that there is some degree of inhibitor-ion orientation at the cathodes on the metal surface in the case of nitrogen derivatives. Thus, Mann, Lauer, and Hutlin,[150] conclude that amine cations are adsorbed on the cathodic regions of the metal surface in such a manner that the nitrogen atom is linked directly to the metal. The result is a monomolecular layer of amine ions on the surface. Hackerman and Sudbury,[151] on the other hand, in studying the polarization phenomena of amine additives in water and sulfuric acid, found indications that both anodic and cathodic areas might be affected by the amine inhibitor. The anodic inhibition is explained on the basis of migration of electrons from the metal to the positively charged inhibitor rather than toward the cathodic areas within the metal.

Kuznetsov and Iofa[152] also note that nitrogenous inhibitors showed anodic inhibition as well as cathodic inhibition. They explain it by postulating that the adsorbed layer of positively charged inhibitor ions retards the transfer of metal cations from the surface into the solution and thus slows down the anodic reaction.

There is no question, however, that the polar end of the molecule is the active participant in the adsorption process. Whether the initial adsorption is really chemisorption or physical adsorption by van der Waals forces followed by chemisorption has not been satisfactorily resolved. Breston[153] states that these probably both occur simultaneously, the chemisorption taking place at the "active spots" and the remainder of the surface being covered by the balance of the inhibitor held by physical forces. However, after a short period there does exist a strong covalent bond between the polar group of the inhibitor and the metal surface. The literature is replete with examples showing a direct relationship between the strength of this bond and the effectiveness of inhibitor.

The "wetting" or degree of coverage of metal surface by inhibitor is really a function of two factors: (1) the strength of the chemical bond and (2) the orientation, shape, and size of the long-chain portion of the molecule. The orientation of the nonpolar portion of the molecule will directly determine the fraction of metal surface which is covered by it, and this amount, in turn, will directly determine the effectiveness of the protective film. Nathan[154] shows that branching of the alkyl chain decreases inhibitor efficiency. He postulates that the geometrical nature of the nonpolar radical should be such that a close interlocking of the hydrocarbon chains is possible. Molecular models show that such interlocking is not possible when the chains are branched as is shown by Bigelow *et al.*[155] The length of the carbon chain appears to have a direct bearing on the effectiveness of the inhibitor. In the case of straight-chain primary aliphatic amines, Wilkes, Denman, and Obrecht[156] state that the carbon chain must be in the C_{10} to C_{18} range for maximum effectiveness. Denman[157] in a patent of a formulation based on octadecylamine states that the C_{12-20} chains are preferred, and Osipowe[158] requires C_{13-21} for his long-chain amide-alcohol mixture. Mann *et al.*[150] found that the efficiency increased as a direct function of chain length. They also state that the efficiency of an amine inhibitor is directly related to the amount of surface area it covers.

Octadecylamine is frequently formulated so as to improve its feeding characteristics and also to aid the inhibitor in wetting the surface rapidly. It is generally used as the acetate salt for feeding purposes. The wetting characteristics are improved by blending or emulsifying it with a suitable wetting agent. Thus Denman,[157] for example, has blended octadecylamine with a nonionic surfactant and a small amount of cyclohexylamine in the ratios of 90 to 9 to 1 and treated the mixture in a colloid mill to make a stable emulsion. This mixture also has the advantage of eliminating the corrosion at the point of introduction which frequently occurs with the acetate salt. Sato and Kato[159] evaluated salts of octadecylamine with (1) "maleinated methyloleate," (2) octadecanol, and (3) oleic acid, and they found the degree of effectiveness as rust inhibitors was in that same order.

Other film-forming inhibitors which have been reported in the patent literature include the following:

1. Ryznar and Kirkpatrick: Reaction product of an organic carboxy acid and a polyamine; e.g., amide mixture from reacting oleic acid, tall oil, and diethylenetriamine.[160]

2. Osipowe: Mixture of high-molecular-weight primary aliphatic amides and alcohols of the general formulas $C_nH_{2n+1}CH_2OH$ and $C_nH_{2n+1}CONH_2$ where n = 13 to 21.[158] *An example is a mixture of octadecyl alcohol and stearamide.*

3. Denman and Hwa: Imidazolines with side chains from C_{12} to C_{18} and pyrimidines with similar side chains.[161]

The film-forming inhibitors, as well as the emulsifying or dispersing materials that may be used with them, have strong surface-active properties. Consequently, their introduction into the system can result in the loosening of previously formed deposits and clogging of the lines by these materials. For that reason it may be better to clean the lines before starting use of the inhibitor or alternately to clean out the system after the loosened deposits have begun to accumulate. The result of this cleaning action is to improve heat transfer as well as impart corrosion inhibition.

The use of film-forming inhibitors becomes economical when the CO_2 content of the steam becomes high enough so that the cost of using sufficient neutralizing amine becomes excessive. By contrast, the dosage of filming amines is independent of dissolved-gas concentration. Typical dosage levels are stated by Denman[157] to be 0.5 to 10 ppm with 2 ppm as the recommended level. Kahler and Brown,[137] on the other hand, recommend levels of 15 to 20 ppm to establish and maintain the desired corrosion-resistant film on the metal surfaces. Akolzin, Zaitseva, and Lazareva[162] achieved satisfactory inhibition of corrosion of the distribution system of a large-process steam plant caused by 2 ppm O_2 and 4 to 5 ppm of CO_2 in the condensate and make-up by using a treatment level of 3 to 4 ppm of octadecylamine. Interruption of treatment for a few hours could be tolerated because of the film that had been built up. Osmond and Welder[71] investigated corrosion in a desuperheating condensate system where low-pressure shells were badly corroded and fittings in the spillover system and piping from the condensate storage were severely attacked. They used a commercially available formulation based on octadecylamine and reduced the corrosion rate of steel panels in the desuperheating condensate system from 1,285 mg/dm^2/day to less than 1 mg/dm^2/day with 4 ppm of treatment and 5 to 10 mg/dm^2/day with 2 ppm of inhibitor. Ryznar and Kirkpatrick[160] recommend the use of 10 ppm of their inhibitor, while Denman and Hwa[161] use 1 to 10 ppm of their imidazolines and pyrimidines. Osipowe[158] cut the corrosion rates of steel panels exposed to water and steam in half by using 25 ppm of his alcohol-amide mixture. Elliott and Gaughan[163] claimed to have saved $14,200 per year in corrosion costs at one plant by the use of octadecylamine. Other savings in dollar figures cited for the use of film-forming amines include those of Maguire[136] who quotes a yearly reduction of $8,000 maintenance costs by a small industrial plant producing 300,000 lb of steam daily and a reduction of $40,000 by a plant generating 5,000,000 lb of steam daily.

The rate at which the protective film builds up is quite important. Ulmer and Wood[66] ran time studies on two proprietary film-formers. One was the "octadecylamine type" at 30 ppm, and the other was a "quarternary ammonium salt type" at a dosage of 20 ppm. They found that the corrosion rate decreased as a function of time, but there was still considerable attack even after 28 days. They point out that the film-forming inhibitors can be classified as "dangerous." If enough inhibitor to form a continuous film is not used, then anodic action leading to several local attacks can occur. Patzelt[140] investigated octadecylamine acetate at 10 ppm and an unidentified proprietary material at the same level. He found that corrosion continued over a long period of time although at reduced rates. It would thus appear to be desirable to start treatment at a high-dosage level to lay down the protective film rapidly, and then to reduce the treatment level to that necessary to maintain and repair the film.

There is some disagreement as to the desirable feeding point for film-forming inhibitors. All inhibitor suppliers state that the materials can be fed directly to the steam and condensate systems. Some suppliers recommend adding the inhibitor to the feedwater or directly to the boiler and state that the inhibitor will evaporate with the steam and condense in a thin, continuous film. Others are uncertain of the vaporization characteristics of those inhibitors and prefer direct addition to the lines.

REFERENCES

1. *Boiler Corrosion and Water Treatment* (London: Gt. Brit. Admiralty, 1945, pub. 1947).

2. Brooke, M. Simplify boiler-water treatment. *Petroleum Refiner,* **35,** No. 11, 193–6, 1956.

3. Eisenstecken, F. Corrosion and corrosion protection in the installations of the boiler industry. *Mitt. Ver. Grosskesselbesitzer,* 396–409, 1956.

4. Evans, U. R. Boiler-water treatment to prevent corrosion. *Bull. Centre Belge Etude et Document Eaux* (Liege), No. 19, 34–42, 1953.

5. Fitzpatrick, L. W. Water treatment engineering—chemicals used in water conditioning. *Power Eng.,* **57,** No. 2, 74–5, Feb. 1953.

6. Hamer, P. J. The prevention of scale and corrosion in boilers. *Inst. Heating Ventilating Engrs.* (London), **23,** 476–85, 1956.

7. Laird, A. Boiler corrosion and its alleviation by feedwater conditioning. *Corrosion Prevention and Control,* **5,** No. 2, 35–8; No. 3, 57–62, 1958.

8. Malicet, R. Protection against corrosion in industrial plants using steam. *Corrosion et Anticorrosion,* **5,** 174–84, June 1957.

9. Anon. Symposium on boiler water chemistry. *Ind. Eng. Chem.,* **5,** 953–97, May 1954.

10. van Dongen Torman, P. Protection against corrosion in the boiler room. *Metalen,* **11,** 282–5, 1956; *Chem. Zentr.,* **129,** 1948, 1958.

11. Turner, T. H. Boiler-water treatment: a general review. *Corrosion Prevention and Control,* **3,** No. 9, 37–40, Sept. 1956.

12. Uhlig, H. H. *Corrosion Handbook* (New York: John Wiley & Sons, Inc., 1948).

13. Brindisi, P. Proper water treatment for packaged boilers. *Power,* **97,** No. 6, 76–7, June 1953.

14. Hinst, H. F. Corrosion problems in small heating boilers. *J. Am. Water Works Assoc.,* **48,** 11–8, 1956.

15. Pincus, L. I. Water treatment for low-pressure heating boilers. *Power,* **97,** No. 8, 118–9, Aug. 1953.

16. Arthurs, J., Robins, J. A., and Whitefoot, T. B. Treatment of water for an industrial high-pressure boiler plant. *Trans. Inst. Chem. Engrs.* (London), **37,** 72–88, 1959.

17. Hamer, P. Present-day feedwater treatment for high-pressure boilers. *Eng. and Boiler House Rev.,* **74,** 368–71, 374, 1959.

18. Kagan, D. Y. The corrosion of high-pressure boilers and the methods to fight it. *Vnutrikotlovye Fiz.-Khim. Protsessy, Akad. Nauk S.S.S.R., Energet. Inst. im. G. M. Krzhizhanovskogo,* 339–47, 1957.

19. Potter, E. C. Treatment and control of boiler feedwater: new interpretations. *Chemistry and Industry,* No. 10, 308–14, Mar. 7, 1959; *J. Inst. Fuel,* **32,** 218–24, 1959.

20. Ulrich, J. A. Treating high-pressure boilers. *Mariner,* **1,** No. 3, 28–9, 42, Mar. 1954.

21. Calise, V. J., and Duff, J. H. Treatment of make-up feedwater, condensate, and recyle water for supercritical and nuclear-reactor power-plant cycles. *Trans. Am. Soc. Mech. Engrs.,* **80,** 1659–75, 1958.

22. Tash, J. A., and Klein, H. A. Boiler-water-chemistry operating experience at the Shippingport atomic power station. *U.S. Atomic Energy Commission WAPD-BT-12,* 136–49, 1959.

23. Ulmer, R. C. Significance and application of water analysis data. *Ind. Eng. Chem.,* **46,** No. 5, 975–8, May 1954. Table 2-1 reprinted by courtesy of R. C. Ulmer and INDUSTRIAL AND ENGINEERING CHEMISTRY.

24. Green, J. Reversion of molecularly dehydrated sodium phosphates. *Ind. Eng. Chem.,* **42,** No. 8, 1542–6, Aug. 1950.

25. Straub, F. G. *Univ. of Illinois Bulletin No. 216,* 76–9, 1930.

26. Andrew, W. L. Control of resinous materials in lower-pressure boiler feedwaters. *Proc. Am. Water Conf. Engr. Soc. W. Pa.,* **13,** 113–22, 1952.

27. Clarke, F. E., and Hopkins, R. D. Significance of boiler deposit analysis. *Ind. Eng. Chem.,* **46,** No. 5, 979–91, May 1954.

28. Howells, E., McNary, T. A., and White, D. E. Boiler model tests of materials for steam generators in pressurized water reactor plants. *Corrosion,* **16,** No. 11, 571t–7t, 1960.

29. Zenkevich, Y. V., and Karasik, N. Y. Chemical and phase composition of the slime of boilers operating under superhigh pressure. *Teploenergetika,* **5,** No. 9, 68–70, 1958.

30. Deev, I. T., Rassonskaya, I. S., and Khlapova, A. N. Phase composition of boiler scales and sludges. *Vnutrikotlovye Fiz.-Khim. Protsessy, Akad. Nauk S.S.S.R., Energet. Inst. im. G. M. Krzhizhanovskogo,* 251–60, 1957.

31. Fitzpatrick, L. W. Stop scale formation in your boiler with proper treatment. *Power,* **99,** No. 2, 106–8, Feb. 1955.

32. Hanlon, R. T. Boiler-tube deposit composition and thickness. *Modern Power and Eng.,* **51,** No. 1, 74–9, 1957.

33. Samilov, Y. F., and Smirnov, O. K. The behavior of calcium hydroxide and calcium chloride in the tubes of a direct flow boiler. *Teploenergetika,* **6,** No. 2, 53–7, 1959.

34. Gerke, F. K., and Tebenikhin, E. F. Effect of surface treatment and composition of metal on scale formation. *Zaschita Metal. ot Korrozii i Obrazovanie Nakipi* (Moscow, Mashgiz) 1953, No. 24, 62–70, 1953.

35. Peters, F. K., and Engell, H. J. The adhesion of scale on steel. *Arch. Eisenhuttenw.,* **30,** 275–82, 1959.

36. Kot, A. A. The quality of the steam and the water regime in cylindrical boilers at high pressures. *Vnutrikotlovye Fiz.-Khim. Protsessy, Akad. Nauk S.S.S.R., Energet. Inst. im. G. M. Krzhizhanovskogo,* 143–78, 1957.

37. Kot, A. A. Scale formation in high-pressure boilers. *Elek. Stantsii,* **30,** No. 8, 74–5, 1959.

38. Wickert, K. Chemical and physical behavior of neutral salts in superheated steam plant operations. *Mitt. Ver. Grosskesselbesitzer,* No. 28, 75–9, 1954.

39. Schudlich, H. M., *et al.* MBMA covers steam and diesel subjects. Oil problems, diesel cooling systems and boilers. *Ry. Locomotives and Cars,* **128,** No. 10, 65–6, Oct. 1954.

40. Tatarinov, B. P. Foaming of boiler water. *Trudy Novocherkassk, Politekh. Inst.,* **25,** 67–79, 1955.

41. Villar, G. E. Theory of inhibiting foam produced by solid dispersed particles in aqueous medium. *Bol. fac. ing. y agrimensure Montevideo*, **6**, No. 8, 211–7, 1955.

42. Styrikovich, M. A. Solubility of impurities present in water and steam and their behavior in the steam tract of power stations. *Trudy Moskov. Energet. Inst.*, No. 25, 106–22, 1955.

43. Andres, R. F. Corrosion in the boiler. *Ind. Eng. Chem.*, **46**, No. 5, 990–2, May 1954.

44. Kaufman, C. E., Trautman, W. H., and Schnarrenberger, W. R. Action of boiler water on steel—attack by bonded oxygen. *Trans. Am. Soc. Mech. Engrs.*, **77**, 423–32, 1955.

45. Francis, H. (personal communication).

46. Akol'zin, P. A., and Ratner, A. V. Intercrystalline corrosion of drums and tubes of high-pressure boilers. *Elek. Stantsii*, **25**, No. 1, 6–10, 1954.

47. Hall, R. E. Conditioning water for steam generation. *Trans. Am. Soc. Mech. Engrs.*, **66**, 457–88, 1944.

48. Tseitlin, K. L., Kurcheninova, N. K., Babitskaya, S. M., and Babakov, A. A. The corrosion of steel with hot alkali solution under pressure. *Khim. Prom.*, 438–40, 1954.

49. Podgornyi, I. G. The alkali brittleness of boiler steels. *Vnutrikotlovye Fiz.-Khim. Protsessy, Akad. Nauk S.S.S.R., Energet. Inst. im. G. M. Krzhizhanovskogo*, 366–83, 1957.

50. Parkins, R. N. Caustic cracking in steam boilers. The intercrystalline corrosion of mild steels. *Chem. and Ind.*, No. 9, 180–4, 1953.

51. Zapffe, C. A. Corrosion resistance of stainless steels. *Trans. Am. Soc. Mech. Engrs.*, **66**, 81–117, 1944.

52. Tajc, J. A. Thermodynamic and colloidal interpretation of the corrosion cracking of stressed mild steel in water solutions. *Proc. Am. Soc. for Testing Materials*, **37**, Part II, 588–99, 1937.

53. Akimov, G. V. *Theory and Research Methods of Metallic Corrosion* (Moscow: Academy of Science, 1945).

54. Dix, E. H., Jr. Acceleration of the rate of corrosion by high constant stresses. *Trans. Am. Inst. Mining Met. Engrs.*, **137**, 11, 1940.

55. Waber, J. T., McDonald, H. J., and Longtin, B. Theory of stress cracking of mild steel in nitrate solutions. *Trans. Electrochem. Soc.*, **87**, 209, 1945; Waber and McDonald, *Corrosion and Material Protection*, **2**, No. 8, 13, 1945; No. 9, 13, 1945; and **3**, Nos. 1–8, 13, 1946.

56. Clarke, F. E., and Ristanio, A. J. Investigation of chemical inhibitors for stress-corrosion cracking of stainless steel. Report for Jan. 1954 to June 1957, Naval Engineering Experiment Station, Annapolis, Sept. 9, 1957.

57. Williams, W. L. Chloride and caustic stress corrosion of austenitic stainless steel in hot water and steam. *Corrosion*, **13**, No. 8, 539t–45t, Aug. 1957.

58. Niederberger, R. B. Report 04007CS, U.S.N. Eng. Expt. Station, Nov. 30, 1956.

59. Phillips, J. H., and Singley, W. J. Screening tests of inhibitors to prevent chloride stress corrosion. *Corrosion*, **15**, No. 9, 450t–4t, Sept. 1959.

60. Edeleanu, C., and Snowden, P. P. Chloride and caustic stress corrosion of austenitic stainless steel in hot water and steam. *J. Iron and Steel Inst.*, **186**, Part 4, 406–22, Aug. 1957.

61. Schoofs, J. The examination of a case of corrosion in a reheater of a power-station boiler. *Bull. Centre Belge Etudes Document. Eaux*, No. 83, 436–9, 1957.

62. Kovacs, K. New developments in the investigation and prevention of corrosion of kettles. *Metalloberflache*, **13**, 167–8, June 1959.

63. Grobner, P., and Bret, Z. Oxidation of steels in superheated steam. *Hutnicke Listy*, **12**, No. 2, 125–31, 1957.

64. Hass, E. Salts and salt decomposition in Benson boilers. *Mitt. Ver. Grosskessel-besitzer,* 287–300, 1953; *Fuel Abstr.,* **14,** No. 1, 103–4, 1953.

65. Styrikovich, M. A. The solubility of low volatility substances in high-pressure steam. *Radioisotopes Sci. Research, Proc. Intl. Conf., Paris I,* 411–25, 1957 (pub. 1958).

66. Ulmer, R. C., and Wood, J. W. Inhibitors for eliminating corrosion in steam and condensate lines. *Ind. Eng. Chem.,* **44,** No. 8, 1761–5, Aug. 1952.

67. Straub, F. G. Wall tube corrosion in steam generating equipment. *Proc. Midwest Power Conf., Chicago,* 295–6, 439–42, 1948.

68. Collins, L. F., and Henderson, E. L. Corrosion in steam heating systems. *Heating, Piping, Air Conditioning,* **11,** Sept. to Dec. 1939; **12,** Jan. to May 1940. Quotation reprinted by courtesy of L. F. Collins and HEATING, PIPING, AND AIR CONDITIONING.

69. Skaperdas, G. T., and Uhlig, H. H. Corrosion of steel by dissolved carbon dioxide and oxygen. *Ind. Eng. Chem.,* **34,** No. 6, 748, 1942.

70. Collins, L. F. Corrosion in steam heating systems. *Power Plant Eng.,* **48,** 88–9, Mar. 1944.

71. Osmond, M. E., and Welder, B. Q. Filming amine solves tough corrosion problem for make-up system. *Power Plant Eng.,* **63,** No. 3, 75–6, Mar. 1959.

72. McKinney, D. S., McGovern, J. J., Young, G. W., and Collins, L. F. Preventing the solution of CO_2 in condensates by venting of the vapor space of steam heating equipment. *Heating, Piping, Air Conditioning,* **17,** 97–104, Feb. 1945.

73. Rozenfel'd, I. L., and Zhigalova, K. A. Method of investigation of corrosion of metals under condensation conditions. *Zavodskaya Lab.,* **25,** No. 2, 172–4, 1959.

74. Mamet, A. P., and Glushenko, V. V. Oxygen removal from boiler feedwater by steel shavings. *Elek. Stantsii,* **21,** 19–22, 1950.

75. Archibald, F. L., and Purcell, J. W. Progress in iron pickup control in the generating station water-steam cycle. *Proc. Am. Power Conf.,* **XIV,** 443–58, 1952.

76. Homig, H. E., and Richter, H. Alkalizing the water-steam cycle in condenser-type boilers. *Mitt. Ver. Grosskesselbesitzer,* No. 36, 615–20, 1955.

77. Grabowski, H. A., Ongman, H. D., and Willsey, W. B. Field studies of preboiler corrosion in higher pressure steam plants. *Combustion,* **27,** No. 11, 46–51, 1956.

78. Decker, J. M., and Marsh, J. C. Evaluation of several alkaline compounds for controlling corrosion-erosion in boiler feedwater systems. *Proc. Am. Power Conf.,* **16,** 569–79, 1954.

79. Deev, I. T. The corrosion of water economizers after treating the feedwater with sulfite. *Vnutrikotlovye Fiz.-Khim. Protsessy, Akad. Nauk S.S.S.R., Energet. Inst. im. G. M. Krzhizhanovskogo,* 334–8, 1957.

80. Oertel, R. Ger. 1,000,295, Jan. 3, 1957.

81. Ongman, H. D. Reducing solutions at steam boiler temperatures. *Combustion,* **24,** No. 8, 40–4, 1953.

82. Fiss, E. C. The use of hydrazine to prevent oxygen corrosion. *Southern Power and Ind.,* **73,** No. 12, 46–9, 1955.

83. Woodward, E. R. Hydrazine: new aid to water treatment. *Power,* **97,** No. 11, 91–3, 212–8, Nov. 1953.

84. Harshman, R. S., and Woodward, E. R. Hydrazine for boiler-feedwater treatment. *Trans. Am. Soc. Mech. Engrs.,* **77,** 869–73, 1955.

85. Woodward, E. R. Hydrazine for boiler-feedwater treatment. *Power,* **100,** No. 11, 80–2, 1956.

86. Woodward, E. R. Hydrazine for boiler-feedwater treatment. *Petroleum Refiner,* **35,** No. 12, 208–10, 1956.

87. Zanchi, C. The use of hydrazine in high-pressure boiler feedwaters. *Calore,* **25,** 264–70, 1954.

88. Zanchi, C. The use of hydrazine in high-pressure boiler feedwaters. *Chim. and Ind.* (Paris), **72,** 941, 1954.

89. Zimmerman, M. Chemical fixation of oxygen in water. *Tek. Tidskr.,* **88,** 1157–61, 1958.

90. Hartmann, H., and Resch, G. *Mitt. Ver. Grosskesselbesitzer,* No. 52, 54–60, 1958.

91. Nissen, W. The use of hydrazine for removing residual oxygen from high-pressure boiler feedwater. *Energietech,* **6,** 108–12, 1956.

92. Dickinson, N. L., Felgar, D. N., and Pirsh, E. A. Experimental investigation of hydrazine-oxygen reaction rates in boiler feedwater. *Proc. Am. Power Conf.,* **19,** 692–702, 1957.

93. Leicester, J. The chemical deaeration of boiler water—the use of hydrazine compounds. *Trans. Am. Soc. Mech. Engrs.,* **78,** 273–85, 1956.

94. Zimmerman, M., and Brinkmann, G. Prevention of corrosion in boilers. Ger. 970, 310, Sept. 4, 1958.

95. Stones, W. F. The use of hydrazine as an oxygen scavenger in H.P. boilers. *Chem. and Ind.,* No. 5, 120–8, Feb. 2, 1957.

96. Massart, R., and Missa, L. Treatment of boiler water with sulfite or hydrazine. *Bull. Centre Belge Etude et Document. Eaux* (Liege), No. 42, 276–87, 1958.

97. Dow Chemical Company. *Separan NP-10 in Water Treatment.* (Midland, Mich.: Dow Chemical Company, no date.)

98. Schwarz, L. Increasing the heat transfer of surface condensers by degasification of cooling water. *Brennstoff-Warme-Kraft,* **10,** 224, 1958.

99. Hatch, G. B., and Rice, O. Corrosion control and scale prevention with glassy phosphate. *Ind. Eng. Chem.,* **37,** No. 8, 710–5, Aug. 1945.

100. Rice, O., and Partridge, E. P. Threshold treatment—elimination of calcium carbonate deposits from industrial waters. *Ind. Eng. Chem.,* **31,** No. 1, 58, Jan. 1939.

101. Buehrer, T. F., and Reitemeier, R. F. Inhibiting action of minute amounts of sodium hexametaphosphate on the precipitation of calcium carbonate from ammoniacal solutions. *J. Phys. Chem.,* **44,** 552, 1940.

102. Anon. Prevention of scale and corrosion with phosphates and filming amines. *Corrosion Technology,* **5,** 363–8, Nov. 1958.

103. Gray, J. A. Boiler-water treatment: a formula for the control of sludge and scale in internal (carbonate) treatment. *J. Inst. Fuel,* **30,** 577–91, 1957.

104. Gerard, W. F. Boiler-water treatment: a formula for the control of sludge and scale in internal (carbonate) treatment. *J. Inst. Fuel,* **31,** 139, 1958.

105. Anchev, K. Boiler scale and the fight against its formation in thermal electric stations. *Khim. i. Ind.,* **29,** No. 6, 25–8, 1957.

106. Jacklin, C. Deposits in boilers. *Ind. Eng. Chem.,* **46,** No. 5, 989–90, May 1954.

107. Holmes, J. A. The development of organics for water treatment. *Proc. Midwest Power Conf.,* **13,** 238–45, 1951.

108. L'Auxiliare des Chemins de fer et de l'Industrie. Boiler-antiscaling composition. Fr. 988,592, Aug. 29, 1951.

109. Lecornu, A. P. Scale-preventing compositions. Fr. 1,007,555, May 7, 1952.

110. Johnson, C. E. Reduction of boiler scale. U.S. 2,723,956, Nov. 15, 1955.

111. Jursich, M. J. Reduction of scale in steam boilers. U.S. 2,749,305, June 5, 1956.

112. Wollerman, E., Jorss, R., and Kadner, R. Prevention of boiler deposits. Ger. (East) 11,735, June 11, 1956.

113. Boelke, M. Compositions preventing the formation of boiler scale. Ger. 838,277, July 19, 1956.

114. Akahane, M., and Kurosawa, A. Removal of silica in the boiler water. Test of basic magnesium compounds as the silica-removing agent for locomotive boiler. *J. Chem. Soc.* (Japan Ind. Chem. Sect.), **58,** 402–4, 1955.

115. Hall, R. E. Treatment of steam-boiler water. *Proc. Ninth Annual Water Conf. Eng. Soc. W. Pa.,* Oct. 18–20, 1948.

116. Ulmer, R. C., Whitney, J. H., and Wood, J. W. Inhibitors for eliminating corrosion in steam and condensate lines. *Proc. Am. Power Conf.,* **XIV,** 459–67, 1952.

117. Kahler, H. L. Iron retention in water supplies with water-soluble lignin. U.S. 2,744,866, May 8, 1956.

118. Denman, W. L. Foam inhibition in steam generating systems. *Ind. Eng. Chem.,* **46,** No. 5, 792–4, May 1954.

119. Johnson, C. E. Prevention of foaming in steam generation. U.S. 2,609,344, Sept. 2, 1952.

120. Denman, W. L. Foam inhibition in steam-generating systems. U.S. 2,727,867, Dec. 20, 1955.

121. Ryznar, J. W. Compositions for inhibiting foaming in steam generation. U.S. 2,701,239, Feb. 1, 1955.

122. Johnson, C. E. Inhibition of foaming in steam generation. U.S. 2,875,156, Feb. 24, 1959.

123. Bird, P. G., and Jacoby, A. L. Foam inhibitors for steam boilers. U.S. 2,717,881, Sept. 13, 1955.

124. Auxiliaire des Chemins de fer et de l'Industrie. Antifoaming agents for boiler feedwater. Fr., 999,437, Jan. 31, 1952.

125. Rath, R. Caustic cracking in steam boilers. *Chem. and Ind.,* No. 25, 600–3, June 20, 1953.

126. Akolzin, P. A., Kagan, D. Y., and Kot, A. A. Safe regimes for alkaline boiler waters. *Teploenergetika,* **4,** No. 6, 32–5, 1957.

127. Schroeder, W. C., Berk, A. A., and Partridge, E. P. *Proc. A.S.T.M.,* **36,** Part 2, 1936.

128. Purcell, T. E., and Whirl, S. F. Protection against caustic embrittlement by coordinated phosphate–pH control. *Trans. Am. Soc. Mech. Engrs.,* **64,** 397–402, 1942.

129. Weir, C. D., and Hamer, P. Caustic cracking in boilers: prevention by chemical methods. *Chem. and Ind.,* No. 43, 1040–9, Oct. 25, 1952.

130. Stanisavlievici, L. Prevention of caustic corrosion in steam boilers. *Energetic,* **4,** 269–72, 1956.

131. American Railway Engineers Society. *Amer. Ry. Eng. Soc. Bull. 490.* (Chicago: Amer. Ry. Eng. Soc., 1950.)

132. Akolzin, P. A., and Ratner, A. V. Intercrystallite corrosion of the metal of cylinders and pipes of high-pressure boilers. *Vnutrikotlovye Fiz.-Khim. Protsessy, Akad. Nauk S.S.S.R., Energet. Inst. im. G. M. Krzhizhanovskogo,* 384–95, 1957.

133. Straub, F. G. *Mech. Eng.,* **61,** 199–202, 1939.

134. Akolzin, P. A. The role of the boiler-water components in the development of intergranular cracks in boiler's metal. *Korroziya Metal. i Metody Borbys Neyo Sbornik,* 71–86, 1955; *Referat. Zhur. Khim.* 1956, Abstr. No. 41943.

135. Leick, J. *Arch. Metallkunde,* **3,** 100–5, 1959.

136. Maguire, J. J. After-boiler corrosion. *Ind. Eng. Chem.,* **46,** No. 5, 994–7, May 1954.

137. Kahler, H. L., and Brown, J. K. Experiences with filming amines in control of condensate line corrosion. *Combustion*, **25**, No. 7, 55–8, 1954.

138. Sperry, S. M. Reduction of iron and copper corrosion in steam and water cycle with amines. *Combustion*, **27**, No. 5, 65–71, 1955.

139. Jacklin, C. Amines for corrosion prevention in steam condensate systems. *Corrosion*, **9**, No. 7, 1, July 1953.

140. Patzelt, H. A laboratory method for the study of steam condensate corrosion inhibitors. *Corrosion*, **9**, No. 1, 19–24, Jan. 1953.

141. Mondoux, R. G. Reduce corrosion in your return system. *Modern Power and Eng.*, **48**, No. 9, 84–86, 154–6, Sept. 1954.

142. Jacklin, C. Experimental boiler studies of the breakdown of amines. *Trans. Am. Soc. Mech. Engrs.*, **77**, 449–53, 1955.

143. Ashcroft, W. K., and Heron, P. N. Cyclohexylamine in water treatment. *Eng. and Boiler House Rev.*, **74**, 51–3, 1959.

144. Anon. Good capacity for absorbing carbon dioxide makes amine useful in corrosion inhibiting formulations. *Chem. Processing*, **14**, No. 1, 20, Jan. 1951.

145. Ashcroft, W. K., and Heron, P. N. Cyclohexylamine for corrosion prevention in steam-raising equipment. *Corrosion Technology*, **6**, No. 3, 85–8, Mar. 1959.

146. Hagan Chemicals and Controls. *Hagamin—Neutralizing Amine Condensate Corrosion Inhibitors* (Product Bulletin No. 342). (Pittsburgh: Hagan Chemicals and Controls, no date.)

147. Balezin, S. A., and Kleshcheva, G. V. Effects of amines on corrosion of carbon steels in neutral solutions. *Sbornik, Komitet po Korrozii i Zashchite Metal. Vseoyuz. Sovet. Nauch.-Tekh. Obshchestv,* No. 2, 124–30, 1957.

148. Hanlon, R. T. Causes and prevention of condensate return line corrosion. *Proc. Midwest Power Conf.*, **10**, 134–40, 1948.

149. Cannon, D. R. More heat less corrosion. Chemicals and raw materials. *Chem. Engr.*, **62**, 140–2, Apr. 1955.

150. Mann, C., Lauer, B., and Hutlin, C. Organic inhibitors of corrosion—aliphatic amines. *Ind. Eng. Chem.*, **28**, No. 9, 1049, Sept. 1936.

151. Hackerman, N., and Sudbury, J. D. Effect of amines on the electrode potential of mild steel in tap water and acid solutions. *J. Electrochem. Soc.*, **97**, 109, 1950.

152. Kuznetsov, V. A., and Iofa, Z. A. Inhibitor action on solution of iron in acids. *Zhur. Fiz. Khim.*, **21**, 201, 1947.

153. Breston, J. N. Corrosion control with organic inhibitors. *Ind. Eng. Chem.*, **44**, No. 8, 1755–61, Aug. 1952.

154. Nathan, C. C. Studies on the inhibition by amines of the corrosion of iron by solutions of high acidity. *Corrosion*, **9**, No. 6, 199–202, June 1953.

155. Bigelow, W. C., Pickett, S. C., and Zisman, W. A. Oleophobic monolayers. I. Film adsorbed from solution in nonpolar liquids. *J. Coll. Sci.*, **1**, 513, 1946.

156. Wilkes, J. F., Denman, W. L., and Obrecht, M. F. Filming amines. Use and misuse in power plant water-steam cycles. *Natl. Eng.*, **59**, No. 6, 20–3, 42, 1955.

157. Denman, W. L. Corrosion inhibitors. U.S. 2,882,171, Apr. 14, 1959.

158. Osipowe, L. I. Corrosion inhibition in steam and water systems. U.S. 2,890,928, June 16, 1959.

159. Sato, S., and Kato, Y. Rust-preventive additives. Salts of some organic acids with octadecylamine. *Kogyo Kagaku Zasshi*, **61**, 69–72, 1958.

160. Ryznar, J. W., and Kirkpatrick, W. H. Inhibition of corrosion in steam-condensate lines. U.S. 2,771,417, Nov. 20, 1956.

161. Denman, W. L., and Hwa, C. M. Corrosion inhibitors for steam and condensate lines. U.S. 2,998,193, June 2, 1959.

162. Akolzin, P. A., Zaitseva, Z. I., and Lazareva, L. I. The prevention of oxygen and carbon dioxide corrosion with the use of octadecylamine. *Teploenergetica,* **5,** No. 10, 54–5, 1958.

163. Elliott, E., and Gaughan, P. J. Plant stops return-line corrosion—saves $14,200 a year. *Power Plant Eng.,* **55,** No. 8, 104–9, Aug. 1951.

3

Cooling Water—
Cooling-Tower
Systems

There are several different types of cooling systems which require the use of corrosion inhibitors. Any breakdown of these systems into various categories for examination must perforce be arbitrary. One could make a distinction between recirculating systems and "once-through" systems, but this classification would not be of too much significance, since most of the systems discussed will be recirculating systems. These systems will therefore be examined by use-categories, since this method should have the most practical significance to the reader. The breakdown of use-categories will be as follows:

1. *Cooling-tower systems.*
2. *Internal combustion engine systems.*
3. *Once-through systems.*
4. *Refrigerating brine systems.*

The reasons for these arbitrary classifications will become clear as the discussion of each category proceeds. The cooling-tower systems will be examined in detail in this chapter, while the other systems will be studied in the next chapter. Many of the principles enunciated here for cooling-tower systems will also apply to the other systems.

The initial and probably still the largest use of corrosion inhibitors in the petroleum and processing industries has been for heat-exchange units associated with cooling towers. In this application, the problem of corrosion per se cannot be set apart from the other water problems. Dirt, formation of carbonate scale, phosphate sludges, iron and aluminum deposits, contamination by H_2S or SO_2, various bacteriological growths, and delignification of the wood in the tower all interfere with corrosion inhibition and not only increase the amount of attack but also considerably change its nature and location. For this reason, cooling-tower systems are generally treated for scale and deposit prevention and bacteriological control in addition to corrosion prevention. The discussion of cooling-tower systems in this section will therefore include these aspects of the problem.

LITERATURE

Thorough discussions of cooling-tower water treatments have appeared in a wide variety of technical and trade journals. Some more useful recent articles which present discussions of all of the various phases of cooling-tower problems and treatments were written by Brooke,[1] Thornley,[2] Forbes,[3] and Dalbke and Masterson.[4] Discussions of over-all water treatment at specific cooling-tower installations were presented by Kennedy[5] for cooling towers used by the Kansas Gas and Electric Company and Gossom and Johnson[6] for equipment at the D-X Sunray Oil Company. A review of water utilization and treatment efficiency of cooling towers at 16 Gulf Coast refineries and chemical plants was presented by the Recirculating Cooling Water Work Group of the National Association of Corrosion Engineers.[7] Helwig and McConomy[8] surveyed 31 refineries and found that fouling and corrosion occurred in all open circulating systems supplied by fresh make-up water when treatment was not practiced.

Earlier discussions of cooling-water treatment problems were presented by Cook,[9] Drane,[10] Paulsen,[11] Gibson,[12] Winzig,[13] Fitzpatrick,[14] Slough,[15] Evans,[16] and Miller.[17] McConomy[18] gathered a literature survey from 1940 to 1953 of corrosion in cooling-water systems, while Rice[19] presented a comprehensive review of all published work from 1940 to 1952 on the treatment of recirculated cooling water.

ECONOMICS

Chemicals which are sold directly for cooling-tower applications include the following:

1. *Antifoams.*
2. p*H adjustment materials.*
3. *Bactericides.*
4. *Scale preventives.*
5. *Corrosion inhibitors.*

It was estimated by the Recirculating Cooling Water Work Group of the National Association of Corrosion Engineers[20] (N.A.C.E.) that the annual American cost of chemicals for this purpose in the chemical and refining industries was $22.5 million in 1955, with the bulk of the money going for scale and corrosion control, including pH adjustment. This figure has increased considerably by 1961, but no more current data are available.

An interesting study of treatment costs at 16 Gulf Coast refineries and chemical plants which have a total of 49 cooling towers was conducted by the same N.A.C.E. subcommittee.[7] These 16 plants were spending a total of $407,000 annually from 1956 to 1957 for water-

TABLE 3-1. Cost Data for an Average Gulf Coast Cooling Tower[7]

CONTROL	AMOUNT (lb/day)	UNIT COST	DAILY COST
pH	702	$0.01	$ 7.02
Algae	58	0.06	3.48
Scale and corrosion	99	0.18	17.82
Total			$28.32

Treatment: pH control: assumed to be sulfuric acid.
Algae control: assumed to be chlorine.
Scale and corrosion control: assumed to be one of the synergistic treatments.

TABLE 3-2. Cost Data for an Average Tower[7]

CONTROL	COST/10^9 BTU
*p*H	$1.80
Algae	0.89
Scale and corrosion	4.57
Total	$7.26

treating chemicals. Table 3-1 is taken from their report and presents data for an average Gulf Coast cooling tower.

The same committee also calculated costs in terms of dollars per billion BTU's for a typical tower, and arrived at the figures shown in Table 3-2.

They then found that if the towers were operated at 100 per cent efficiency, the total cost could be reduced to $4.20, with $2.87 of the $3.06 total savings coming from a reduction in the costs of scale and corrosion control.

THE PROBLEM

In view of the intimate relationship of the problems of scale and bacteria to the corrosion of metals in open recirculating cooling systems, they will also be treated in this section. Attempts to minimize corrosion without considering these other problems are generally unsuccessful, and corrosion inhibitors are usually added as part of the package treatment for this system. Because we are dealing with a recirculating system, the topic breakdown in this section will be by the type of problem, rather than by location in the system.

Deposits

Undesirable deposits are quite varied in nature and can come from many sources. For the purpose of this discussion, they are classified as precipitated suspended solids, inorganic scaling, phosphate sludge, and metal deposits. Each will be discussed separately.

Suspended solids may be present in the recirculating water because of incomplete preclarification, poor filtration, dust, or contamination by such things as bird droppings. Many river waters are subjected to clarification processes prior to use for cooling purposes. Techniques involved vary from the use of only sedimentation ponds to elaborate coagulation procedures. These procedures may include the use of conventional flocculants such as alum, lime, soda ash, sodium aluminate, and Ferrifloc, and also the addition of the newer polymeric coagulants. The latter group includes both natural polymers, such as starch or guar gum, or synthetic polymers, such as polyacrylamides or polyamines. Elaborate clarification units can be employed, since such factors as residence time, stirring, mode of addition, and pH can be critical.

Improper clarification can result in the presence of suspended solids in the cooling water for one of two reasons. Either settling time and the basin were insufficient so that floc carried over with the clarified water or else postflocculation occurred. This phenomenon of postflocculation results when some of the floc formation is retarded and takes place after the clarified water has entered the cooling system. It is especially objectionable since the presence of aluminum ions will cause the removal of phosphate ions from the treated cooling water and thus interfere with corrosion and scale inhibition. Laboratory experiments conducted on this problem[21] show that formation of a floc based on alum in cooling water which has been treated with polyphosphate results in rapid absorption of phosphate and polyphosphate ions by the growing floc with a consequent appreciable decrease of the concentration of these ions remaining in solution. In actual practice, this problem can become so severe that either the preclarification treatment must be radically changed or else the phosphate water treatment must be replaced by some other technique.

Poor filtration is another major cause of suspended solids. The diatomaceous earth filters which are commonly used frequently do not operate at maximum efficiency, and leakage of clay particles occurs. The problem may be one of operation above rated capacity or, more likely, the lack of backwashing and filter-bed cleansing according to specifications.

Bird droppings are often a serious cooling-tower problem. Large flocks of birds may find the tower to be a convenient roosting place and produce a quantity of droppings sufficient to cause considerable tower difficulties. In addition, many of the larger cooling-tower systems in the United States are located in areas where dust storms are frequent.

Another source of external contamination can be process solids or other chemicals blown into the towers.

The problems caused by precipitation of suspended solids are obvious. Accumulation of solids in stagnant areas (as in bends of tubing) will interfere with heat transfer, provide excellent sites for bacterial growth or development of local corrosion cells, and lead to tube failures at those points. These deposits also act as filters which entrap other particles that normally might not settle out, thus providing an auto-accelerated growth mechanism.

The term *inorganic scale* is used to cover a number of chemical compounds which adhere tightly to the metal surface and reduce heat transfer. The most common scale and the one which is generally of the most concern is calcium carbonate, but calcium sulfate, magnesium compounds, and iron oxides are also part of this group. In practice, these scales are present at the same time in a mixture, and the deposit is heavily interspersed with corrosion product.

Calcium carbonate precipitates because of the nature of the operation of the cooling-tower system. The make-up water fed to the system generally has only a small amount of calcium in it and has little carbonate and some bicarbonate ions. During the course of the operation, however, several things happen which build up the $CaCO_3$ concentration to a point where it comes out of solution and forms very adherent deposits on the hot metal surfaces. The major cause is the gradual increase in the concentration of solids to anywhere from four to six times their original concentration in the make-up water. The degree to which the solids content can be increased by keeping the make-up water at a minimum is, of course, a direct measure of the efficiency of the system. Therefore the concentration is raised to the maximum value possible before scale and corrosion problems dictate a halt.

The temperature plays an important role in scale formation. As it increases because of heat exchange with the process side, the bicarbonate decomposes, CO_2 is lost, and the much more insoluble (with calcium) carbonate forms. Hatch and Rice[22] published a graph which shows that for samples heated for 1 hr at various temperatures, the maximum calcium bicarbonate concentration which can be maintained without deposition drops from 200 ppm as $CaCO_3$ at 40° C to about 67 ppm at 100° C. They point out that when a hard (i.e., containing Ca^{++} and Mg^{++}) bicarbonate water is heated, the *p*H of saturation decreases and deposition is a result. The value of the *p*H of saturation is such that the partial pressure of CO_2 (hence the rate of loss) is relatively high.

The pH as already mentioned is an important factor. It should also be noted that, in practice, for better corrosion inhibition the pH is kept as high as possible without having scaling occur. Thus the pH is being constantly maintained right at the edge of the scaling value. Furthermore, the alkalinity of the system generally increases with the total solids. Finally, other suspended solids or deposits present in the system can act as seeding materials for the precipitation of calcium carbonate.

The physical nature of the calcium carbonate scale is such that it is especially objectionable in heat-transfer systems. A hard, tenaciously adherent, and occasionally baked scale causes the heat exchange to drop off markedly and the tube walls to become overheated. In addition, the scale builds up rapidly, entraps other materials, cuts down the effective water-passage volume, and can even plug the tube entirely.

Calcium sulfate can form as a scale in the case of certain water which is high in sulfate ions and which is used at high temperatures (160 to 170° F). Magnesium hydroxide or carbonate may be entrapped by the scale. Iron oxide can deposit because of the presence of either (1) dissolved iron in the make-up water or (2) corrosion products. These deposits are all objectionable and are generally found together with the calcium carbonate scale.

Phosphate sludge is an artificial condition brought about by the addition of polyphosphates as scale minimizers or as corrosion inhibitors. As already described, the polyphosphates revert to orthophosphates, although at a much slower rate than under boiler conditions. There is sufficient orthophosphate present, however, so that iron or aluminum ions which may be present in the water form insoluble phosphate sludges. These sludges form sticky deposits and serve to deplete the desirable phosphate concentration of the treated water.

Metal deposits can be caused by the presence of copper or iron in the water as a result of corrosion somewhere in the system. They are very undesirable since they form galvanic couples when deposited on other metals and promote pitting corrosion.

Bacteria

Reviews of microbiological fouling in recirculating cooling-water systems were published by Maguire, Betz, and Betz,[23] Talbot *et al.*,[24] and Williams.[25] Updegraff[26] published a more general discussion of microbiological corrosion of iron and steel, while Brooke[1] presented a chart identifying bacteria, algae, and fungi found in recirculating cooling water.

The two major groups of organisms which cause deposit and corrosion problems in cooling-tower systems are *slime* and *algae*. They manifest themselves in somewhat different manners and therefore will be treated separately. *Sulfate-reducing bacteria* have also been found occasionally in these systems and are mentioned briefly.

Slime-forming bacteria form a gelatinous mass which is composed mostly of airborne organisms and contains fungi, yeasts, bacteria, and protozoa. In addition, this mass entraps other solid material, both inorganic and organic in nature. The slime frequently forms in areas of low light-intensity[23] since these microorganisms are not dependent upon sunlight but instead derive their food from the water. The gelatinous outside coating gives the slimy mass considerable resistance to chemical and physical agents. These deposits are doubly injurious to cooling-water metal surfaces in that they seriously retard heat transfer and also form local corrosion cells and cause pitting attack. The growth of slime formers is aided by increases in temperature and in concentration of dissolved and suspended solids as well as by airborne contamination.[23]

Exposure of the recirculating water to sunlight in cooling towers and spray ponds promotes the growth of algae. The algae are found in both fresh and salt water and require sunlight for their growth. Large growths are found in the spray ponds and cooling towers which interfere with water distribution and proper cooling. They also plug screens and restrict flow in pipelines and sumps. In addition, they will promote pitting corrosion. Maguire, Betz, and Betz[23] state that the corrosive mechanism of living algae is the depolarizing action of the oxygen liberated by the algae in the photosynthesis process, while dead algae lodge in heat-exchange units and cause local cell formation.

Sulfate-reducing bacteria are anaerobolic in nature, and one would normally not expect to find them in the highly oxygenated cooling-tower systems. Their occasional deleterious presence comes about, however, because they can take root under a covering of slime-formers which protect them from oxygen. Thus encouraged, they produce H_2S and cause severe pitting attack. Contamination of water with sulfides and mercaptans, because of the presence of hydrocarbons, provides nutrient for the sulfate reducers. Dirt or debris helps form the covering slime layer.

The corrosive mechanism of the sulfate-reducing bacteria is believed to be one of depolarization. The reduction of sulfates to sulfides by the bacteria must be accompanied by an oxidation reaction which removes the protective hydrogen film from the metal surface and starts localized corrosion.

Wood Deterioration

There appear to be two modes of deterioration of cooling-tower lumber: *chemical* and *microbiological*. The chemical attack involves leaching out soluble natural preservatives, reaction of chlorine with organics in the wooden towers, attack by sodium carbonate or other alkaline materials which cause the recirculating water to have a pH greater than 7.5, and the formation of salt on and in the wood.

The biological attack on wood is due to various fungi and can occur at any place in the tower. Various species of fungi preferentially attack different constituents of wood. The most severe problems usually occur in the mist sections of the tower, at or beyond the eliminators, but attack can also occur in the fill sections. There is considerable speculation that chemical attack occurs first and leaves the wood in a condition which is more prone to biological attack.[23]

Gas Contamination

Cooling towers in refineries are frequently subject to contamination by gases in the refinery atmosphere. These gases can interfere with the cooling-system treatment and destroy its effectiveness, or they may change the corrosive nature of the water and require a different treatment approach. Precipitation or fouling, pH changes, bacteriological effects, and deterioration of cooling-tower lumber can also be influenced.

Hydrogen sulfide is one of the most common gas contaminants, especially in refineries. Its major effect is the reduction of chromates which are used to inhibit corrosion. This reduction can be sufficiently severe to prohibit the use of chromates and require other less effective inhibitors. Sulfur dioxide is another common gaseous contaminant which can cause corrosion trouble by lowering the pH of the recirculating water. Ammonia can act as a contaminant and raise the pH while attacking copper or Admiralty parts severely. Other contaminants can be present that are derived from the unique composition of the liquid on the process side. It thus becomes apparent that gaseous contamination of recirculating water cannot be overlooked as a source of difficulties.

Corrosion

While the number and the sizes of cooling-tower units vary considerably, the corrosive factors are limited in number and are common to all of them. The discussion of the corrosion problem is therefore in terms of these factors.

Corrosion occurs mainly in the heat-exchange units, although pitting can occasionally be found in the pipes carrying the water to and from these units. Figure 3-1 presents a picture of severe localized attack in the water side of a refinery heat exchanger. The most common locations in the heat-exchange units are in the tubes, the points where the tubes and the header are joined, the header itself, and any place in the system where stagnant conditions can arise. The corrosive factors and the type of corrosion vary depending on the nature of the metal of construction. The initial part of this discussion therefore deals with iron corrosion, and the differences in the cases of other metals are discussed subsequently.

IRON. *Water Composition.* The cooling water will contain a very high concentration of dissolved solids because the efficiency of the system (in terms of cost) is a direct function of the number of concentrations that can be carried. The limit to which the circulating water can be concentrated is governed by its hardness and its pH. These factors determine the deposit formation and also affect the corrosiveness. The pH is especially important, and most cooling systems are generally kept in a narrow range of 6.0 to 7.5. The lower limit is the one below which appreciable corrosion takes place, while the upper limit is imposed because of scale formation. Many cooling-water systems have sulfuric acid or some other acid fed into them at a constant rate to lower the natural pH to the desired range. It is easy to visualize how an upset in the feeding system or an unexpected change in water composition could result in a rapid shift to an appreciably acidic pH value with consequent severe corrosion damage.

A high-dissolved solids content in the recirculating water increases

FIGURE 3-1. Severe Localized Attack in a Refinery Heat Exchanger—
Water Side

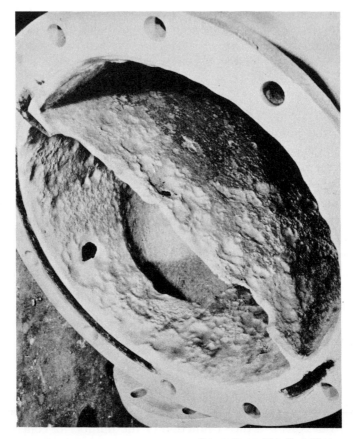

Photograph Courtesy of Nalco Chemical Company

the conductivity. The result is a larger corrosion current. Cathodic
areas further away from any specific anodic area can now take part
in the corrosion reaction and thus produce an effective increase in
the available cathodic area.

The nature of the ions which give the high-dissolved solids content
is quite important. Thus chloride is the most corrosive anion usually
present due to its small size and its ability to penetrate protective
films. In addition, it will complex iron and stimulate the corrosion
reaction and interfere with the formation of protective corrosion-
product films. The presence of a certain amount of calcium is actually

desirable, while excesses of calcium, magnesium, carbonate, sulfate, or phosphate ions are undesirable because of deposit formation.

Gases. The cooling water entering the heat exchangers is saturated with dissolved oxygen. This situation is inherent in these systems because of their nature. Chlorine is frequently present as a bactericide and can cause corrosion. Wormwell and Nurse[27] show that free chlorine levels up to 0.4 ppm can be tolerated, but beyond that point appreciable corrosion takes place. Other gases can enter the system as a result of atmospheric contamination peculiar to a particular location and can cause severe attack. These gases can include H_2S, SO_2, NH_3, HCl, or various organic compounds.

Water Velocity. Flow velocity can range anywhere from stagnant conditions to very rapid flow. Stagnant conditions, which can occur readily at bends in the tubing, at the point where the heat-exchange tube is joined to the header or under deposits and in crevices, lead to intense local attack with rapid pit development. A rapid flow is generally desirable since, among other things, it tends to keep the heat-transfer surface clean of fouling, scaling, and corrosion products. It serves to keep up the oxygen supply throughout the system and therefore minimize the formation of local cells. Too rapid a flow rate can be undesirable, especially on Admiralty metal tubes, since protective films of corrosion products may not form.[28]

Temperature. Temperatures in cooling-tower heat-exchange units range within a narrow band with 85 to 130° F as typical limits for ferrous systems. In this region, the corrosivity increases with the temperature, since decreasing oxygen solubility is not yet of any consequence. The higher temperatures also cause calcium carbonate scaling problems because of the decrease in the solubility of this material with increasing temperature.

In evaluating temperature effects, heat transfer must also be considered. Localized overheating for any reason, scale, corrosion products, or bacteria, results in rapid tube failure at that point.

Deposits. Throughout this discussion, continuous reference is made to the effect of deposits upon corrosion. The two factors are intimately associated, and the presence of deposits, almost irrespective of their nature, enhances the rapid development of localized corrosion. Calcium carbonate or phosphate scales can produce localized overheating and consequent rapid tube failure. Clay, alumina, or salt can foul heat-transfer surfaces and cause severe oxygen-concentration cell attack.

Microbiological growths will provide ideal conditions for local cells to arise. In addition, it is possible for sulfate-reducing bacteria to take root and grow well under a protective cover of slime. Hydrogen sulfide is produced with rapid metal pitting. This phenomenon has been reproduced on a laboratory scale[29] with evidence of sulfate reducers, H_2S, and typical pitting attack under the protective (to sulfate reducers) slime film.

An example of severe microbiological corrosion[30] is described as taking place in a large petroleum refinery in the southern part of Texas. Corrosion rates of 35 mils per year were occurring even though an inhibitor program was in effect. Test coupons were covered with a slimy black deposit and had an unusual type of pitting attack which manifested itself in the form of smooth-sided pits with concentric circles around the main penetration. Microbiological analyses showed very high counts of both sulfate-reducing and slime-forming bacteria. Treatment with proper microbiological agents eliminated both the corrosion and the bacteria.

It therefore becomes obvious that there can be no valid separation of the problem of deposit formation from that of corrosion and that the plant engineer who is responsible for corrosion prevention must also be concerned with the prevention of deposits.

COPPER. Copper and Admiralty metals are frequently used in cooling-tower heat-exchanger systems and have certain peculiar problems connected with them. Admiralty metal is the most commonly used material of construction next to steel. It has the advantage of being much more corrosion resistant than steel but also has the disadvantage of being much more expensive. There are certain conditions under which the Admiralty metal can be attacked, and these most commonly involve pH extremes. Low pH values (5 or less) or high pH values (9 or more) can be very deleterious. The low pH values can be brought about by poor acid feed control or else by the presence of acid gases in the air. The high pH is frequently the result of pick-up of ammonia from the air. This pick-up is especially undesirable as the ammonia will complex copper very readily and put it into solution. The formation of deposits as discussed previously for iron also causes corrosion of Admiralty.

The introduction of Admiralty metal into a system raises the possibility of galvanic effects. The entire system will rarely be made completely of Admiralty, and an extremely dangerous situation is therefore created at the point where the Admiralty and steel form a junction. Severe attack of the steel can take place at that junction.

Another danger which must be considered when Admiralty metal is used is the corrosive nature of the copper which is dissolved out of the Admiralty. This copper will plate out on the steel surfaces and will cause intense localized corrosion. The plated copper becomes cathodic to the steel and a corrosion couple is set up which is extremely difficult to eliminate.[31] The prevention of Admiralty corrosion thus becomes of twofold importance because (1) the Admiralty itself must be protected and (2) attack of the steel by the Admiralty corrosion products must be prevented.

In recent years, the use of copper for heat-exchange systems has grown appreciably, especially at Atomic Energy Commission plants. These exchangers are generally operated at higher temperature and velocity conditions than is the case with steel exchangers, and much better heat transfer is obtained. For example, Powell[32] has described the cooling facilities at the Atomic Energy Commission plant near Paducah, Kentucky, where several billion BTU per hr must be removed from a Freon coolant. Here the condenser tubes are made of pure copper, while supply headers and associated piping are of wrought steel. There are hundreds of the condensers with heat-transfer areas ranging from 8,000 to 14,000 ft^2 each. The cooling water in these systems undergoes a large temperature rise; the temperature of the water leaving the process condenser is anywhere from 130 to 180° F. Severe pitting occurred here, and examination showed that some of the pits were 0.042 in. deep after less than one year. The pitting was attributed to the presence of copper oxide deposits on the tubes and to use of an improper inhibitor.

Murray and Tester[33] studied the corrosion of copper condenser tubes for the Atomic Energy Commission. They found some pitting in tubes where the water velocity was low and severe pitting at high temperatures. Picarazzi[34] showed that under certain conditions involving brackish water and microbiological growths, service life of Admiralty may be poor and 70-30 copper-nickel is preferable. Other adverse effects on copper would be expected, of course, from the presence of H$_2$S or NH$_3$ in the atmosphere.

ALUMINUM. Aluminum cooling towers are used on occasion to replace wood towers. A large metallic surface area thus becomes exposed to the possibility of corrosion. DeHalas[35] states that the corrosion rates are apparently governed by the mean temperature of the oxide film formed on the surface of the aluminum plate. The Water Service Laboratories[36] point out that acid gases scrubbed from the large volumes of contaminated air passed through a cooling tower increases the acidity of the circulating water to such an extent that it attacks aluminum. Since aluminum is amphoteric, either a slightly acidic or basic pH value is deleterious, and the pH of the cooling water has to be closely maintained.

Sverepa[37] conducted an interesting study on the corrosion of aluminum alloys in which he found that recirculating waters were much more corrosive than river waters or make-up waters. The attack manifests itself in the form of pitting. Copper, chloride, calcium, and bicarbonate ions in the presence of oxygen were the most destructive. The rapid pitting due to copper brought about by the plating out of copper ions on aluminum is well known and must be avoided. There have been actual field cases where microbiological treatments containing copper were used in an aluminum system, with an ensuing rapid destruction of the aluminum. The chloride ion appears to have the ability to penetrate the protective aluminum oxide film, probably because of its small size. Bicarbonate ion can be harmful because it is a "dangerous" inhibitor; i.e., although it inhibits general attack, an insufficient amount can lead to serious pitting problems.

Haygood and Minford[38] divide the natural waters into four main classifications insofar as aluminum corrosion is concerned. These are

1. *Waters containing heavy metals.*
2. *Neutral or nearly neutral waters (pH 6 to 8).*
3. *Acidic waters (pH 4.5 to 6).*
4. *Alkaline waters (pH 8 to 9).*

They point out that aluminum alloys are susceptible to pitting in waters containing heavy metals such as copper, nickel, and lead. The effect of copper ion decreases as the pH is raised and its solubility drops. Sussman and Akers[39] point out that the heavy metal contaminants can be picked up by the water as a result of corrosion when recirculated in the evaporative cooling equipment.

Aluminum alloys are resistant to the acid waters (down to pH 4.5) even in the presence of large amounts of chloride.[38] Sussman and Akers[39] point out that in many areas where the waters have little buffering or acid-neutralizing capacity (such as in New York City), the pH may drop to values of 3.2 to 4.5 and other metals such as iron or copper in the system may be attacked. The dissolved heavy metals will then plate out on the aluminum and cause severe pitting. The neutral waters, as such, have little or no action upon aluminum.[40] The presence of heavy metals or excessive concentrations of particular water components can change this situation, however. The build-up of scales or deposits can form oxygen-concentration cells which result in pitting. The solution potential-relationships between the other metals present and aluminum can be such as to actively promote corrosion. Oxygen, carbon dioxide, and hydrogen sulfide, all of which will attack steel, will not be harmful to aluminum cooling-tower systems.

The alkaline waters (pH 8 to 9) darken the surfaces of aluminum alloys but generally do not cause any significant weight losses. The problem of scaling becomes troublesome at these pH values, however, and then corrosion can follow.

The deposition of suspended dirt becomes quite frequent in evaporative cooling equipment in urban and industrial areas. The dirt settles in the pan or basin of the equipment, and promotes the formation of concentration cells and localized corrosion below it.[39] Sussman and Akers cite an example of a cooling tower which was shut down for the winter by draining out the water. A three-quarter inch layer of muck remained on the bottom of the pan, which stayed damp for several weeks. When inspected later, hundreds of white tubercles were found scattered all over the surface of the dark dirt layer. Each tubercle had a pit underneath it.

INHIBITION

Deposits

The prevention of *suspended solids* such as those due to incomplete preclarification, bird droppings, or dust is generally accomplished by the installation of a suitable slipstream filter. Recent developments in this area include the treatment of this filter with a polymeric coagulant which increases removal capacity and rate of the filter by large amounts. When the problem is one of postprecipitation due to the presence of aluminum ion in the clarified water, the neutralization of polyphosphate ions can be such a serious problem that it may become necessary to avoid the use of polyphosphates for scale prevention or corrosion inhibition.

Channabasappa[41] has recently described the use of an organic-inorganic additive to corrosion-inhibitor formulations which prevents the deposition of suspended solids. Thus, for example, 40 ppm of a chromate treatment plus 15 ppm of the additive gave better corrosion inhibition than did 75 ppm of chromate alone, since the suspended solids did not precipitate and aggravate corrosion in the former case, but they did in the latter.

Calcium carbonate is both desirable and undesirable in a cooling-tower system. The undesirable features have already been discussed. It is not generally realized, however, that a thin film of calcium carbonate on the metal surfaces is a necessary feature for corrosion inhibition. This film must be thin enough to prevent any appreciable interference with heat transfer, but at the same time it protects the metal surface from corrosive attack and is the most economical corrosion inhibitor known for this purpose. For this reason, water-treatment recommendations for cooling-tower systems invariably specify a minimum calcium content as well as a maximum.

There are a number of methods commonly employed for the prevention of calcium carbonate scaling. These include the following:

1. *Control of pH.*
2. *Softening externally.*
3. *Maintenance of proper calcium and alkalinity levels by controlled blowdown.*
4. *Use of "threshold" polyphosphate treatments.*
5. *Use of surface-active agents.*
6. *Use of chelating agents.*
7. *Combinations of these approaches.*

The first three approaches are all based on the principle of maintaining the proper calcium, bicarbonate, and carbonate levels so that the solubility product of calcium carbonate will not be excessive.

Detailed semiempirical formulations, such as the Langelier and Ryznar indices, were developed which show the scale-forming tendency of any given water as a function of pH. As a general rule, however, one may say that the lower the pH value is, the less the tendency of cooling water to deposit calcium carbonate scale. In practice, scale and corrosion-inhibition formulations are kept in the pH range of about 6.0 to 7.5. The lower value is the one below which corrosion will be aggravated, while the higher figure is the one above which severe scaling may occur. Sulfuric acid is the most common chemical added for *p*H reduction, while citric or oxalic acids can be used in special cases. Acid addition is generally conducted on a continuous basis since the water is invariably too alkaline. Sodium hydroxide can be used in those rare occasions when the water is too acidic or if an unexpectedly large amount of acid is added and results in a sudden drop in the *p*H.

External softening means the use of various techniques to keep to a minimum the calcium content of the water which enters the cooling systems. These techniques were adequately described in the chapter on boiler-water chemistry. *Controlled blowdown* means the periodic removal of concentrated solutions from the cooling water and their replacement by fresh water. Here again, the calcium and carbonate values build up to the danger point and must be removed. The alkalinity of the system is important since the conversion of bicarbonate to carbonate ion must be prevented.

The mechanism of the threshold polyphosphate treatment to control calcium carbonate scaling was discussed in detail in the chapter on boiler-water treatment. This method of scale prevention appears to find almost universal application to cooling-water systems and generally meets with considerable success. There are a variety of polyphosphates in use today, but the most common ones are Calgon, tripolyphosphate, and pyrophosphate. In addition, certain complex, glassy, and "very slowly soluble" polyphosphates are also used. A convenient feeding method is to pelletize or ball the material, frequently together with other chemicals used for other treatment purposes, and hang it in a wire cage in the path of the water or else put it into a line through which the water must pass.[42] The major disadvantage of the polyphosphate treatment is its possible reversion to orthophosphate along with the formation of insoluble calcium phosphate sludge. Some of the articles dealing with the subject of threshold treatment include those by Hatch and Rice,[22] Kleber,[43] and Reif.[44]

In an interesting variation of the polyphosphate approach, Stone[45] claims that metallic phosphates, which are used primarily as corrosion inhibitors, will also be more effective in preventing scale than regular polyphosphates. He cites phosphate derivatives of 14 different metals. Some are effective scale removers, while others appear to retard the breakdown of sodium bicarbonate to the carbonate.

Surface-active agents or good dispersants inhibit scale deposition by keeping the metal surface clean, and, in some cases, the functional group of the dispersant itself ties up the calcium ion. Thus, Oxford[46] describes the use of a mixture of (1) high-molecular-weight substituted glyoxalidines and (2) acylated amino alcohols as very effective in controlling both scale and corrosion. Oxford[47] also patented the use of acylated derivatives of amino alcohols as such as scale inhibitors. Drane[10] states that the use of dispersives, such as tannins or lignins, reduces the tendency of calcium carbonate to come out of solution. Chittum and Rohrback[48] have patented a combination of an alkali-metal polyphosphate, a water-soluble alkyl sulfonate, and an oil-soluble alkyl aryl sulfonate for the prevention of carbonate scale deposition. Other materials are added to the formulation for good stability and solubility, but the polyphosphate and the sulfonates are the effective ingredients.

The most common chelating agent used for scale prevention is the sodium salt of ethylenediaminetetraacetic acid, EDTA. This material and similar chelating agents are effective for the prevention of scale, but by themselves are generally too expensive to compete with the more common scale inhibitors. Roche[49] has described the use of EDTA for this purpose and has shown figures of crystal structures of treated and untreated heating surfaces to illustrate the appearance of modified residues as compared with untreated surfaces. Lecornu[50] has patented the use of derivatives of vegetable products containing at least one flavone, or similar products of the same class, e.g., fisetin, quercetin, luteolin, or their derivatives, especially glucosides which they form with certain glucides, e.g., isodulcitol. Gambill[51] has patented a scale-preventing combination of an alkali-metal polyphosphate, an EDTA-type chelating agent, and a cactus extract. The cactus extract is used for its polyglycoside content and is obtained from the common elephant-leaf-type cactus of Texas.

A very unusual type of carbonate control is described by Nagel.[52] He found that the growth of green algae in a pond was directly related to the drop in scaling tendency in the cooling water taken from that pond. The algae appeared to liberate free CO_2 and drop the pH.

Prevention of *calcium sulfate* deposits can be readily attained by control of the sulfate content of the cooling water. *Magnesium hydroxide* or *carbonate* are rarely troublesome as such and are of concern only when entrapped by calcium carbonate scale.

Iron oxide is frequently difficult to prevent. One obvious answer is the prevention of corrosion in the system by means to be discussed later.

The dissolved iron in the make-up water, however, is generally treated with chelating agents or dispersants to prevent it from coming out of solution. Kahler[53] states that water-soluble lignins are more efficient than polyphosphates for preventing iron precipitation from water supplies. The prevention techniques for *phosphate sludge* and *metal deposits* are obvious.

Bacteria

The most widely employed microbiological agent for cooling-tower systems is chlorine. It is also generally considered to be the most economical. As an example of its widespread use, the survey by the N.A.C.E. work group[20] shows that at 16 Gulf Coast plants and refineries continuous chlorination was employed in 24 towers and intermittent chlorination in 10 towers.

The chlorine is fed from a cylinder or occasionally in liquid form, which involves some handling and feeding problems. It is fed in an amount sufficient to maintain a residual chlorine level of 0.5 to 1.0 ppm. This maintenance level means that in waters which have a high chlorine demand because of the presence of various contaminants which can be oxidized easily, it may be necessary to use other bactericides. These undesirable contaminants may include organic matter, H_2S, or Fe^{++} ion.

The 0.5 to 1.0 ppm residual is usually sufficient to keep bacteria under control. Chlorine is generally less effective in alkaline waters than in neutral or acidic waters. It is fed either on a continuous basis or intermittently; the former is much more effective, but the latter is more economical.

A variation of the chlorine treatment that has been used is a feed of chloramine, which is the reaction product of chlorine and ammonia or other nitrogenous materials. The combination was used in distribution systems to reduce chlorine demand. The effectiveness of this material is much less than that of chlorine alone, both on a chlorine-content and on a time basis.

An excellent summary of the use of chlorine for recirculating cooling-water systems has been given by Maguire, Betz, and Betz[23] and the reader is referred to this article for more details.

Both bromine and iodine can be used as possible alternatives for

chlorine. Bromine was tried in a number of cooling systems with incon-
clusive results. It is severely limited by the hazard involved in handling
it, while iodine was not evaluated because of its high cost.

Phenols and chlorinated or brominated derivatives represent another
major class of cooling-tower bactericides for slime control. Fitzpatrick[14]
describes the use of phenol and cresol for this purpose. Most operators
agree that the halogenated derivatives are much more effective. Williams[25] describes the use of 15 to 20 ppm of sodium pentachlorophenate
to keep a cooling-water system free of slime. Maguire, Betz, and Betz[23]
state that this compound is the most frequently used chlorinated phenol,
either alone or in combination with the trichlorophenol salt. They state
that a combination of the two is more effective than either one alone and
that the addition of a metallic ion, such as copper or zinc, further improves the biocidal properties.

Table 3-3 is taken from the paper and is a comparison of various
phenol derivatives when used for a number of different standard test
organisms.

The table illustrates the wide variation in the effectiveness of these
materials and the desirable characteristics which would accrue to a
properly chosen blend of chemicals. Maguire, Betz and Betz[23] give a
formula for calculating the theoretical depletion of a slime-control agent

TABLE 3-3. A Comparison of Phenolic Compounds[23]

COMPOUND	INHIBITING CONCENTRATION (ppm)			
	Aerobacter aerogenes	Bacillus mycoides	Aspergillus niger	Penicillium expansum
Chloro-o-phenylphenol	40	25	35	35
2-tert-Butyl-4-chloro-5-methylphenol	35	6	95	75
o-Benzyl-p-chlorophenol	55	5	80	80
4,6-Dichlorophenol	30	0.7	2,000	40
Sodium salt of				
o-Phenylphenol	200	200	150	150
2,4,5-Trichlorophenol	20	15	15	7
Chloro-2-phenylphenol	60	30	55	30
2-Chloro-4-phenylphenol	45	20	65	50
2-Bromo-4-phenylphenol	60	15	150	80
2,3,4,6-Tetrachlorophenol	400	7	20	30
Pentachlorophenol	200	4	25	30

and thus determine how often it should be fed. This formula is as follows:

$$\log C_f = \log C_i - \frac{BD \times T}{2.303V}, \qquad [3\text{-}1]$$

where C_f is the final concentration in ppm, C_i is the initial concentration in ppm, BD is the blowdown and windage loss in gal/min, V is the system capacity in gal, and T is the time in min. The authors state that a practical treatment program is to repeat the slug of treatment when the concentration has been depleted to 25 per cent of the original amount. This repetition reduces the above equation to the following:

$$T = 1.385\frac{V}{BD}, \qquad [3\text{-}2]$$

where T is the retention time or the frequency with which the slug of treatment should be repeated in days, V is the system capacity in gal, and BD is the blowdown and windage loss in gal/day.

Robinson[54] and Stone[45] both describe heavy-metal polyphosphates as algicides. Robinson suggests the use of a heavy-metal residual content of 2.5 to 10 ppm. Copper salts, especially copper sulfate, are very effective as algicides and function at very low concentrations, generally less than 1 ppm. They must be used at low pH values, otherwise insoluble copper hydroxide can precipitate. In addition, the concentrated solution is very corrosive and even the extremely dilute use-level will severely pit aluminum. The use of wetting agents along with copper sulfate is frequently practiced with improved results.[23] The use of copper or mercury must be avoided in the case of aluminum cooling towers; otherwise severe localized corrosion will occur.

Silver can also be used as a bactericide, but no favorable reports in cooling-tower systems are available and the economics are poor. Potassium permanganate is also suggested because of its strong oxidizing ability, but it is not effective because it lacks selectivity. Organic mercurials are used in some systems, but with the inorganic mercurials they are generally considered to be too toxic to humans for use.

Quaternary ammonium compounds have received considerable attention recently. While their bactericidal properties are not as effective as many other materials on a ppm basis, they have the added advantage of excellent surface-active properties. By this means they keep the metal surfaces free of slime accumulations and are effective for slime-control purposes. They can be used in formulations. For example,

Cross[55] patented a combination of quaternary ammonium salts, poly-glycol ethers, and long-chain amines. The quaternaries can be ineffective under certain conditions. Chambers *et al.*[56] show that bicarbonates, sulfates, and chlorides of calcium and magnesium can interfere with their action. Organic matter can react with quaternaries, and volatilization can deplete their concentration. Nevertheless, these materials are coming into widespread use today.

Chemicals which inhibit growth of sulfate-reducing bacteria are discussed in the chapter on petroleum production. In cooling-tower systems, prevention of destruction by these bacteria can be accomplished readily in an indirect manner. The prevention of slime accumulations removes favorable conditions for the growth of sulfate reducers and thus effectively controls them. A recent article in *Chemical Processing*[80] describes the reduction of microbiological corrosion from 35 mpy to 1 mpy by use of an amine formulation. The corrosion was caused by a combination of sulfate reducers and slime bacteria.

Wood Deterioration

An excellent series of papers was written by Hurst[57, 58] on this subject, and the reader is referred to them for a detailed discussion. Talbot,[24] Maguire,[23] Brooke,[1] and Comeaux[59] also describe the problem and present recommended solutions for it.

The initial preventive measures must be taken when the new tower is *leached.* At this point, a number of natural preservatives, such as resins and carbohydrates, are removed from the wood; this raises its susceptibility to deterioration and also provides an excellent nutrient for microbiological organisms. During the initial leaching period the pH should be carefully controlled within a range of 6.0 to 7.0 to keep the leaching to a minimum. In addition, since the leached materials will react with chlorine, halogenated phenol derivatives should be used as bactericides for the entire system rather than chlorine. After the first few weeks of cooling-tower operation, when all of the leaching has occurred, the water can be dumped and chlorine used for treatment of the fresh water.

Another technique for the solution of the leaching problem is to impregnate the wood with preservatives insoluble in cooling water. These preservatives can function by one of two mechanisms. Either they produce a surface which is fungistatic or else they react with the wood to form a product which blocks the pores and hinders penetration by organisms. Frequently, a combination of both approaches is used.

One of the earliest preservative treatments depends on a "double-diffusion" procedure. A recent technique is to spray the wood with copper sulfate and allow this material to penetrate into the lumber. The process is then repeated with sodium chromate. The result is a copper chromate fungistatic precipitate formed within the wood itself. Sodium pentachlorophenate, arsenic acid, and zinc sulfate are also used in this manner. The presence of copper or zinc ions in the water can lead to severe pitting or fouling problems elsewhere in the system and should be borne in mind when using these materials. The initial portion of recirculating water used after impregnation will contain large concentrations of these metal ions and should be dumped.

Control of *delignification* generally depends upon the effective control of pH and oxidizing agents. Deposition of alkaline salts, such as sodium carbonate must be prevented and maintenance of pH below a critical value goes a long way toward controlling this problem. Hurst lists this pH value as 8.5, Talbot says 7.5, while Comeaux prefers 7.0.

The strong oxidizing power of chlorine which promotes delignification is controlled by keeping the chlorine residual below 1.0 ppm. Many authors[58] claim that even at this level chlorine is harmful to wood. The mechanism of attack is uncertain, but a more rapid delignification of wood when chlorine is the bactericide was proven conclusively.

In addition to deterioration due to excessive leaching or chemical delignification, microbiological attack on the cellulose portions of the wood can also occur. This attack may result in either surface decay or deep internal decay. The preventive measure here is the use of specific fungicides or microbiocides. These are generally the same materials used for microbiological control elsewhere in the system and include such chemicals as copper sulfate and sodium pentachlorophenate.

An interesting case of lumber deterioration is presented by Reif[44] who describes a system where the thinned hurdles of a wooden water-cooling tower were loaded with carbonate until the internal structure collapsed. To avoid recurrence, the water was decarbonated and stabilized with polymeric phosphates.

Gas Contamination

Control of gas contamination by preventive measures at the source of the leak can be critical to the cooling system. If the contamination cannot be prevented, then the type of inhibitor used may have to be varied.

Thus, for example, the use of chromates may be impossible if too much hydrogen sulfide is present.

Corrosion

IRON. The first part of this discussion is limited to the inhibition of the corrosion of iron. Other metals are treated subsequently as was the case in the presentation of the problem earlier in this chapter. Inhibitors are discussed individually, and then combinations are considered. No good, over-all discussion of all inhibitors used for cooling-tower systems is available today, but partial lists can be obtained from articles by Wise[60] and Brooke.[61]

CALCIUM CARBONATE. The cheapest corrosion inhibitor for cooling-tower systems was already mentioned: *calcium carbonate*. A very thin, very adherent, protective film of calcium carbonate can be extremely effective, and for this reason most water-treatment concerns recommend that at least 50 ppm of calcium expressed as calcium carbonate be carried in the recirculating water. While this protective film may not be sufficient by itself, it does minimize the dosages required of other inhibitors.

The theory of protection by the calcium carbonate film is discussed by Stumm,[62, 63] Splittgerber,[64] Powell *et al.*,[65] Evans,[66] and Atkins.[67] The film of calcium carbonate must be laid down properly, since formation of a slimy nonadherent film, which can occur readily, promotes corrosion as shown by Haase[68] and Thornhill.[69] A protective film of calcium carbonate (generally in the form of a mixture with ferric oxide) is formed only if the carbon dioxide content of the water is limited to the amount needed to stabilize the calcium bicarbonate that is present. In this way the smallest rise in pH suffices to render the liquid next to the metal supersaturated with calcium carbonate.[66]

The well-known Langelier Index, which is the difference between the actual pH value of water and the pH value reached when water is brought into equilibrium with calcium carbonate, indicates the possibility of formation of a protective film. The first value must be higher than the second for this to occur, and addition of lime may be necessary if it is not. Atkins[67] shows that for South African Cape coastal waters, the calcium content is frequently too low, and the use of a calcium carbonate-pH equilibrium curve determines what the minimal calcium carbonate concentration must be made by the addition of lime water.

Reference was made to the need for ferric oxide in the calcium carbonate film. Splittgerber[64] shows that sufficient oxygen must be present in the water so that this oxide can form. In the presence of oxygen, the primary iron oxyhydrate absorbs the free and combined carbonic acid, leading to a supersaturated calcium solution at the surface of the iron oxide; consequently, calcium carbonate and ferric oxide precipitate together as a protective layer. In the absence of oxygen, the layer of rust formed is practically free from calcium carbonate and is not protective. Thus the oxygen content is critical to the calcium carbonate film protection.

Most authors assume that calcium carbonate is primarily deposited on cathodic areas and functions as a cathodic corrosion inhibitor. Stumm[63] points out that the actual situation is far more complicated. First he presents data showing that the amount of calcium carbonate deposited cannot be calculated from the saturation equilibrium alone. The pH of the solution immediately adjacent to the metal surface is higher than the pH in the bulk of the solution. The deposition of calcium carbonate is therefore primarily controlled by the electrochemical changes at the metal surface. It is influenced by the corrosion rate and also the buffer capacity and flow rate of the solution.[58]

Stumm then conducted some experiments which showed that the calcium-carbonate deposition and corrosion-rate reduction are accompanied by an ennoblement (shift to positive) of the corrosion potential. If the calcium carbonate functioned only by blocking the cathodic area more than the anodic area, the corrosion potential would have shifted in the negative (base) direction. The shift to a positive direction could be explained by the assumption that in addition to cathodic areas, the calcium carbonate is also deposited on the boundaries between the cathodic and anodic areas, thus decreasing the anodic area by clogging the pores. Since the cathodic area is much larger than the anodic area, the reduction in anodic area affects the anodic exchange current much more significantly than the cathodic-area change affects the cathodic-exchange current, and thus the corrosion potential is ennobled and the corrosion current is reduced. This theory was further proven by varying the size of anodic areas by adjusting the pH and showing that the reduction of anodic areas and corrosion current is more effective at the lower pH values where the anodic areas are smallest.

The control of pH is an essential part of water treatment for open recirculating cooling-water systems. The effect of pH on scaling tendencies and the consequent need for maintaining a pH value below 7.5 or 8.0 was already discussed. A similar pH requirement applies for corrosion prevention. Here a value of 6.0 and preferably 6.5 is usually the minimum value that must be maintained, since below this value corrosion proceeds rapidly.

Most cooling-tower waters are naturally alkaline and after concentration have pH values of 8.0 to 9.0. The conventional method of treating these waters is to add sulfuric acid continually to drop the pH to the required value of 6.0 to 6.5. On occasion the water has an acidic pH value. New York City, for example, has water with a very low alkalinity. When the untreated recirculating water is exposed to the heavily contaminated air in the metropolitan area, it tends to pick up sulfur dioxide and carbon dioxide in large quantities and pH values which may range from 3 to 6 result. Sussman[70] tabulated analyses for ten such typical waters scattered all over New York City and found that they have pH values ranging from 3.2 to 6.1. He found that the constant feeding of alkali was necessary to keep the pH at the higher values needed for effective protection by additional inhibitors. Almost every cooling-tower system today is treated with acid or lime for pH adjustment.

CHROMATE. Probably the most effective corrosion inhibitor for cooling-tower systems, all things considered, is the *chromate* ion. This material is now generally used as the key ingredient in a combination of inhibitors, but it is also quite effective when used alone. A discussion of the mechanism by which the chromate ion provides corrosion inhibition follows.

The initial conception of the inhibiting power of chromate was that it is a function of the oxidizing ability of that ion. Presumably, the rapid oxidation of ferrous to ferric oxide at the metal surface is the protective mechanism. This postulate can only be partially correct since other strong oxidizing agents, e.g., permanganate, are not necessarily effective inhibitors. Similarly, other hexavalent oxide anions which should be as effective because of their chemical similarity to chromates, e.g., molybdates and tungstates, are not nearly as effective as chromate. An alternative or supplementary mechanism would thus appear to be indicated.

Another possible mechanism, that of the formation of an insoluble iron chromate compound on the surface, does not appear to be borne out by analyses of the surface film from iron samples which were protected by chromates. Mayne and Pryor[71] showed that the film consists mostly of cubic oxide, while several authors[72-74] show that some chromium is also present. The amount of chromium present appears to vary considerably, depending on the concentration of oxygen and the original state of the iron. The greater oxygen concentration and the longer period of pre-exposure of the metal to air or oxygenated water result in the least amount of chromium being present. The generally accepted composition of the protective film is that it consists of a mixture of γ-ferric oxide and chromic oxide.

Based on that analysis, the protective mechanism is generally considered to be the following, which is similar to that proposed by Cohen and Beck:[75] Iron corrodes to form ferrous hydroxide. The ferrous ion is then oxidized to a ferric oxide film on the surface by oxygen in the system. The presence of chromate results in the oxidation taking place right at the surface giving a protective film of iron oxide with some chromic oxide (reduction product of the chromate) mixed in with it. If the sample was already allowed to form a protective iron oxide film, as by pre-exposure, then the function of the chromate is to repair weak places in the film and strengthen and thicken it with the ferric oxide-chromic oxide mixture. Pryor and Cohen[76] state that the normal protective film of γ-ferric oxide due to oxygen in solution is about 200 A thick and that oxidizing inhibitors, such as chromate, act as film repair agents at discontinuities present during the early stages of film formation. A radioactive tracer study by Erwall[77] on the sorption of Cr^{51} on steel from solutions containing Cr^{+++} and $CrO_4^=$ shows that at low chromate concentrations ($10^{-5}M$) the amount sorbed was 5.2×10^{15} atoms of Cr/cm^2, or 0.65 monolayers. Chromium was sorbed as chromic oxide, and the film growth in contact with air was logarithmic. Gerischer[78] compared this surface film to that which is present on chromium steels (stainless steel). Data to support the variation of the chromium content of the surface film with the oxygen content of the liquid were presented by Brasher et al.[74, 79, 80]

Kingsbury[81] suggests a somewhat different mechanism. He postulates that a layer of chromate ions is first adsorbed on the surface. This adsorbed layer obstructs the electrode processes involved in corrosion and acts as a reservoir of oxidants in intimate contact with the surface and as a shield against ions which could interfere with the orderly growth of an oxide film beneath it. Oxidation by chromate ions and by oxygen then proceeds under the adsorbed layer. Evans has suggested still another mechanism for protection of iron by chromates. He states that $CrO_4^=$ is pushed up against the anodic parts of the metal by the potential gradient, with the positive parts of $CrO_4^=$ being furthest from the metal. A possible reaction then becomes the union of the CrO_2^{++} group with the two nearest water molecules forming chromic acid

$$\begin{matrix} HO \\ \diagdown \\ \diagup \quad CrO_2 . \\ HO \end{matrix}$$

The two protons displaced from the water molecules will switch to the next pair of water molecules and so on until the cathodic area is reached. Meanwhile two oxygens are left at the metal at the anodic areas, forming an oxide layer. At the cathode, the reaction is either the reduction of oxygen by arriving H^+ or, in the absence of oxygen, the reduction of chromate, which ties in with observations that more chromium is in the film when oxygen is absent.

A very interesting piece of work conducted by Japanese investigators[82] shows that at a threshold concentration of chromate (7×10^{-4} mole/liter for steel wire), the corrosion rate suddenly falls off while the potential suddenly rises. It is then possible to drop the concentration to lower levels and retain passivity. Further resistance measurements of iron wire in 0.1 mole/liter of chromate show that a film is formed, which thickens fast at the beginning and then proceeds at a much slower rate. This fact, coupled with the retention of protection when the chromate concentration is dropped below the threshold value after initial protection, strongly argues for the film theory as against the adsorption theory. Their film thickness values were calculated to be 46 to 55 A.

The above data lead into a practical point in the application of chromate treatments as well as many other types. Much better protection is generally obtained in a more economic manner when a high inhibitor dosage is used at the beginning of treatment. This high dosage establishes the protective film very rapidly and permits subsequent continuous operation at a much lower dosage than would be possible without the initial slug treatment. This fact was first shown for chromates by Darrin[83] who presented data to show that for typical cooling towers an initial concentration of 500 to 1,000 ppm of chromate could subsequently be reduced to 100 ppm or less safely, while the lack of the initial slug resulted in poor protection. This general principle is still in use in water treatment of cooling towers today, although dosage levels have decreased as treatments have improved. For example, a recent article by Hess[84] describes successful treatment with an inorganic chromate formulation at a level of 30 to 40 ppm as CrO_4 for the first few days, followed by a subsequent drop to 15 to 20 ppm.

While sodium chromate by itself is a good inhibitor, it has certain drawbacks. One of the most serious ones is the adverse effect of the chloride ion which leads to greatly increased dosage requirements. Darrin's data[83] show that the protection by chromates drops with increasing chloride content. The chloride ion is able to penetrate the protective film and cause corrosion to occur beneath it.

A more serious disadvantage of the use of chromate as a corrosion inhibitor is its failure under certain conditions to give satisfactory protection against pitting. The chromate ion is a member of the class of dangerous anodic inhibitors which can promote pitting when present in insufficient quantities to give complete protection. Presumably, the attack is intensified at weak points or discontinuities in the oxide film, and perforation occurs readily. This pitting tendency of chromates presents a serious drawback to the use of this chemical alone in a cooling system.

Another serious disadvantage of chromates is the toxicity. The treated discharge to a stream may be toxic to fish and plant life. A number of states have begun to adopt rigid regulations concerning pollution of streams, and these laws present a possible threat to full-scale use of chromate without some sort of neutralization or removal prior to discharge. Chromates can also cause serious damage to the people handling the chemicals if precautions are not taken. It is desirable that breathing of chromate dust be avoided and contact with the body prevented.

On the positive side of the picture, the effectiveness of chromate, its relatively low cost, and its applicability to many different metals all combine to favor this treatment. Today, chromate-based formulations are the most widespread and effective treatments available. They are discussed in detail later in this chapter.

Molecularly Dehydrated Phosphates. Molecularly dehydrated phosphates represent the second major class of corrosion inhibitors in use today for cooling-tower systems. Like the chromates, these materials were first used by themselves but now are more commonly found as members of an inhibitor formulation. They serve a dual function— scale prevention and corrosion inhibition. The former use has already been mentioned and the latter is discussed here.

There are a variety of these phosphates in use today. Some of the more common ones for corrosion inhibition include orthophosphate, pyrophosphate, tripolyphosphate, a wide variety of glassy polyphosphates, and particularly their calcium and/or magnesium salts. The chemistry of the polyphosphates is not discussed here in any detail. Van Wazer[85] published a thorough and systematic study of phosphorus chemistry, and the reader is referred to his book for details. The structures of the simpler water-treatment phosphates (where M is a monovalent cation) are essentially the following:

Orthophosphate:

$$M_3PO_4 = M—O—\overset{\displaystyle O}{\underset{\displaystyle O}{\overset{|}{\underset{|}{P}}}}—O—M\,.$$
$$\underset{M}{\overset{|}{}}$$

Pyrophosphate:

$$M_4P_2O_7 = M—O—\overset{\displaystyle O}{\underset{\displaystyle O}{\overset{|}{\underset{|}{P}}}}—O—\overset{\displaystyle O}{\underset{\displaystyle O}{\overset{|}{\underset{|}{P}}}}—O—M\,.$$
$$\underset{M}{}\quad\underset{M}{}$$

Tripolyphosphate:

$$M_5P_3O_{10} = M—O—\overset{\displaystyle O}{\underset{\displaystyle O}{\overset{|}{\underset{|}{P}}}}—O—\overset{\displaystyle O}{\underset{\displaystyle O}{\overset{|}{\underset{|}{P}}}}—O—\overset{\displaystyle O}{\underset{\displaystyle O}{\overset{|}{\underset{|}{P}}}}—O—M\,.$$
$$\underset{M}{}\quad\underset{M}{}\quad\underset{M}{}$$

Structures of higher condensed or polyphosphates are much harder to define. They are generally mixtures of various polyphosphate chain lengths. The vitreous sodium metaphosphate $(NaPO_3)_x$ had been assumed by early workers to have a value of 6 for x and was called "hexametaphosphate" until recently. Today these glasses are preferably characterized in terms of the molar ratio of their Na_2O and P_2O_5 contents. The commercial glass Calgon, which is probably the most commonly used polyphosphate for water conditioning, has a Na_2O/P_2O_5 mole ratio of about 1.1 and has also on occasion been called "hexametaphosphate." Other glasses in common usage have been the anhydrous ones with Na_2O/P_2O_5 mole ratios of $(n + 2)/n =$ 1.50 and 1.285 (where n is the chain length). These glasses have been called "tetrapoly-" and "septapolyphosphate," respectively.

Two papers by Hatch and Rice[22, 86] published in 1945 provide the basic data on the use of glassy phosphates as corrosion inhibitors. Working with Calgon, they found that a thin protective film of the glassy phosphate or one of its complexes is deposited which does not interfere with heat transfer. The film formation is not critical with respect to normal variations of temperature or pH. The rate of film formation is a function of the rate of supply of the glassy phosphate to the metal surface; hence higher initial PO_4 concentrations and good flow rates are helpful. The inhibitor dosage level varies with the system and in practice can vary anywhere from 2 to 100 ppm calculated as PO_4, although for cooling towers the range of 10 to 25 ppm is the most common. Also in the case of phosphates a high initial dosage leads to rapid film formation and allows subsequent treatment at lower dosage levels than would be the case in the absence of the initial slug. The flow rate is important since the rate of supply of the inhibitor to the metal surface is primarily dependent upon diffusion. In cooling-tower systems the flow rate in most of the system is no problem; but where stagnant pockets occur, it is very difficult to maintain the desired film.

The protective film survives for a considerable period, even after treatment has stopped. This is another reason for the rapid establishment of the film. Apel'tsin and Zolotova[87] found that for effective protection, a large dose (35 to 100 ppm) of calcium or magnesium metaphosphate or sodium hexametaphosphate should be used for the first two days and then the dosage should be reduced to 5 ppm. Hatch and Rice[86] show that polyphosphates give protection over a range of 4 to 99° C and over a wide pH range provided that the lower limit is 5. Like many other inhibitors, however, the glassy polyphosphates are corrosive when they are present in concentrated solutions, a factor which must be borne in mind when setting up feeding procedures.

Performance-wise, the polyphosphates appear to be somewhat less effective than chromates on a dosage basis. They require somewhat higher levels and tend to give slightly higher corrosion rates. They suffer from reversion to orthophosphates. Although the orthophosphates are also inhibitors they are rapidly removed from solution by calcium, thus both depleting the PO_4 concentration and creating a sludge or scale which can promote serious corrosion. On the other hand, the polyphosphates do not suffer from some of the disadvantages that chromates do. They are not toxic and are used instead of chromates in many systems for that reason. In addition, phosphate treatments do not appear to be as susceptible to pitting attack when present in insufficient dosages as do chromates.

The mechanisms of inhibition by ortho- and polyphosphates appear to be different from each other. The orthophosphate inhibits by an anodic mechanism, while the polyphosphates appear to be cathodic inhibitors. A brief discussion of each mechanism follows.

Pryor and Cohen[76] postulate that when sodium orthophosphate is used as an inhibitor in the presence of oxygen, the protective mechanism is one of passivity by the oxygen through its heterogeneous reaction with surface iron atoms to form a thin, self-repairing film of γ-Fe_2O_3 about 200 A thick. The phosphate acts as a film-repairing agent at discontinuities present during the early stages of film formation with the anodic product, an iron phosphate, being the agent. The protection is thus due to both oxygen and phosphate. The film is largely cubic oxide, but it contains plugs of ferric phosphate presumably located at points where anodic corrosion would have occurred in the absence of phosphate.

Pryor, Cohen, and Brown[88] show that a surface pretreatment which involved destruction of the original air-formed oxide film resulted in increasingly higher PO_4 contents in the eventually formed protective film as the severity of the pretreatment and the exclusion of oxygen increased. Mayne and Menter[89] examined the film found on iron in 0.1 N solutions of NaH_2PO_4 and Na_3PO_4 by electron diffraction. They found it was mostly a cubic oxide having the composition of Fe_3O_4, γ-Fe_2O_3, or an intermediate compound. With Na_2HPO_4 large particles of $FePO_4 \cdot 2H_2O$ were found imbedded in a matrix of cubic oxide. A small amount of $FePO_4$ was found with Na_3PO_4. Abd El Wahed and Pourbaix[90] also found that, if all other conditions are the same, protection by oxidizing phosphatization is more effective than by nonoxidizing phosphatization.

Evans[66] points out that the fact that the iron phosphate is hydrated and that ferric (rather than ferrous) phosphate is produced suggests that the substance is formed at the outside of gaps in the film, where the ions are on the point of escape. The quantity of phosphate in the film decreases as the pH rises, so that the film PO_4 content is half as great with Na_3PO_4($pH = 12.2$) as with Na_2HPO_4($pH = 9.1$).[86]

Protection by polyphosphates appears to be the result of the deposition of a film at the cathode. Hatch[91] found that in the case of the galvanic corrosion of steel coupled to cathodic metals, inhibition by polyphosphates was chiefly the result of a marked polarization of the cathode. He states that a glassy film was present at the cathode which appeared to be laid down by an electrodeposition process. With uncoupled steel, the film deposition occurred at local cathodic areas. Raistrick[92] found that if the cathode was removed from a cell which had been inhibited with Calgon and it was then cleaned, the current would increase. The lack of such a result on cleaning the anode is an argument for cathodic control. Lamb and Eliassen[93] suggest that while polyphosphates are primarily cathodic inhibitors, they may also have some anodic effects. They show that the film at the cathode contains iron, calcium, and phosphate and that iron appears to be helpful for polyphosphate protection. Mansa and Szybalski[94] studied the influence of Calgon on potentials of electrodes in a differential aeration cell. They found it decreases the cathode potential by adsorption and thereby inhibits oxygen access to the surface. The potential of the anode increases because the Calgon interferes with anodic depletion of the oxygen. The corrosion current thus decreases because of both effects and also because of increasing internal resistance of the cell resulting from formation of layers of Calgon and of corrosion products with low electrical conductivity.

Mears[95] analyzed data on inhibition by sodium hexametaphosphate which were developed by Hatch[91] and concluded that the short-range effect of the sodium hexametaphosphate (24 hr) is to increase the cathodic polarization. After a longer period of time (120 hr), the slope of the cathodic polarization curve does not alter much from the 24-hr value. The open-circuit potential difference, however, has decreased greatly, and this change now accounts for much of the inhibiting action.

Raistrick[92] believes that CO_2 is important in polyphosphate protection. He states that alteration of the crystal structure of the cathodically deposited calcium carbonate by polyphosphates results in layers of crystals which protect far greater surfaces than if the crystals grew out in their normal forms. He shows that CO_2 is essential for inhibition in a Zn-Fe cell inhibited by metaphosphate.

Evidence of the requirement for the presence of oxygen in the successful use of polyphosphate inhibitors is presented by Uhlig, Triadis, and Stern.[96] They found that a minimum amount of oxygen (1 ml/liter) was necessary and in its absence, solutions containing 60 ppm of sodium polyphosphates actually accelerated corrosion. In the presence of calcium, the level of this critical oxygen content dropped.

The requirement for the presence of calcium or magnesium for satisfactory protection by polyphosphates is well known. Some inhibitors, like Micromet, which is a glassy polymer of sodium calcium metaphosphate, have the divalent ion as a part of the inhibitor itself. Others require it in solution, and cooling towers invariably have far more than a sufficient amount of these cations present. Parham and Tod[97] state that the ratio of phosphate to calcium carbonate must be less than 2. Uhlig, Triadis, and Stern[96] conducted detailed studies to show the need for Ca^{++}. Thus, for example, the presence of Ca^{++} decreased the critical level of oxygen needed for protection by sodium polyphosphate from 1 ml/liter to 0.15 ml/liter. It also raised the limit on the amount of chloride ion which could be present and not harm protection. They postulate that the calcium salts lead to formation on cathodic areas of a diffusion barrier film of unknown structure containing both Ca and P. Takeuchi[98] found that the optimum weight ratio of calcium chloride to sodium hexametaphosphate is 1:2.

The role of soluble iron in the protection by polyphosphates was reported to be both detrimental and yet favorable. This apparent anomaly comes from the fact that soluble iron will use up the polyphosphate by forming a strong complex with it, while some authors reported that iron is needed in the protective film. Rice[99] points out that two parts of the phosphate are used up in complexing each part of iron in the water. Lamb and Eliassen,[93] on the other hand, found that iron helped the protective polyphosphate film at the cathode to build up more rapidly. The liquid contained colloidal particles, and the cathodic film had calcium, iron, and phosphate all present.

Sodium Silicate. One of the inhibitors used to a lesser extent for cooling-tower systems is sodium silicate. There are two articles by Shuldener *et al.*[100, 101] to which the reader is referred for a detailed discussion of its behavior as an inhibitor. The major use of sodium silicate is for water distribution once-through systems. This application is discussed in a subsequent chapter; the present discussion is limited to cooling-tower systems.

Sussman[70] states that with good control of the amount of silica, it is possible to obtain good corrosion inhibition with no danger of scale formation. Streicker[102] points out earlier that excessive quantities of silicate could lead to serious scaling problems. Corrosion rates with silicates are generally somewhat higher than with chromates,[76] but Sussman points out their value where chromates cannot be used. He gives examples of treatment of air washers and cooling towers with SiO_2 levels of 51 to 184 ppm and corrosion rates of 0.6 to 2.9 mils per year. It is interesting to note that his pH ranges were 7.9 to 9.2 in accordance with the higher values that must be maintained when silicates are used.

Dosages are generally maintained in the range of 40 to 60 ppm as SiO_2 in cooling towers with a minimum level of about 25 ppm. With silicates also, initial high dosage levels for a brief period allow a rapid cutback to low levels with good protection. This high dosage is especially important with silicates since the protective film initially appears to form very close to the point where the inhibitor is applied and then to extend out gradually. The initial protective film appears to take much longer to form with silica than with most other inhibitors.

Wood, Beecher, and Laurence[103] made a detailed study of the factors involved in the use of crystalloidal sodium silicate as a corrosion control agent for open-recirculating cooling-water systems. They found that 30 to 40 ppm provide adequate protection in waters containing more than 500 ppm of chlorides and sulfates. Values of pH of 8.6 and higher have an adverse effect, as does magnesium in concentrations of over 250 ppm as $CaCO_3$. They conclude that before a protective film can be formed, it is necessary to have an initial coating of iron oxide. This fact is advantageous since it indicates that sodium silicate will be a good corrosion inhibitor in systems which have already been corroded.

There are a number of different silicates. The grade which has a ratio of $Na_2O:SiO_2$ of 1:3.22 is the preferred inhibitor for cooling-tower waters and other systems with pH values above 6. Calcium is believed to be beneficial for silicate inhibition,[66] while bicarbonate is stated to be harmful.[104] Use of insufficient quantities of silicates can be dangerous with intensified local pitting as the result. Chlorides are especially harmful to the protective film. Pryor and Cohen[82] in their detailed study of the effect of insufficient inhibitor concentrations on corrosion rates show that sodium silicate accelerates corrosion at dosages just below the minimum required for protection. At that minimum value, however, there is a very sharp drop in the rate of attack. The silicate is more dangerous than molybdate, nitrite, or chromate, but less dangerous than Na_2HPO_4 or sodium carbonate.

The mechanism of inhibition by sodium silicate has often been thought to be solely the result of the pH elevation by the alkaline material. This view was disproved by Duffer and McKinney,[105] who ran passivity curves on polished steel electrodes in aerated sodium silicate solutions and in sodium hydroxide solutions at the same pH value. No corrosion products could be observed for the electrodes subjected to sodium silicate, while the sodium hydroxide electrodes all corroded.

Lehrman and Shuldener[100] show that the protective mechanism involves the formation of a thin film over the metal. They found that there is an equilibrium in the treated solution between the ionic and colloidal forms of silica. The protective film is apparently dependent upon the initial formation of a layer of corrosion product on the surface. The hydrous oxide corrosion product then removes the ionic (negatively charged) silica from solution. This silica deposit is gelatinous and enmeshes mechanically carried particles in the water. Since the water and the film are slightly alkaline, iron and hardness participate in the film. Chemical analysis of the protective layer shows that it is high in silica.[101] The silica gel-like structure of the film makes it semitransparent when wet. When dry, it is a thin coating, colored brown by iron corrosion products. Once the film forms, corrosion stops, and the film itself no longer builds up. The film is thus self-limiting in thickness.[101] Similarly, it is self-healing, since if any of the film is removed from the surface, the metal begins to corrode and a fresh surface film forms by reaction with the silica in the treated water.

Organic Inhibitors. Organic corrosion inhibitors are not used to any appreciable extent in cooling-tower systems. In general, their cost and relative lack of effectiveness under high-oxygen conditions are deterrents to their use. Only the chromglucosates have any degree of use. These compounds were developed by Haering[106, 107] as modifications of natural glucosides which had shown some promise. They are used when the price is not prohibitive[108] and especially in very hot waters (175 to 200° F).[109] There the oxygen content has dropped and the organics begin to become effective.

The mechanism of protection by chromglucosates is not well understood. Presumably it is somewhat a combination of the chromate and organic mechanisms, and involves a protective organic film coupled with iron oxide. The mechanism of organic inhibitors is discussed in some detail in a later chapter.

The chromglucosates suffer from the need for relatively high dosages and possible decomposition and bacterial problems. There are, however, cooling towers that have operated successfully on these chemicals for many years.

Other organic compounds that were evaluated as cooling-tower inhibitors include emulsified or soluble oils, sodium sulfoglucosates,[15] glycerine derivatives,[110] acylation products of polyamines,[46] waste sulfite liquors, alkaline tannates, tannins, and starch.[108] The emulsified or soluble oils showed some promise, but they suffer from oil-water separation, overheating, spotty protection, formation of calcium soaps, and microbiological attack. However, their use was quite successful in closed cooling systems and is discussed in a subsequent chapter.

A material similar to the chromglucosates was recently patented by Martin and Eberman.[111] They reacted 2 to 5 parts of starch with 1 part of CrO_3 to form a new inhibitor. They report this inhibitor to be effective at 3 to 15 ppm of Cr.

Other Anions. Certain other anions would be expected to act as corrosion inhibitors by analogy with chromate. These anions would include permanganate, molybdate, tungstate, pertechnetate, and perrhenate. *Permanganates* and *perrhenates,* which would be expected to be effective because of their strong oxidizing powers, show no effectiveness at all as corrosion inhibitors. A high oxidation potential alone does not appear to be sufficient by itself to give corrosion inhibition.

Molybdates and *tungstates* would be expected to function in a manner similar to chromates because of their similar chemical structures. They are good corrosion inhibitors, but not as effective as chromates on a dosage basis. Their high cost, relative to chromate, rules them out for this application. Robertson[112] was the first to show their effectiveness. Pryor and Cohen[76] showed that they require the presence of oxygen, while chromate does not. Sympson and Cartledge[113] studied the effect of oxygen on the potentials of solutions of molybdates, tungstates, chromates, and pertechnetates. They found that all four solutions maintain iron electrodes at potentials more noble than the Flade potential in the presence of dissolved air. In deaerated solutions of molybdate and tungstate, the potentials are essentially the same as in sodium sulfate. Potentials in deaerated chromate solutions are much more noble than in the molybdate and tungstate solutions, but less noble than in the pertechnetate solutions. Work on molybdates and tungstates in laboratory-simulated cooling-tower systems by the author of this book showed these materials to have inhibitor properties, but not to the same extent as chromates or polyphosphates. Interest in these materials had arisen because they are much less toxic than chromate and are possible substitutes for it where stream pollution laws are a problem.

Cartledge conducted an extensive series of studies on the *pertechnetate ion*[113-116] and discovered that it has excellent corrosion-inhibiting properties. By using radioactive techniques, he showed that inhibition can be achieved without precipitation of more than traces of radiochemical film, which is probably of secondary origin, and that exposures lasting almost 10 years were not accompanied by a continuous increase in the amount of precipitated technetium. Attempts to measure adsorbed pertechnetate ions gave results barely beyond experimental uncertainty. Exceptionally effective inhibition could be obtained at concentrations as low as 5 to 10 ppm. He also found that disturbance of inhibition by added electrolytes involved a specific action and not merely an increase in the conductivity of the solution phase. He concluded that inhibition arises from some intraionic property rather than from forces due to an image charge of the ion as a whole or from some effect due to the tetrahedral oxygen atoms of the TcO_4^- ion.

Erwall[77] found that the TcO_4^- ion was effective at a sorption of about 0.01 monolayers; the pertechnetate ion forms a mixed oxide with the iron. By contrast, chromate had a thickness of 0.65 monolayers.

Inhibitor Combinations. Practically all major cooling-tower installations today are treated with corrosion-inhibitor formulations or combinations. A proper blend of inhibitors provides improved protection at a much lower cost than individual inhibitors. This protection is frequently brought about by using a mixture of inhibitors which function by different mechanisms and thereby fill in the holes in the protective film which might otherwise have caused local attack.

Probably the best-known cooling-tower inhibitor formulation and still one of the most effective is the *phosphate-chromate* combination. This treatment is described in great detail by Kahler *et al.*[117-119] It was originally developed in an effort to stop the pitting and tuberculation which occurs with chromate at low dosages. While the phosphate alone is no better, the combination of the two inhibitors is extremely effective. For example, a combination of 40 ppm of polyphosphate and 20 ppm of chromate gives a drastically reduced number of pits compared to 60 ppm of either chromate or polyphosphate alone over the *p*H range of 5 to 8. In addition these few pits that developed are only slight surface etchings while the pits which develop by the individual treatments are quite deep. These results were obtained in both laboratory and field evaluations. Devereux[120] describes a test where the average penetration under low phosphate treatments is 21 mpy, under conventional chromate treatment it is 3.3 mpy, and under the combination treatment it is 2.0 mpy.

Both ortho- and polyphosphate were used by Kahler together with chromate. While the orthophosphates were effective, the polyphosphates were much better, and consequently polyphosphates are generally used with chromates. The term "dianodic treatment," which is generally used for this combination, is correct only for the orthophosphate combination, since the polyphosphate is not an anodic inhibitor.

The pH of the polyphosphate-chromate treated water is generally maintained between 6.0 and 6.5. This low value is used to minimize phosphate reversion. Brandel,[121] in describing the successful application of this treatment at a large petroleum refinery for over seven years, points out the importance of good pH control. Failure to maintain it will cause troublesome deposits of either corrosion products or scale. Alternative versions of this treatment wherein the chromate dosage is high and the polyphosphate dosage is low were also very successful there. These variations include such chromate:polyphosphate ratios (expressed in ppm) as 20:1 at a pH of 7.5. The object here is to have just enough polyphosphate to control scale by a threshold mechanism. Hess[84] reports keeping refinery corrosion rates below 5 mpy by using a combination of 20 to 25 ppm of chromate and sufficient metaphosphate to maintain a pH of 6.5 to 7.0. The Kahler patent[122] on this combination states that best results are obtained with a total concentration between 30 and 50 ppm and a phosphate to chromate ratio of 2:1.

The mechanism by which this combination treatment functions has not been satisfactorily elucidated. One likelihood is that the polyphosphate plugs the cathodic holes left by the chromate treatment or that the chromate provides additional anodic protection which the polyphosphate lacks. This theory would not account for the fact that the orthophosphate-chromate combination is effective when both are known to be anodic inhibitors. The mechanism can also vary as the ratio of the two ingredients varies. A careful study of the structure of the protective film might show whether the mechanism is one of simple reinforcement or whether a new process occurs.

The chromate-polyphosphate treatment was improved during the past few years by the addition of *zinc.* The zinc is added in a water-soluble form, generally as zinc sulfate. The dosage used is such that the level of the zinc ion, Zn^{++}, in the treated water is generally about 1 or 2 ppm. Maximum protection appears to be effective at these levels. As one goes to higher levels of zinc, no further increase in the protection is noticed and precipitation problems begin to appear.

The patent by Kahler and Tanzola[123] on this treatment states that it is especially effective when the calcium content of the water restricts the phosphate dosage that can be used. Kahler and George[117] describe the problems of this treatment in some detail and give case histories to illustrate its beneficial results. Bird[124] points out the value of zinc added to chromate alone or zinc added to chromate plus organic matter.

Forbes[3] compared three inhibitors under comparable field conditions during two consecutive 300-hr periods. The inhibitors were (1) phosphate, (2) phosphate-chromate, and (3) zinc-chromate. Zinc-chromate was the most effective in this test.

Smart[125] discusses the electrochemical behavior of zinc in preventing corrosion of iron in aqueous solution. The present thinking is that the zinc ion functions as a cathodic inhibitor. It plugs the cathodic holes that may be left open by the other inhibitors. In addition, in all likelihood, highly insoluble zinc compounds (especially in the presence of phosphate) are formed, mingle with the protective film, and are very adherent.

Rozenfel'd and Marshakov[126] studied the behavior of iron in crevices of various widths. They found that in these crevices, sodium nitrite, disodium hydrogen phosphate, and potassium dichromate accelerated the corrosion of iron whereas zinc sulfate prevented it. They postulated that accelerated iron corrosion in cracks appears because it is difficult for the anodic inhibitors to get into crevices. With the cathodic inhibitors, such as zinc, they believe that the corrosion is low because oxygen access is hindered and the inhibitor decreases the processes of the corrosion micropair: (differential aeration of Fe in crack):(aeration of Fe in the bulk of the solution).

Zinc is not the only cathodic inhibitor which aids chromates or chromate formulations. The *trivalent chromium cation,* Cr^{+++}, was also shown to be very effective for this purpose. A patent by Kahler and George[127] describes the effectiveness of the addition of trivalent chromium. Thus, for example, they state that 2 ppm of Cr^{+++} added to 15 ppm of chromate anion gives excellent protection in a test cooling system that has up to 500 ppm of total hardness, 500 ppm of chlorides,

300 ppm of sulfates, a *p*H range of 3 to 9, and temperatures of 50 to 150° F. By contrast 15 ppm of chromates alone is unable to protect this system.

In further modifications of this treatment, Kahler and George[128] combined chromate, molybdate, and trivalent Cr^{+++}. They found that the addition of molybdate in small quantities gives still better protection. The reason for the behavior of the molybdate in this manner is obscure.

Additives to polyphosphate corrosion inhibitors, in addition to the chromate already mentioned, consist mostly of ferrocyanide and zinc or other cations. A combination *polyphosphate-ferrocyanide* corrosion inhibitor was on the market for a number of years. Ferrocyanide which is present in relatively small amounts compared to polyphosphate functions as a synergist. No reasonable mechanism has been suggested for the fact that it improves the polyphosphate performance very markedly, although ferrocyanide by itself is not very effective. As the ferrocyanide becomes oxidized, its effectiveness drops. This treatment is generally used at a dosage level of 15 to 25 ppm of PO_4 and in the *p*H range from 6.0 to 6.5.

Detailed studies on the effect of adding *zinc* or other cations to the *polyphosphate-ferrocyanide combination* are reported by Bregman and Newman.[129, 130] They found that the addition of a number of cations is beneficial. These cations include cobalt, cerium, chromium, manganese, cadmium, zinc, and nickel. On the other hand, uranium, silicon, thallium, zirconium, iron, copper, antimony, beryllium, and aluminum harm protection by inhibitors. On a cost and solubility basis, zinc appears to be the most practical for incorporation into cooling-tower formulations. An optimum formulation level is reached at dosages of 1 to 2 ppm of Zn^{++} for 25 ppm of polyphosphate. Bird[124] reports a polyphosphate-zinc formulation to be effective. Takeuchi[98] reports that both Zn and Ni aided inhibiting action of hexametaphosphate. The optimum weight ratios of the respective cations to the metaphosphate anion were 25 and 60 to 100. Rama Char[131] reports the effectiveness of Sn, Zn, Ni, Cu, and Pb with pyrophosphate inhibitors.

Kahler and George[128] found that the treatment consisting of 26 ppm of sodium tripolyphosphate, 26 ppm of sodium orthophosphate, and 2 ppm of trivalent chromium as $CrCl_3$ is an effective inhibitor. Brooke[132] reports that a mixture of $CuCl_2$ and any of the molecularly dehydrated phosphates in approximately equal amounts is a good corrosion inhibitor. He cites an example where steel in contact with aerated raw water at a pH of 6.5 had a corrosion rate of 165 mpy. Treatment with $Na_9P_7O_{22}$ cuts the rate to 145 mpy. Treatment with the mixture of this condensed phosphate and $CuCl_2$ reduces the corrosion to less than 1 mpy.

Stone[45] studied metal phosphates for both corrosion inhibition and scale prevention and found that their use made chemical control of acidity in water systems much less critical. A number of metallic phosphates including those of strontium, calcium, barium, lead, cadmium, magnesium, copper, antimony, manganese, molybdenum, vanadium, silicon, iron, and aluminum were prepared and evaluated.

One discrepancy between the work of Bregman and Newman and those of other authors becomes apparent here concerning the effectiveness of Cu^{++}. The former authors found that this cation was ineffective when ferrocyanide was present along with the polyphosphate. Presumably the two ions neutralized each other forming a very insoluble compound nowhere near the surface. In the absence of ferrocyanide, copper was effective.

Fluorides are frequently used in cooling-tower corrosion inhibitor formulations. They are not corrosion inhibitors in themselves. Their purpose is to complex cations, such as aluminum or iron, which might be present in the water and cause problems. The aluminum ion may be present as a result of poor clarification. The iron might be present as soluble iron or corrosion product. The use of fluoride ion has resulted in dramatically improving corrosion inhibition by both chromate and phosphate formulations in a number of large cooling towers, especially in the Texas area.

Kahler, Bishop, and Tanzola[133] patented the addition of sodium fluoride to the chromate treatment for this purpose. They found that corrosion of iron, aluminum, and copper-based alloys is reduced by adding 10 to 200 ppm of fluoride expressed as NaF, and 1 to 200 ppm of chromate expressed as $Na_2Cr_2O_7 \cdot 2H_2O$. The treatment is effective in the presence of sulfide and aluminum ions and prevents the precipitation of aluminum phosphate sludge when the water is treated with phosphate.

Inhibitors that were discussed can be categorized in the following manner:

1. Cathodic: *Polyphosphate, zinc, silicate.*
2. Anodic: *Orthophosphate, chromate, nitrite, ferrocyanide.*

An extremely interesting point that has been called to the author's attention[134] is the fact that most commercial corrosion inhibitors contain both cathodic and anodic inhibitors. Various combinations of the chemicals in the above listing are used. The combination is invariably more effective than the individual inhibitors.

Pretreatment. It is frequently not a simple thing to translate principles of corrosion inhibition from theory or from the laboratory into actual practice in large cooling-tower systems. Thus, for example, the principle of initial slug treatment which was discussed earlier was only used considerably in recent years although the principles involved are as old as the use of corrosion inhibitors themselves. A similar situation holds for the proper pretreatment of metallic surfaces.

It is obvious that optimum corrosion inhibition is obtained with the protective film laid down rapidly and in a very adherent manner. It is also obvious that the condition of the metal surface will markedly influence the nature of adherence of this film. Therefore it has been the practice with laboratories for many years, when a rapid, efficient, protective film was desired, to first properly prepare the surface to be protected and then apply a large amount of corrosion inhibitor. This preparation can consist of removing oily films, dirt, and rust, polishing or sandblasting the surface, and then soaking the metal in a concentrated solution of the inhibitor.

Translation of this protective mechanism to field application is very recent and has met with a considerable amount of success. Palen[135] describes work by the Shell Oil Company to take advantage of the pretreatment procedure. He describes tests which compare the corrosion and fouling of steel tubes which were pretreated against those which were not. In the case of new steel tubing, pretreatment consisted of removing the oily film on condensers and cooling tubes by use of a hot detergent soak, sandblasting, and a cold inhibitor soak. He found a dramatic improvement in protection when the tubes were pretreated in this manner.

A considerable amount of laboratory work on pretreatment was conducted under the direction of the author of this book[136] and is reported by Puckorius and Ryzner.[137, 138] This work shows that proper preparation of metal surfaces results in much more effective and economical inhibition with conventional inhibitor formulations. The study was conducted on small lengths of new and rusted heat-exchange tubes of mild steel. The experimental setup was one in which the corrosion and fouling of the tube could be followed visually. Tubes were run in inhibited water side by side, one set of tubes having been pretreated and the other not. Striking differences were soon apparent. The tubes which had been pretreated were kept free of corrosion at low levels of commercial inhibitors, whereas tubes which had not been pretreated corroded at much higher levels of those same inhibitors. This same effect was subsequently shown in the field by Puckorius[138] for both mild steel and Admiralty heat-exchanger bundles.

There are two basic procedures for pretreatment of cooling towers. Whenever possible, it is desirable to remove the heat-exchange bundles from the system and to soak them in a proper pretreatment solution. This solution might contain the necessary detergent and cleaning agents as well as the inhibitor all in one, or else a two-step soaking might be necessary. When it is not convenient to do this, the heat-exchange bundles can be pretreated *in situ*. In this case pretreatment solutions are circulated through the system. This method may not be as effective as the soaking technique because the volumes of water involved are so great that the pretreatment concentrations may have to be drastically reduced so that the economics does not get out of bounds. This reduction can result in a borderline operation.

COPPER. Generally, if the system containing both iron and a copper alloy, such as Admiralty metal, is designed properly (i.e., no galvanic couples, stresses, or "dead spots"), then the corrosion of the copper alloy cannot be considered to be much of a problem compared to that of iron. However, introduction of any of these factors or "overprotection" of iron can result in considerable attack on the copper alloy. A combination of inhibitors to protect both metals is therefore a necessary precaution.

With one exception, which is discussed in detail later, corrosion inhibitors were not developed specifically for copper in cooling-tower systems. Rather, inhibitors which were developed for steel were also evaluated for copper. Some of these inhibitors which are stated to be of value for copper in cooling-tower systems are calcium carbonate, polyphosphates and other combinations with chromates, polyphosphate-ferrocyanide combinations, polyphosphate-organic combinations such as phosphoglucosate, polyphosphate-silicate combinations, and silicates. A list of inhibitors of this nature can be found in the N.A.C.E. inhibitor reference list.[139] Whitney[140] studied a number of these corrosion inhibitors for Admiralty metal and concludes that the most effective inhibitor is a combination of chromate and hexametaphosphate.

Shields, Sorg, and Stutz[141] describe the selection of corrosion inhibitors for Admiralty metal at the Standard Oil Refinery at Sugar

Creek, Missouri. They found that the chromates are best, with organic chromates being better than inorganic chromates, especially when supplemented by a small amount of hexametaphosphate.

Hatch[91] states that the corrosion of Fe-Cu or Zn-Cu couples can be minimized by use of glassy polyphosphates. He postulates that the glassy polyphosphates are adsorbed on the copper, thereby acting as cathodic inhibitors.

Cavallaro and Indelli[142] evaluate chromates, nitrites, chlorates, sulfites, and organic compounds for the Fe-Cu system. Tanzola[143] shows that the combination chromate-polyphosphate treatment is better for Admiralty metal than either component alone.

Powell[32] reports on the selection of corrosion inhibitors for the high-temperature Atomic Energy Commission installation at Paducah, Kentucky. Here the system consists of pure copper condenser tubes and the supply headers and associated piping are of wrought steel. During a three-year period, five different types of water treatment were evaluated. These treatments are as follows:

1. *Straight polyphosphate.*
2. *Zinc-polyphosphate.*
3. *Ferrocyanide-polyphosphate.*
4. *Zinc-chromate-polyphosphate.*
5. *Chromate-polyphosphate.*

The best inhibitor found was the chromate-polyphosphate treatment. This inhibitor was applied to the system which had developed pitting while using the ferrocyanide-polyphosphate system. The chromate-polyphosphate treatment appeared to stop the pitting and gave subsequent protection.

By far the outstanding corrosion inhibitor in use today for copper and its alloys in cooling-tower systems is *2-mercaptobenzothiazole.* This chemical appears to be unique in its protective action on copper and is not of much value for other metals. It functions at extremely low dosages and is generally present in cooling-tower formulations at levels of 1 to 2 ppm. It can be used with chromates or polyphosphates or both. A number of commercial formulations are available today containing 2-mercapto-benzothiazole although the material is fed separately. It is also commonly known as MBT or BTT and will be referred to here as the former.

MBT has certain drawbacks for application to cooling-tower systems. It is high in cost (approximately \$0.50/lb) and relatively insoluble. This insolubility increases with decrease in pH because MBT is a thio-acid chemical. There is some question as to its effectiveness in the presence of chlorine. The two are reported to interact and destroy each other's effectiveness. However, even with these disadvantages, the chemical is such an excellent corrosion inhibitor that its use is becoming more widespread.

MBT is generally believed to be an anodic inhibitor for copper. It is thought that a strong, extremely adherent, highly insoluble bond is formed between copper ions and MBT at the surface of the metal. This bond prevents any copper from further going into solution. Low dosages of MBT suffice in view of its effectiveness. As the pH of the system drops, however, the dissociation of the —SH group lessens until it can be considered to be completely undissociated at pH values less than 6. Solubility then vanishes as does the value of the MBT as a corrosion inhibitor.

Mercaptobenzothiazole has the following structure.

In aqueous solution, it ionizes as a weak acid as illustrated below.

The ionic species forms insoluble salts with metal ions, such as copper, and conceivably the protective coating consists merely of the insoluble copper salt of MBT. However, a more plausible structure for the protective coating would take into account the fact that the MBT possesses not only an ionized sulfur group but also a ring sulfur and a ring nitrogen, both capable of forming coordinate bonds with the metal or the metal ion. If the surface of the copper becomes partially oxidized, one mode of attachment of MBT to the surface can be visualized as shown below.

Cu — O — Cu — O — Cu
Cu — O
S — C = N
S
O — Cu — Cu
O — Cu — Cu
O

This structure is a pictorial representation only; the precise geometry would be dependent upon the structure of the oxide film and the geometry of the MBT molecule. It does show, however, that it would be firmly bonded to the surface by several bonds and a similar type of bonding to the unoxidized metal surface would also be visualized.

ALUMINUM. Verink and Murphy[144] give a broad description of the use of aluminum in solving refinery corrosion problems and present a detailed bibliography. Haygood and Minford[38] discuss the subject of aluminum cooling towers and their treatment in some detail as have Sussman and Akers.[39] A considerable amount of the discussion in this section is based upon their papers.

Haygood and Minford state that aluminum cooling towers in an all-aluminum system can be operated without water treatment in many localities. Introduction of heavy metals or else a high-dissolved solids content will increase the pitting and scaling hazards and require treatment. There has been little research done on the development of inhibitors designed specifically for aluminum cooling-tower systems. Instead, conventional inhibitor formulations were evaluated for this purpose.

Sussman and Akers[39] note that zinc dissolved in the cooling water acts as an inhibitor. Aluminum test coupons removed from cooling towers built with appreciable amounts of galvanized steel have only a limited number of pits. The remainder of the metal surface has an unusual dark gray or black coating which is extremely adherent and very thin. The reason why the cathodic inhibitor, zinc, should function so effectively by itself in this case has not been explained.

Chromate formulations are generally effective for the protection of aluminum systems just as they are for steel. The normal protective film is one of aluminum oxide. For this film to be effective it must have continuity and sufficient thickness. The presence of alloying constituents or their oxidation products affects this continuity in an adverse manner. The film also tends to be adsorptive, particularly with respect to water and CO_2, which harms its effectiveness. A detailed study of this protective film and the factors affecting it is presented by Keller and Edwards.[145] Presumably, the chromates keep this oxide film in good repair and assure its continuity. Haygood and Minford[38] state that the chromate is an excellent filming agent on aluminum. Sussman and Akers[39] describe protection of a number of cooling towers by maintaining a pH of 7.0 to 8.5 and a sodium chromate concentration of 200 to 500 ppm. In every case corrosion was negligible and most of the test specimens removed from the tower waters still had their original bright lustre, including some that had been exposed for 321 days. By contrast, specimens in untreated systems corroded heavily. Average penetrations of about 5 mpy for the specimens in the untreated systems were reduced to about 0.1 mpy for the specimens in the chromate-treated waters.

Polyphosphates received considerable attention as corrosion inhibitors for aluminum systems. Sussman and Akers describe tests on hexametaphosphate-treated systems. A number of different aluminum systems were subjected to a polyphosphate treatment. The degree of protection varied from very good to very poor. There was some question as to the proper application of the treatment and whether it might have been responsible for some of the poor results.

Haygood and Minford describe two successful polyphosphate treatments. The first was a proprietary treatment which was found to be effective at a level of 35 ppm of PO_4 and a pH of 6.0 to 6.5. The cooling water (Pittsburgh tap) was concentrated 5 times. More concentrations —up to 10—could have been employed if necessary. The ratio of polyphosphate to calcium had to be kept at less than 2 for satisfactory protection, as is the case with steel.

The second polyphosphate treatment described by Haygood and Minford was developed for multimetallic systems of aluminum, steel, and copper. It is based on phosphate and contains other unspecified inhibitors as well. The operating level is about 10 ppm of PO_4 and 3 to 5 ppm of additives. The water used in the system is highly concentrated and the pH is kept at 7.0 to 7.5. Chromate-polyphosphate combinations are also being used for aluminum cooling systems with a considerable degree of success.

Silicates are known to be extremely effective corrosion inhibitors for aluminum when used under the right conditions. These conditions involve alkaline *p*H values in the range of 8.0 to 9.5. This condition limits the use of silicates for cooling-tower systems since it introduces a danger of scaling. Silicates are used, however, with considerable success for cooling systems where little make-up water is necessary and the hardness does not achieve a level where scaling is a danger. Systems of this type are described in the next chapter.

Various organic compounds have been suggested as inhibitors. It is known that in other systems, materials such as peat extracts, agar, starches, and soluble oils are very effective inhibitors for aluminum. Sussman and Akers evaluated a commercial tannin-extract inhibitor. They found extremely poor protection results from the use of this material. Oil-soluble sulfonates, such as those described by Simonoff,[146] are promising for this application. The sulfonate molecule contains a polar grouping and a hydrocarbon portion. The polar group bonds to the metal surface and the hydrocarbon residue has a strong affinity for oil. Use of an appropriate oil solvent for this sulfonate therefore results in an oil film which adheres tenaciously to the metal, barring penetration by the water. Sulfonates used should have a molecular weight of over 400 in order to be sufficiently oleophilic. The drawbacks to such a treatment are the same as those mentioned earlier for soluble oils—oil breakout, overheating, and localized attack.

REFERENCES

1. Brooke, M. Cooling-water treatment: a review. *Petroleum Refiner,* **36,** 142–8, Feb. 1957.

2. Thornley, J. L. Corrective water treatment prevents scale deposit, corrosion. *Heating, Piping, and Air Conditioning,* **31,** No. 8, 112–15, Aug. 1959.

3. Forbes, M. C. Approaching problems of cooling-water corrosion. *Petroleum Refiner,* **36,** No. 4, 164–5, 216, Apr. 1957.

4. Dalbke, R. G., and Masterson, J. M. Treat your cooling water right. *Power Plant Eng.,* **61,** No. 7, 56–9, July 1957.

5. Kennedy, E. F. Cooling-tower treatment (Paper No. A157-6-2). *Proc. Natl. Conf. Instr. Methods Anal.,* Chicago, 1957.

6. Gossom, J., and Johnson, J. O. Cooling-tower water treatment. *Oil Gas J.,* **55,** No. 49, 91–5, Dec. 9, 1957.

7. Recirculating Cooling-Water Work Group. Water utilization and treatment efficiency on Gulf Coast cooling towers. *Corrosion,* **13,** No. 8, 527t–30t, Aug. 1957. Tables 3-1 and 3-2 reprinted by courtesy of CORROSION.

8. Helwig, J. D., and McConomy, H. F. How 31 refineries condition cooling-water systems. *Oil Gas J.,* **55,** No. 48, 101, 103–6, Dec. 2, 1957.

9. Cook, C. H. Corrosion and deposit control in cooling water systems. *Combustion,* **27,** No. 3, 53–6, Mar. 1956.

10. Drane, C. W. Water treatment for recirculating systems. *Chem. and Ind.,* No. 46, 1367–72, Nov. 24, 1956.

11. Paulsen, G. C. Water-treatment problems in open-type recirculating cooling systems. *National Eng.,* **60,** No. 8, 26–7, 39, Aug. 1956.

12. Gibson, J. W. A survey of water conditioning practices. *Petroleum Engr.* **27,** No. 10, C44–6, C48–9, C53, Sept. 1955.

13. Winzig, W. J. Water treatment for cooling towers. *Blast Furnace Steel Plant,* **42,** No. 7, 812–6, July 1954; *World Oil,* **138,** No. 5, 261–4, 266, Apr. 1954.

14. Fitzpatrick, L. W. Treatment for cooling waters. *Power Plant Eng.,* **58,** 82–4, Feb. 1954.

15. Slough, J. M. Right water treatment extends cooling-tower life, saves money. *Power,* **98,** No. 5, 100–1, 232–8, May 1954.

16. Evans, U. R. Corrosion problems arising from water in chemical industry. *Chem. and Ind.,* No. 53, 1193–200, Dec. 31, 1951.

17. Miller, D. Objectives and techniques of cooling-water treatment. *Oil Gas J.,* No. 16, 139+, Aug. 23, 1951.

18. McConomy, H. F. Literature survey of corrosion in cooling-water systems—1940–1953. *Proc. Am. Petroleum Inst., III,* **35,** 32–79, 1955.

19. Rice, J. K. Treatment of recirculated cooling water. *Corrosion,* **8,** No. 11, 375–80, Nov. 1952.

20. Recirculating Cooling Water Sub-Committee. Some of the economic data on chemical treatment of Gulf Coast cooling waters. *Corrosion,* **11,** 61–2, Nov. 1955.

21. Bregman, J. I., and Newman, T. R. (unpublished data).

22. Hatch, G. B., and Rice, O. Threshold treatment of water systems: corrosion control and scale prevention with glassy phosphate. *Ind. Eng. Chem.,* **37,** No. 8, 710–5, Aug. 1945.

23. Maguire, J. J., Betz, W. H., and Betz, L. D. Biological fouling in recirculating cooling-water systems. *Ind. Eng. Chem.,* **48,** No. 12, 2162–7, Dec. 1956. Table 3-3 reprinted by courtesy of the authors and INDUSTRIAL AND CHEMICAL ENGINEERING.

24. Talbot, L. E., *et al.* Treatment of water for cooling purposes. *Am. Ry. Eng. Assoc. Bull., 525,* 339–42, 1955.

25. Williams, A. E. Control of slime and algae in cooling-water systems. *Cheap Steam,* **37,** 74–5, Oct. 1953; *Fuel Abstr.,* **15,** 94, 1954.

26. Updegraff, D. M. Microbiological corrosion of iron and steel. *Corrosion,* **11,** No. 10, 442t–6t, Oct. 1955.

27. Wormwell, F., and Nurse, T. J. The corrosion of mild steel and brass in chlorinated water. *J. Appl. Chem.,* **2,** Pt. 12, 685–92, Dec. 1952.

28. Uhlig, H. H. *Corrosion Handbook* (New York: John Wiley & Sons, Inc., 1953), p. 545.

29. Walker, C., and Bregman, J. I. (unpublished data).

30. Anon. Microbiological corrosion controlled by amine-type treatment. *Chem. Processing,* **23,** 127–8, Sept. 1960.

31. Hurst, E. H. Water treatment for polymetallic cooling systems. *Proc. Nineteenth Annual Am. Water Conf. Engr. Soc. W. Pa.,* 17–32, 1958.

32. Powell, J. L. Corrosion of copper in open recirculating water systems. *Ind. Eng. Chem.,* **51,** No. 3, 75A–6A, Mar. 1959.

33. Murray, R. G., and Tester, M. E. Four-tower water treatment test facility. *U.S. Atomic Energy Comm. Publication GAT-247,* Sept. 23, 1958.

34. Picarazzi, J. J. Cities Service tackles brackish-cooling-water corrosion. *Oil Gas J.,* **50,** No. 45, 271–4, May 17, 1952.

35. DeHalas, D. R. Heat-transfer effects on aluminum corrosion. I. *U.S. Atomic Energy Comm. Publication HW-42585, Rev.,* 1956.

36. Corrosion characteristics of aluminum cooling towers. *Heating and Ventilating,* **51,** No. 1, 88, Jan. 1954.

37. Sverepa, O. Corrosion of aluminum and its alloys in waters of various compositions. *Werkstoffe u. Korrosion,* **9,** 533–6, 1958.

38. Haygood, A. J., and Minford, J. D. Aluminum cooling towers and their treatment. *Corrosion,* **15,** No. 1, 36–40, Jan. 1959.

39. Sussman, S., and Akers, J. R. Corrosion and its control in aluminum cooling towers. *Corrosion,* **10,** No. 5, 151–9, May 1954.

40. Binger, W. W., and Fritts, H. W. Aluminum alloy heat exchangers in the process industries. *Corrosion,* **10,** 425, Dec. 1954.

41. Channabasappa, K. Prevention of solid deposits by new additive. Paper presented at N.A.C.E. Technical Committee T-5C-2 All-Day Meeting, Chicago, Apr. 25, 1961.

42. Flamand, R. J. J. Y. Polyphosphate distribution process for water treatment. Belg. 566,341, Apr. 30, 1958.

43. Kleber, J. P. Chemical conditioning of cooling waters. *Combustion,* **22,** No. 11, 45, May 1951.

44. Reif, K. The use of phosphates in water treatment. *Gas-u. Wasserfach,* **99,** 1354–6, 1958.

45. Stone, W. J. Metallic phosphates in cooling-water treatments. *Corrosion Technology,* **2,** 13–7, Jan. 1955.

46. Oxford, W. F., Jr. Use of surface-active agents in cooling-tower treatments. *Petroleum Processing,* **7,** No. 5, 620–2, May 1952; *Oil Gas J.,* **50,** No. 51, 176–7, 263–4, May 5, 1952.

47. Oxford, W. F. Inhibition of scaling and corrosion. U.S. 2,720,490, Oct. 1955.

48. Chittum, J. F., and Rohrback, G. H. Inhibition of deposition of carbonate scale on metals. U.S. 2,934,503, Apr. 26, 1960.

49. Roche, M. The incrustation of heating surfaces by calcium carbonate. *Inds. Aliment et Agr* (Paris), **75,** 281–8, 1958.

50. Lecornu, A. P. Scale-preventing compositions. Fr. 1,007,555, May 7, 1952.

51. Gambill, M. Scale in oil wells. U.S. 2,777,818, Jan. 15, 1957.

52. Nagel, H. Removal of carbonate hardness from cooling water by algae. *Mitt. Ver. Grosskesselbesitz.,* 403–6, 1951.

53. Kahler, H. L. Iron retention in water supplies with water-soluble lignin. U.S. 2,744,866, May 8, 1956.

54. Robinson, W. W., Jr. Treatment of industrial waters. U.S. 2,657,178 and U.S. 2,657,179, Oct. 27, 1953.

55. Cross, J. M. Water-soluble compositions containing water-insoluble organic amines. U.S. 2,779,741, Jan. 29, 1957.

56. Chambers, C. W., Kabler, P. W., Bryant, A. R., Chambers, L. A., and Ettinger, M. B. Bactericidal efficiency of quaternary ammonium compounds (Q.A.C.) in different waters. *Public Health Repts.* (U.S.), **70,** 545–53, 1955.

57. Hurst, E. H. Wood deterioration in cooling towers. *The Plant,* 25–9, Oct. 1959; *Nalco Reprint No. 85* (Chicago: Nalco Chemical Company, no date). Paraphrased by permission of Nalco Chemical Co.

58. Hurst, E. H. Wood deterioration in cooling towers. *The Plant,* 40–2, Nov. 1959; *Nalco Reprint No. 85* (Chicago: Nalco Chemical Company, no date). Paraphrased by permission of Nalco Chemical Co.

59. Comeaux, R. F. Redwood cooling towers—a look at causes of deterioration and methods of maintenance. *Oil Gas J.,* **52,** No. 20, 343–7, 1953.

60. Wise, R. S. Some corrosion inhibitors—a reference list. *Corrosion,* **11,** No. 4, 65–7, Apr. 1955.

61. Brooke, M. Corrosion inhibitor checklist. *Chem. Engr.,* **61,** No. 12, 230–4, Dec. 1954.

62. Stumm, W. Calcium carbonate deposition at iron surfaces. *J. Am. Water Works Assoc.,* **48,** 300–10, 1956.

63. Stumm, W. Estimating corrosion rates in water: polarization data permit rapid determination of instantaneous corrosion rates and evaluation of the effects of environmental variables on the extent of corrosion. *Ind. Eng. Chem.,* **51,** 1487–90, 1959.

64. Splittgerber, A. Corrosive action of tap waters in terms of the equilibrium: carbonic acid-calcium oxide. *Energietch.,* **4,** 131–2, 1954.

65. Powell, S. T., Bacon, H. E., and Knoedler, E. L. Corrosion prevention by controlled calcium carbonate scale. *Ind. Eng. Chem.,* **40,** 453–7, Mar. 1948.

66. Evans, U. R. *The Corrosion and Oxidation of Metals* (London: Edward Arnold Ltd., 1960; New York: St. Martin's Press, Inc., 1960), pp. 160–5.

67. Atkins, G. R. Soft-water corrosion and calcium carbonate saturation. *S. African Ind. Chemist,* **8,** 104–11, 1954.

68. Haase, L. W. *Arch. Metallk.,* **3,** 114, 1949.

69. Thornhill, R. S. Corrosion control by water treatment. *Chem. and Ind.* (London), 403, 1956.

70. Sussman, S. Cooling water problems in the New York metropolitan area. *Ind. Eng. Chem.,* **44,** No. 8, 1740–4, Aug. 1952.

71. Mayne, J. E. O., and Pryor, M. J. J. The mechanism of inhibition of corrosion of iron by chromic acid and potassium chromate. *J. Chem. Soc.,* 1831–5, 1949.

72. Hoar, T. P., and Evans, U. R. Time-potential curves on iron and steel and their significance. *J. Chem. Soc.,* 2476, 1932.

73. Simnad, M. T., and Evans, U. R. Influence of stress on the electrode potential and polarization of iron and steel in acid solution. *J. Metals,* **188,** 1220, 1950.

74. Brasher, D. M., and Stove, E. R. The use of radioactive tracers in the study of the mechanism of action of corrosion inhibitors. *Chem. and Ind.* (London), No. 8, 171–2, Feb. 23, 1952.

75. Cohen, M., and Beck, A. F. Passivity of iron in chromate solution. (I) Structure and composition of the film. *Z. Elekrochem.,* **62,** 696, 1958.

76. Pryor, M. J., and Cohen, M. J. The inhibition of the corrosion of iron by some anodic inhibitors. *J. Electrochem. Soc.,* **100,** No. 5, 203–15, May 1953.

77. Erwall, L. G. Radioactive tracers in corrosion research. *Jernkontorets Ann.,* **143,** 646–72, 1959.

78. Gerischer, H. Passivity of metals. *Angew. Chem.,* **70,** No. 10, 285–98, May 21, 1958.

79. Brasher, D. M., Kingsbury, A. H., Mercer, A. D., and De, C. P. Passivation of iron by chromate solutions. *Nature,* **180,** 27–9, 1957.

80. Brasher, D. M., and Kingsbury, A. H. Passivity of metals in inhibitor solutions using radioactive tracers. *Trans. Faraday Soc.,* **54,** 1214, 1958.

81. Kingsbury, A. H. Passivation of iron and steel in chromate solutions. *J. Australian Inst. Metals,* **4,** 12–8, May 1959.

82. Okamato, G. O., Nagayoma, N., and Mitami, Y. Corrosion phenomena. IV. Passivation mechanism of iron in chromate solution. *J. Electrochem. Soc. Japan* (English), **24,** 69, 1956.

83. Darrin, M. Chromate corrosion inhibitors in chloride systems. *Ind. Eng. Chem.,* **38,** 368, 1946.

84. Hess, W. A. Refinery corrosion rates below 5 mils/year achieved by chromate water treatment. *Corrosion,* **16,** No. 7, 20–1, July 1960.

85. Van Wazer, J. R. *Phosphorus and Its Compounds,* Vol. I (New York: Interscience Publishers, Inc., 1958).

86. Hatch, G. B., and Rice, O. Corrosion control with threshold treatment: factors in formation of protective films upon steel by waters treated with glassy phosphates. *Ind. Eng. Chem.,* **32,** 1572–9, 1940.

87. Apel'tsin, I. E., and Zolotova, E. F. The application of difficultly soluble metaphosphates to water works. *Vodosnabshenie i Sanit. Tekh.,* No. 4, 34–6, 1959.

88. Pryor, M. J., Cohen, M., and Brown, F. *J. Electrochem. Soc.,* **99,** 542, 1952.

89. Mayne, J. E. O., and Menter, J. W. The mechanism of inhibition of the corrosion of iron by solutions of sodium phosphate, borate, and carbonate. *J. Chem. Soc.,* 103–7, 1954.

90. Abd El Wahed, A. M., and Pourbaix, M. Use of polarization curves for the study of the conditions for corrosion and protection of iron in presence of chlorides. *Proc. Sixth Meeting Intern. Comm. Electrochem. Thermodynam. and Kinet.,* 351–9, 1954.

91. Hatch, G. B. Protective film formation with phosphate glasses. *Ind. Eng. Chem.,* **44,** 1775–80, Aug. 1952.

92. Raistrick, B. Condensed phosphates and corrosion control. *Chem. and Ind.* (London), No. 19, 408–14, May 10, 1952.

93. Lamb, J. C., and Eliassen, R. Mechanism of corrosion inhibition by sodium metaphosphate glass. *J. Am. Water Works Assoc.,* **46,** 445–60, May 1954.

94. Mansa, J. L., and Szybalski, W. Corrosion due to tuberculation in water systems. 1. The effect of Calgon on the potential of iron electrodes in differential aeration cells with running tap water. *Corrosion,* **8,** No. 11, 381–90, Nov. 1952.

95. Mears, R. B. The electrochemistry of inhibitor action. *Corrosion,* **11,** No. 8, 50–2, Aug. 1955.

96. Uhlig, H. H., Triadis, D. N., and Stern, M. Effect of oxygen, chlorides, and calcium ion on corrosion inhibition of iron by polyphosphates. *J. Electrochem. Soc.,* **102,** 59–66, 1955.

97. Parham, P. N., and Tod, C. W. Condensed phosphates in the treatment of corrosive waters. *Chem. and Ind.* (London), 628–31, June 1953.

98. Takeuchi, K. Corrosion inhibition by hexametaphosphate in the presence of bivalent metal ions. *Boshoku Gijutsu,* **8,** 147–9, 1959.

99. Rice, O. Corrosion control with Calgon. *J. Am. Water Works Assoc.,* **39,** No. 6, 552–60, June 1947.

100. Lehrman, L., and Shuldener, H. L. Action of sodium silicate as a corrosion inhibitor in water piping. *Ind. Eng. Chem.,* **44,** No. 8, 1765–9, Aug. 1952.

101. Shuldener, H. L., and Sussman, S. Thirty years' experience with silicate as a corrosion inhibitor in water systems. *Corrosion,* **16,** 354t–8t, July 1960.

102. Streiker, W. Experiences with silicate inhibitors. Paper presented at 12th Annual Am. Water Conf. Eng. Soc. W. Pa., Oct. 1951.

103. Wood, J. W., Beecher, J. S., and Laurence, P. S. Some experience with sodium silicate as a corrosion inhibitor in industrial cooling waters. *Corrosion*, **13**, No. 11, 719t–24t, Nov. 1957.

104. Shuldener, H. L., and Lehrman, L. Influence of bicarbonate ion on inhibition of corrosion by sodium silicate in a zinc-iron system. *J. Am. Water Works Assoc.*, **49**, 1432–40, 1957.

105. Duffer, E. F., and McKinney, D. S. New method of studying corrosion inhibition of iron with sodium silicate. *J. Electrochem. Soc.*, **103**, No. 12, 645–7, Dec. 1956.

106. Haering, D. W. Film inhibitors in industrial aqueous systems. *Ind. Eng. Chem.*, **30**, No. 12, 1356–61, Dec. 1938.

107. Haering, D. W. *Organic Methods of Scale and Corrosion Control*, 5th ed. (Chicago: D. W. Haering and Co., Inc., 1943).

108. Breston, J. N. Corrosion control with organic inhibitors. *Ind. Eng. Chem.*, **44**, No. 8, 1755–61, Aug. 1952.

109. Speller, F. N. *Corrosion, Causes and Prevention*, 3rd ed. (New York: McGraw-Hill Book Co., Inc., 1951), pp. 396, 409.

110. Oakes, B. D. Corrosion inhibition. U.S. 2,931,700, Apr. 5, 1960.

111. Martin, A. E., and Eberman, J. W. Reaction product of starch with chromium trioxide as corrosion inhibitor in water systems. U.S. 2,658,817, Nov. 10, 1953.

112. Robertson, W. D. Corrosion: new rust preventives. *J. Electrochem. Soc.*, **98**, 94, 1951; *Chem. Eng.*, **57**, 290–2, Apr. 1950.

113. Sympson, R. F., and Cartledge, G. H. The mechanism of the inhibition of corrosion by the pertechnetate ion., Part IV. Comparison with other $XO_4{}^{n-}$ inhibitors. *J. Phys. Chem.*, **60**, No. 8, 1037–43, Aug. 1956.

114. Cartledge, G. H. The inhibition of corrosion by the pertechnetate ion. *U.S. Atomic Energy Comm. Publication ORNL-1833*, Jan. 18, 1955.

115. Cartledge, G. H. The mechanism of the inhibition of corrosion by the pertechnetate ion. Part II. The reversibility of the inhibiting mechanism. *J. Phys. Chem.*, **60**, 28–32, Jan. 1956.

116. Cartledge, G. H. Studies in corrosion. *Sci. American*, **194**, 35–40, May 1956.

117. Kahler, H. L., and George, C. Decreasing cooling water corrosion. *Petroleum Refiner*, **34**, No. 7, 144–8, July 1945.

118. Kahler, H. L., and George, C. Protection of metal against pitting, tuberculation, and general corrosion. *Corrosion*, **6**, 331–40, Oct. 1950.

119. Kahler, H. L., and Gaughan, P. Protection of metals against pitting, tuberculation, and general corrosion. *Ind. Eng. Chem.*, **44**, No. 8, 1770–4, Aug. 1952.

120. Devereux, T. J. Controlling corrosion in cooling systems. *Western Metals*, **13**, No. 6, 53–6, June 1955.

121. Brandel, A. J. Recirculation of cooling water in petroleum refining. *Ind. Eng. Chem.*, **48**, No. 12, 2156–8, Dec. 1956.

122. Kahler, H. L. Phosphate-chromate protection in water systems. U.S. 2,711,391, June 21, 1955.

123. Kahler, H. L., and Tanzola, W. A. Inhibiting corrosion in industrial water systems. U.S. 2,900,222, Aug. 18, 1959.

124. Bird, P. G. Stopping deterioration in recirculating cooling water systems. *Ind. Refrig.*, **133**, 1, 15–8, 60, 1957.

125. Smart, A. H. Zinc as an anti-corrosive. *Paint Manuf.*, **17**, No. 11, 383–5, 1947.

126. Rozenfel'd, I. L., and Marshakov, I. K. Metal corrosion mechanism in narrow fissures and crevices. II. Corrosion of iron in solutions of inhibitors. *Zhur. Fiz. Khim.,* **31,** 72–82, 1957.

127. Kahler, H. L., and George, C. B. Corrosion inhibition. U.S. 2,793,932, May 28, 1957.

128. Kahler, H. L., and George, C. B. Corrosion inhibition of water-metal interfaces. U.S. 2,872,281, Feb. 3, 1959.

129. Bregman, J. I., and Newman, T. R. Developments in the handling of circulating water. Multivalent ion-polyphosphate inhibitors. *Werkstoffe u. Korrosion,* **9,** 379–83, 1958.

130. Bregman, J. I., and Newman, T. R. Developments in cooling tower system treatments. Part I. Polyvalent ion-polyphosphate inhibitors. *Corrosion,* **15,** No. 2, 61–4, 1959.

131. Rama Char, T. L. Anodic corrosion of metals and alloys in pyrophosphate solutions. *Corrosion Prevent. and Control,* **5,** No. 4, 37–8, 1958.

132. Brooke, J. M. Corrosion inhibition agent. U.S. 2,813,075, Nov. 12, 1957.

133. Kahler, H. L., Bishop, C. A., and Tanzola, W. A. Corrosion inhibition in water systems. U.S. 2,848,299, Aug. 19, 1958.

134. Boies, D. B. (personal communication).

135. Palen, T. Reduce cooling-system corrosion. *Petroleum Refiner,* **38,** No. 5, 239–42, May 1959.

136. Bregman, J. I., and Boies, D. B. (unpublished data).

137. Puckorius, P. R., and Ryzner, W. J. Cooling water inhibitor performance. *Corrosion,* **16,** No. 10, 473t–8t, Oct. 1960.

138. Puckorius, P. R. Pretreatment—the key to effective production cooling water systems. Paper presented at Twenty-First Annual Am. Water Conf. Engr. Soc. W. Pa., 23–33, Oct. 1960.

139. N.A.C.E. Technical Committee T-3A. Some corrosion inhibitors—a reference list. *Corrosion,* **11,** 195t–7t, 1955.

140. Whitney, F. L. Inhibiting a cooling-water tower system. *Corrosion,* **13,** 711t–8t, 1957.

141. Shields, H., Sorg, L. C., and Stutz, R. L. Selecting corrosion and scale inhibitors for cooling water. *Corrosion,* **15,** No. 5, 233t–6t, 1959.

142. Cavallaro, L., and Indelli, A. Corrosion inhibitors and stimulators in liquid medium. *Rev. Met.,* **49,** No. 2, 117–24, 1952.

143. Tanzola, W. A. Corrosion control in cooling water systems. *Petroleum Engr.,* **25,** No. 4, C57–C60, 1953.

144. Verink, E. D., and Murphy, F. B. Solving refinery corrosion problems with aluminum. *Corrosion,* **16,** No. 12, 16–20, Dec. 1960.

145. Keller, F., and Edwards, J. D. The behavior of oxide films on aluminum. *Pittsburgh International Conference on Surface Reactions,* 202–12, June 1948.

146. Simonoff, R. Sulfonates as rust preventives. *Petrochemical Ind.,* **1,** 35–7, June 1958.

4

Cooling Water—
Other Systems

There are a number of additional cooling-water systems which require corrosion inhibitors. These systems are broken down into three different categories in this chapter as outlined in the introduction in Chapter 3. The problems, the inhibition principles, and the techniques are similar in many of these systems both to each other and to those already discussed for cooling towers.

INTERNAL COMBUSTION ENGINES

The problems associated with the inhibition of corrosion of internal combustion engines are similar in many respects to those already described for cooling-tower systems. For this reason this category is examined first. The main difference between the cooling systems of the internal combustion engines and those of the cooling towers is that the former are essentially "closed" recirculating systems while the latter are "open." The resultant difference in the loss by evaporation and the oxygen content gives a somewhat easier system to protect.

The problems associated with cooling systems in internal combustion engines can be further broken down as follows:

1. *Diesel engine cooling systems.*
2. *Automotive cooling systems.*
3. *Antifreeze in either system.*

There are other recirculating systems which are treated with corrosion inhibitors and antifreeze, but the diesel and the automotive systems are the major ones. They are treated separately here for reasons which become obvious in this chapter. The addition of antifreeze imposes new corrosive conditions. Inhibitors for use with antifreeze are similar in both diesel and automotive systems and therefore are considered as a unit.

Literature

DIESEL ENGINES. The major use of corrosion inhibitors for diesel engines is in the railroad industry. For this reason, most of the literature dealing with this subject is oriented in the direction of railroad problems. In 1948 Hanson[1] wrote an article in the *Journal of the American Water Works Association* which summarized the problem of combating scale and corrosion in diesel-locomotive cooling systems to that date. This problem was relatively new since most railroads had been using the steam engine and were just in the process of switching to diesels. In 1953 Wise[2] discussed the problem of corrosion and the use of inhibitors for diesel engines. During the same year, the American Locomotive Company published the papers presented at the Symposium on Diesel Locomotive Engine Maintenance[3] which included sections on cooling-water treatment. More recent surveys of the field have been published by Talbot,[4] Crossett,[5] and Blackwood.[6] A survey of literature dealing with corrosion in engine-cooling systems which contain aluminum was published by Benton.[7]

A major corrosion problem in diesel engines is that of cavitation erosion. This term "cavitation erosion" is the commonly used contraction of the more correct term *cavitation corrosion-erosion.* Corrosion and erosion are actually two separate phenomena which are associated in the present context. A large amount of literature describing this problem has been presented, including articles by Godfrey[8, 9] and Piltz[10] and a book by Nowotny[11] which presents an excellent theoretical discussion of the phenomenon of cavitation and the processes which cause the destruction of materials. Joyner[12] discusses the problem specifically with relation to diesel-engine cylinder liners.

AUTOMOTIVE COOLING SYSTEMS. Although this problem received a great deal of attention, most generalized literature describing it is the popular science variety. An exception is that of Wukman[13] who discusses the problem and presents possible solutions. Good descriptions of the problem are given in articles dealing with specific inhibitors which are presented later in this chapter.

ANTIFREEZE. This problem is the subject of a great many publications. A thorough description is given in the Bureau of Standards circular[14] which presents a general survey based on 191 references. The required properties of the various antifreezes are presented with comments on the corrosion aspects in each case. Separate sections are presented on cooling-system corrosion, depletion of corrosion inhibitors, and properties of coolant materials.

Ondrejcin[15] discussed automotive antifreezes, the need for them, the pros and cons of methanol-based and glycol-based types, and the use of corrosion inhibitors. Agnew, Truitt, and Robertson[16] as well as Collins and Higgins[17] studied the corrosive factors in ethylene glycol solutions for automotive systems.

Economics

DIESEL ENGINES. There are no published figures on the dollar volume of chemicals sold as corrosion inhibitors for diesel engines. Practically every engine in use in the railroad industry is being treated constantly with inhibitors at dosage levels of from 0.4 to 1.5 ounces of inhibitor per gallon of cooling water. The total annual sale of inhibitors for this purpose is probably in the neighborhood of two to four million dollars in the United States. This amount is exclusive of inhibitors in the antifreeze used in these engines.

AUTOMOTIVE COOLING SYSTEMS. Sales of inhibitors of automotive cooling systems must be divided into two categories: those added to the cooling water during the summer months and those present in the antifreeze used during the winter. Almost all antifreeze sold has a corrosion inhibitor in it. By contrast, despite an intensive educational campaign, only a small fraction of the automotive cooling systems which do not contain antifreeze are treated with corrosion inhibitors. Corrosion inhibitors for this purpose are usually available at gasoline stations at a price of about $1.00 per can, one can being sufficient to treat the average radiator. A figure of $2 to $3 million would be a fair estimate of the dollar volume of inhibitors sold annually in the United States for this purpose.

ANTIFREEZE. The market for corrosion inhibitors for antifreeze is much greater. A recent issue of *Chemical and Engineering News*[18] states that 121 million gallons of antifreeze were sold in 1960. It further says that glycol-base material now accounts for 91 per cent of all antifreeze sales. The cost of the corrosion inhibitor that the antifreeze manufacturer places in his mixture varies considerably depending on the type and the effectiveness of the inhibitor. Estimated costs to him may be from two cents per gallon to as much as 10 or 15 cents per gallon. Using an average figure of five cents per gallon for the purpose of making a rough estimate, one arrives at a figure of about six million dollars per year of corrosion inhibitors for this purpose.

A new type of coolant-antifreeze system has been introduced during the past few years. This consists of a glycol base containing corrosion inhibitors and pH indicators. The material is "permanent," i.e., the suppliers recommend that it be kept in the cooling system permanently instead of being replaced annually like most antifreeze materials. The initial cost is much higher than the conventional glycol antifreezes, but there is little or no subsequent cost. While it is still too early to gauge the impact of this type of material on the antifreeze market, it is apparent that sales thus far have been disappointing.

The Problem

DIESEL ENGINES. Hanson[1] states that no water is suitable for use in a diesel-locomotive cooling system without treatment for corrosion prevention. This statement is rather broad but experience indicates that it can be considered as a generalized truth. The diesel-cooling system presents a closed circuit which operates under conditions such that severe corrosion in the absence of an inhibitor almost becomes a certainty. There are a number of different makes of diesel locomotives in use today and all major diesel locomotive builders specify that corrosion inhibitors must be used in the cooling water. In some cases, they go much further and lay down strict requirements as to the types of treatments and the concentrations which are to be maintained.

Corrosivity of the system occurs because of unavoidable factors in design which result in the use of a number of different metals, high-temperature, high-oxygen-content, high-velocity and turbulent conditions, the possibility for contamination, and foaming. In addition, a phenomenon known as cavitation-corrosion-erosion is quite common because of the design of certain types of engines.

A large number of different metals are used in the diesel engine. These metals may number as many as nine or 10 and may be insulated from each other or coupled in a galvanic manner; the latter would especially accelerate corrosion. These metals include cast iron, steel, copper, brass, a variety of solders, aluminum on occasion, and perhaps even stainless steel and various other alloys. All of these are subject to corrosion. They can affect the corrosion of other metals both by galvanic attack and also by deposition of their corrosion products on the other metals. For this reason new solutions for this problem must be designed so as to protect all of the metals.

Accumulation of scale and sludge in the diesel-cooling system must be prevented. This prevention is generally easy to accomplish since the amount of make-up water in a properly treated system is generally quite low. As an extra precaution, demineralized or softened water is frequently used in these systems. Phosphates are avoided because of the formation of phosphate sludge.

There are a number of nonmetallic compounds in the system which must not be attacked or allowed to deteriorate. These include such things as natural and synthetic rubbers, carbon, and asbestos. The problem here is generally not so much to prevent attack on these non-metallic materials by the water, but rather to be sure that materials added as corrosion inhibitors for metals will not attack the nonmetallic materials. For example, many soluble oils which are excellent metallic corrosion inhibitors swell rubber quite badly.

Water temperatures vary from ambient (when the engine is idle) to about 180° F under normal operation. Recently, this range was extended with the introduction of vapor-phase cooling.[19] The acceleration of corrosion by increasing temperature is a well-known fact.

The velocity of the water in the cooling system varies considerably. In operation, the bulk of the water has a flow rate of 5 to 10 ft/sec. Water may be stagnant in certain areas in the system and, of course, when the engine is standing idle. In addition, undesirable turbulence can occur which will play a major role in the development of corrosion-erosion.

Copson[20] presents a detailed discussion of the effect of velocity on the corrosion of metals with emphasis on those metals such as iron, copper, and other alloys that are generally found in cooling systems of this type. He points out that generally corrosion will increase with velocity but not always. Sometimes motion can either eliminate or cause local attack. It will have a marked effect on galvanic couples. A detailed knowledge of operating conditions is essential for the analysis of a particular problem.

The chemical composition of the water is important. Many railroads and inhibitor suppliers place a limit of 10 grains per gallon of total hardness and also of sodium chloride on the water which can be used for cooling purposes. Water of much greater hardness or chloride content can find its way into the system when the engine takes on water at points where there are no treatment facilities. Pressures in the system can range from atmospheric to about 15 psig.

Schudlic[21] shows that oil in cooling systems can cause overheating of cylinders and destruction of hoses and seals, and interfere with corrosion inhibitors and testing. Blackwood[6] points out that high water velocity and sleeve deflection are accelerating factors in corrosion areas. Addition of insufficient corrosion inhibitors also accelerates corrosion. Tennyson[22] shows that a combination of precipitated calcium and magnesium hardness with oil forms a sticky sludge which causes local overheating and obstructs water passages.

Field conditions and practices by the engineers responsible for treatment may vary drastically from one railroad to another and even from one area to another within the same railroad system. Some engineers may keep the treatment level at recommended dosages, while others allow it to drop to levels which turn inhibitor use into a "dangerous" one promoting attack. Such unusual contaminants as burlap or cotton rags and bags were found in corroded diesel-cooling systems. It has frequently been said that the best treatment for the diesel cooling system is a conscientious operator.

For a more detailed discussion of the corrosion problems involved in diesel cooling systems, the reader is referred to articles by Bregman and Boies,[23] Wilkes,[24] Hanson,[25] and Hold.[26]

A large number of diesel engines that are in use in locomotion are subjected to the phenomenon of cavitation-erosion. This extremely destructive process appears to occur when the cylinder liner and the jacket are separated from each other. In the case of those engines in which the liner and the jacket form an integral unit, little or no cavitation-erosion is generally found.

There has been a great deal of dispute about whether or not cavitation-erosion is strictly a mechanical problem or a chemical one (and therefore can be considered as corrosion) or both. There has been a great deal of literature on this question. Ramsay[27] in 1912 suggested that cavitation-erosion is really a form of electrolytic corrosion occurring at the strain-hardened indentation where cavitation bubbles have collapsed on the metal surface. Fittinger[28] proposes that the mechanical destruction process is predominant and any electrochemical effects are minor. Nowotny[11] set forth a theory which postulates the destruction by cavitation to be completely physical in nature. In more recent times, the generally accepted theory is that the cavitation, as it occurs initially, is essentially physical. The result of the cavitation, however, is to leave a surface which is eroded and weakened considerably. This surface now becomes highly susceptible to corrosion, especially at those points where bubble-collapse resulted in the initiation of the pitting pattern. Corrosion then proceeds rapidly in a pitting manner. The portions of the metal that have been corroded are further weakened and are more susceptible to cavitation. The net result is a catastrophic situation in which the cavitation and the corrosion each accelerate the effect of the other and pitting all through the liner occurs rapidly.

Nowotny[11] defines cavitation as the formation of bubbles (cavities) which appear in an agitated liquid with resultant material destruction. A two-phase condition (liquid-steam) is formed on the surface of the metal. He postulates that cavitation is composed of a "primary incident" and a "secondary incident." The primary incident is a hydro-dynamic effect which is caused by formation of small cavities of vapor in the water. This formation occurs because pressure is induced locally so that boiling occurs. Return of the pressure to normal causes an implosion as the cavities collapse. If the cavities are in contact with metal, deep spongy pitting can occur. The damages are influenced strongly by the factors affecting the condition of the bubbles, such as external pressure, saturation pressure, temperature, surface tension, and viscosity. The stability and the destructive force of the bubble increase with increasing pressure difference, while the number of bubbles increases with increasing temperature. A high surface tension causes severe damage. The viscosity appears to have a very small influence upon the intensity of the cavitation damage. The secondary incident consists of the effects of localized high temperatures and high pressures that are created at the point of the bubble-collapse.

Richardson[29] made measurements of the number and the size of gaseous nuclei that give rise to cavitation. He states that the nuclei can be removed by long standing or by application of pressure. Crewdsen[30] states that the secondary incident referred to by Nowotny is really the one that causes the major portion of the cavitation. He says that the major part of the energy available for the attack is stored in the bubbles and not in the surface waters. The high temperatures attained in bubbles assist the attack. The resulting temperature gradients in the metal can produce thermoelectric effects which lead to electrolytic attack. He further states that high pressure and high temperature of gas within the bubbles can account for the damage instead of the bubble-collapse.

The properties of the material which is subjected to cavitation are important in determining the extent to which damage occurs. These properties include surface hardness, corrosion fatigue, resistance, strength, surface workability, and porosity and composition of the metal. Nowotny states that a porous surface is more evenly attacked. Bogachev and Mints[31] present a detailed study of the effect of graphite form in cast iron, chemical composition, and heat-treatment. With respect to the cavitation damage resistance of cast iron, they found that the most favorable type of graphite was globular. They state that the damage in cast iron starts from graphite inclusions. In laminar graphite cast iron, an easy path is provided for the development of the damage. The sharp discontinuities in the matrix generated by graphite erosion aid rapid failure, whereas in globular graphite the damage is local and confined to isolated volumes of graphite. Martensitic and ferritic matrices appear to be disadvantageous, while finely dispersed pearlitic, behnitic, or sorbitic structures are the most resistant.

Glikman, Tekht, and Zobachev[32] made microscopic studies of metal surfaces during cavitation. They found that a surface layer of plastically deformed metal, 20 to 40μ thick, grew during the test and then microcracks and ridges formed. When the specimens were not of the same structure, cavitation-erosion always began at the weakest part. The surface layer increased in hardness by as much as 20 to 50 per cent.

Resistance to cavitation was determined not only by the macroscopic properties of the specimens but also by the properties of any microscopic inclusion.

Additional factors in the acceleration of the destruction by corrosion, can be the removal of the protective oxide film from the surface of the increased reactivity of the water associated with the cavitation.[33] Copson[20] points out that pitting roughening of the surface by corrosion increases the damage. A material which pits can cause turbulence that leads to cavitation-erosion. Both exhaust gas leakage into the system and suction of air on the inlet side of the pump contribute to the damage.

Leith and Thompson[34] conducted an excellent laboratory study in which they evaluate the effects of corrosion on cavitation damage. They confirm the inferior resistance of ferritic metals. They show that cavitation proceeds more rapidly in tap water than in distilled water, while sea water gives the worst damage. This fact correlates directly with the corrosivity sequence of these waters. The effect of temperature is quite striking. Destruction increases up to a temperature of 120° F and then decreases with further increase in temperature for a cast-iron cylinder liner. Decreasing pressure results in rapidly increasing cavitation so that a reduction from 10 to 5 psig nearly doubled the cavitation damage. They point out that a pressure release valve now maintains the back pressure in all engines at 20 psig in order to give minimum cavitation damage. Under conditions of field operation, some of the most severe cavitation damages occur in diesel engines in the Rocky Mountains.

AUTOMOTIVE COOLING SYSTEMS. This section deals with the problems involved in the corrosion of automotive cooling systems, but it should be realized that the same basic problems would apply to aircraft cooling systems as well. The automotive cooling system is one which represents a general corrosive situation to the metals therein and which should be protected by inhibitors to a far greater extent than is the case today. Rowe[35] itemized the factors influencing the process of corrosion in a multimetal engine cooling system as follows:

1. Coolant flow.
2. Aeration.
3. Operating temperatures.
4. Water composition variables.
5. Corrosion byproducts.
6. Antifreeze characteristics.
7. Couples of dissimilar metals.
8. Exhaust gas leakage into coolant.
9. Metal hot spots.
10. Metal stresses.
11. Operating conditions.[35]

He listed the following metals as being typical of those found in auto-motive systems:

1. Aluminum (type 3003).
2. Steel (SAE 1010).
3. Copper (electrolytic).
4. Brass (Cu-70, Zn-30).
5. Cast iron.
6. Solder (Pb-70, Sn-30).[35]

The ASTM corrosion method also lists the same metals but with some-what different specifications.[36]

The coolant flow varies from a static condition to a flow rate similar to that found in a diesel engine. The water is, for all practical purposes, saturated with oxygen. Operating temperatures vary from ambient (which may be as low as −20 or −30° F) to about 180° F. The water composition varies from city to city and may contain antifreeze. Exhaust gas leakage into the cooling system or glycol breakdown can cause an acidic condition. Local hot spots or stresses can develop which influence pitting.

Another factor which can be very dangerous so far as corrosion is concerned is the use of an acidic compound to clean out the cooling system. Quite frequently this acid is not followed by sufficient rinsing and addition of a neutralizer composition. The result is that the pH of the water drops and a local highly acidic situation can develop in stagnant areas.

The recent advent of aluminum radiators and blocks introduces new corrosion problems. Several different aluminum alloys are being used for this purpose. The aluminum is much more susceptible to pitting and corrosion than conventional metals would be, and it is especially im-portant that it be protected with inhibitors. There has been some dis-cussion of using closed aluminum systems so that proper conditions can be maintained.

The rubber hose that is part of the cooling system presents another problem. In addition to the normal susceptibility of the hose to swelling and cracking, it can be attacked severely by certain of the corrosion inhibitors that are popular for radiators. The use of glycol antifreeze can also damage the rubber hose.

ANTIFREEZE. Ethylene glycol, which is the major antifreeze material for automotive and diesel engines, oxidizes to a mixture of corrosive acids of which formic acid is the major constituent.[17] This oxidation is promoted by mechanical defects, such as air suction at water pump shaft seals or lower hose connection and exhaust gas leakage.[15] The resulting solution will be much more corrosive than tap water to which no antifreeze has been added. Collins and Higgins[17] state that the factors believed to be responsible for the rapid oxidation of glycol are excessive aeration of the coolant, the presence of local hot spots in the cooling system, operation of the coolant at consistently high temperatures, and the large amounts of copper or copper alloys in the cooling system. Bregman and Boies[23] presented data showing that the addition of ethylene glycol gives higher corrosion rates for many metals than when water alone is used. Furthermore, in their tests, many commercial antifreeze materials based on glycol which were stated to contain corrosion inhibitors gave higher corrosion rates during one week at 180° F than uninhibited ethylene glycol. This increase was especially the case for aluminum.

Agnew, Truitt, and Robertson[16] conducted a detailed study of the factors which affect the corrosion of metals in ethylene glycol solution. They found that the corrosion rates for all metals and chemical conditions studied are linear with time or decrease with time. The magnitude of corrosion rates under conditions of nonreplacement of solution is either equal to or lower than those obtained under the conditions of solution renewal. Copper and brass are affected to a much greater extent by solution replacement than steel or solder. The pH range for optimum protection is 6 to 9. Below and above these values the corrosion rate increases rapidly. Aluminum and solder are especially susceptible to rapid failure when the pH increases to about 10. In a 40 per cent ethylene glycol-water solution, the corrosion rates do not follow a simple pattern with increasing temperature. They do not fall off as the temperature approaches the boiling point of the solution, as is expected, due to the rapidly decreasing oxygen solubility. Copper and brass show an absolute dependence of corrosion rate on oxygen content while the other metals are less affected. The presence of chloride ion increases the corrosion rate, especially for aluminum and solder. In the case of steel, the corrosion rate decreases almost linearly with increasing glycol concentration in an intermediate pH range.

The ratio of antifreeze material to water varies considerably depending upon the location. The concentration of antifreeze is anywhere from 10 to 60 per cent. The antifreeze mixture can also contain additives which are designed to protect against the swelling of rubber or the foaming of the treated water. In addition, a dye is usually present to color the solution.

Leakage of antifreeze into the combustion space or crankcase of an engine can cause serious damage. When either antifreeze solution or water mixes with engine oil, the subsequent formation of sludge and gum can impair lubrication and cause sticking of valves, hydraulic valve lifters, and piston rings.

Other factors which can shorten the life of ethylene glycol are the presence of cleaning acids in the radiator, the use of a corrosion inhibitor (such as chromate) which is incompatible with the glycol and which reduces it, and the presence of rust deposits. In the case of methanol, loss by evaporation is negligible compared to the overflow loss of liquid because of violent boiling. The use of methanol as an antifreeze does not remove the need for a corrosion inhibitor. Bregman and Boies[37] studied corrosion of methanol-water mixtures and found that in many cases these mixtures are more corrosive and more difficult to inhibit properly than ethylene glycol-water mixtures.

Finally, a number of other materials for possible antifreezes for automotive cooling systems are mentioned briefly. These include salt-base materials, such as calcium or magnesium chloride, petroleum coolants, such as oils or kerosine, or other materials, such as honey, sugar, glycerine, or diacetone alcohol. The salt-base materials are much too corrosive for use in automobiles. The petroleum coolants attack rubber hose severely. The other materials are unsatisfactory because they are either poor freezing point depressants, thermally unstable, or too viscous.

Inhibition

DIESEL ENGINES. The value of inhibitor treatment in a diesel-engine cooling system can be seen by examination of Figures 4-1 and 4-2. Figure 4-1 shows a diesel locomotive cylinder head that was ruined by corrosion. In Figure 4-2 a similar cylinder head is shown which shows very little corrosion after 793,000 miles during which it was protected by proper water treatment.

The oldest, most widely used, and perhaps still the most effective corrosion-inhibitor approach to the problem of diesel-locomotive cooling-system corrosion is the use of formulations based on chromates or dichromates. A paper published in 1945 by Darrin[38] stresses the advantages of chromates for diesel cooling systems, while he earlier (1941)[39] pointed out that sodium chromate inhibited corrosion of iron, galvanized iron, tinned iron, copper, brass, and aluminum, both alone and in contact with each other. A number of papers were published in the next few years which advised the use of chromates.[40-42]

The need for pH control in the use of chromates was observed by several authors. Darrin[38] suggests a suitable mixture of dichromate and caustic while Hanson[1] recommends a pH value between 8.5 and 9.5. This alkaline value is still the most common one used, although variations of the chromate treatment at pH values as low as 6.5 are also utilized.

Darrin[38] states that a concentration of 500 ppm of chromate is usu-

FIGURE 4-1. Corroded Diesel Cylinder Head

Photograph Courtesy of Nalco Chemical Company

FIGURE 4-2. Diesel Locomotive Head Retainer After 793,000 Miles with Corrosion-Inhibitor Treatment

Photograph Courtesy of Nalco Chemical Company

ally sufficient, but recommends a level of 1,000 ppm for extra safety. The use of 0.5 lb of sodium chromate in a diesel which contains about 100 gal of water would suffice. Dosage levels as low as 200 ppm[43] and as high as 2,000 ppm[44] have also been recommended.

A number of formulations based on chromate were developed and some are being used today. Jacoby[45] patented a formulation of 500 to 3,000 $Na_2Cr_2O_7 \cdot 2H_2O$ and 250 to 1,000 ppm of $NaNO_3$. The pH range is kept between 6.5 and 9.5, which is controlled by buffering with borax and Na_2CO_3. This formulation and variations of it are still used today. The nitrate is an inhibitor with the chromate, while the borax adds considerable buffering capacity at the high end of the pH range with the carbonate. Bardwell and Dwyer[46] recommend the use of a mixture of chromates, phosphates, and soda ash with distilled water. The problem here is that if distilled water is not available at some points and water containing appreciable hardness is taken up, the resultant calcium phosphate sludge will be detrimental. Antinori[47] recommends the use of a mixture of equal parts of K_2CrO_4 and Na_2CO_3 as the best inhibitor for diesels. Evans[48] describes a unique treatment which is applied by a large chemical concern in the United Kingdom to a number of different systems including locomotive, land, and ship diesel engines. In applying this treatment to a system which is already severely corroded, about 1,000 ppm of calgon is added to penetrate and remove corrosion products. The system is then drained and about 1,500 to 3,000 ppm of sodium or potassium chromate are added to build up a protective film. The chloride content of the water is kept below 30 ppm, with the pH controlled between 6 and 7. The effectiveness of this approach is subject to some dispute and most authorities prefer the use of mild organic acids.

Patterson and Jones[49] showed that the addition of high salt concentrations, such as 7,500 ppm of NaCl, to distilled water drastically increased the corrosion rate of mild steel, even at $K_2Cr_2O_7$ dosage levels as high as 2,000 ppm of solution. Darrin[50] points out that chromates reduce corrosion at low salt levels but do not prevent it entirely at higher concentrations. He presents data showing that the effect of increased concentration of chloride is to accelerate the consumption of chromate, especially during the first few days and to increase the concentration of chromate required to protect the metal surfaces. After a few months of operation it is not necessary to add the full chromate dosage to the make-up water to maintain the concentration because of evaporation and concentration effects.

The addition of a small amount of sodium metasilicate to a chromate treatment is of especial value when aluminum which is in contact with copper must be protected.[38] Speller[51] also states that 500 ppm of Na_2CrO_4 with 40 ppm of sodium metasilicate is effective in retarding corrosion of aluminum in contact with copper in tap water (pH 7.5 to 8.5). However, if the ratio of copper to aluminum surface is large, no inhibitor will protect the metal above 160° F. Eldredge and Mears[52] postulate that the difficulty in inhibiting attack on the aluminum, when it is in contact with copper metal and in a solution containing chloride ions arises because the potential difference between the copper and aluminum is greater than that between the local electrodes on the aluminum itself, which are involved in local corrosion. They also found that the addition of sodium silicate to chromate solutions aids aluminum protection. The more alkaline silicates are the most effective.

Today, chromate formulations, preferably at slightly alkaline pH values, 7.5 to 9.5, are probably the most common inhibitors used in diesel-locomotive cooling systems. They are generally applied at dosage levels of about 0.4 oz/gal of cooling water. Protection of all metal in the system is usually quite good and fewer corrosion problems appear to occur than with almost any other type of treatment.

The chromate inhibitors are dangerous and if the treatment level is kept too low, accelerated local attack may occur. For this reason, test kits are usually employed by railroad operators to check the treatment level frequently and to apply additional inhibitor as needed. A much more serious drawback of chromates, however, is their toxicity. Frequent handling and failure to remove chromate powders or concentrated liquid from the skin is said possibly to cause dermatitis. Lawsuits were instituted against some railroads during the early fifties by railroad workers who claimed to have contracted dermatitis from working with chromate inhibitors. As a result, many railroads abandoned the use of this type of inhibition in favor of *nonchromate* treatments. A discussion of these alternate treatments follows.

Blended *tannins* of various types were used in a number of English and South American railways. Evans[48] cites a discussion by Hancock,[53] who describes their use on 450 diesels over a seven-year period. The tannins were blended with soda ash and used with waters of medium or low hardness. Both corrosion and scaling were avoided. Evans further cites the case of a South American steam locomotive which had copper corrosion problems caused by soft or very alkaline water. It was overcome by adding a slowly soluble tannin paste to the tenders. Tannins are not used today for diesels.

"Soluble oils" or "emulsifying oils" represent another category of corrosion inhibitors that met with varying degrees of success. These materials consist of a combination of an oil and emulsifying agent. The latter is usually polar in nature with long-chain high-molecular-weight sulfonates being frequently used. This combination is usually applied in a high ratio of oil to emulsifier, anywhere from 10:1 to 100:1. On addition to the cooling water at dosage levels of 0.01 to 1.00 per cent, an oil in water emulsion results with a milky coloring of the treated fluid. Evans[48] states that the oil particles carry a negative charge and are deposited at the anodic points of the incipient-corrosion process or are precipitated by the emergent iron cationics. An oily film is eventually deposited over the entire surface, rendering it noncorrodible. It is the opinion of the author of this book that the sulfonate group is attached to the anodic areas and that the hydrophobic chain at the other end of the molecule brings the oil with it to give the protective oil film which covers the entire surface and prevents the corrosive water from reaching it. Powers and Cessna[54] state that polar-type oils prevent corrosion not only by acting as a diffusion barrier, but also by promoting electrochemical passivation by dissolved oxygen.

A considerable amount of work reported by Patterson and Jones[49] shows that soluble oils can suppress corrosion on steel and cast iron even when appreciable amounts of chloride ion are present as in sea water. They also found that this type of inhibitor can arrest corrosion even when added to a system which is already corroding severely. Hamer, Powell, and Colbeck[55] and Ferri[56] have classified soluble oils as dangerous anodic inhibitors since accelerated attack can occur at points which are not protected. Hamer *et al.* conclude that the oils are suitable only for small circuits. Eldredge and Warner[57] found soluble oils to be effective for Al-Cu couples. Bulow[58] reports that soluble oils reduce both general and galvanic corrosion in closed multimetallic recirculating systems. Evans[59] states that emulsifying oils effectively combat corrosion in cooling waters, while Eldredge and Mears[52] found them to be effective inhibitors for aluminum in waters containing up to about 100 ppm of chlorides.

Bregman and Boies[23] present laboratory data comparing a commercially available soluble oil against boron-nitrite types. The soluble-oil inhibitor gives better protection to aluminum than does the boron-nitrite type, but it is not as good for the other metals. They found that the dosage level is more critical for the soluble-oil inhibitor. In another discussion, Bregman[60] describes results with a new type of soluble-oil inhibitor that gave much better protection than either chromate or boron-nitrite formulations. Hanson[61] also describes corrosion tests with a soluble-oil inhibitor which gives a considerable degree of protection.

Soluble-oil inhibitors suffer from certain shortcomings which harm their value as inhibitors for diesel locomotives: (1) It is extremely difficult to run quick spot tests to determine their concentration in the water. In view of the dependence of their protection on the presence of a sufficiently high dosage and the necessity for occasional make-up of engines, this limitation can be a serious drawback. (2) They tend to break out of solution and give an oily film floating on the water. (3) A layer of oil which is too thick can interfere with heat transfer. (4) The most serious problem of all is the fact that most of the oils attack the rubber, both natural and synthetic, which is present and thus cause radiator hose and gasket problems within a very short period. Bregman and Boies[23] show photographs of the effects of a soluble-oil inhibitor on samples of diesel gaskets and radiator hose. After immersion for a two-week period in a test solution at 180° F, the samples were swollen quite badly.

The petroleum sulfonates that are the key portions of soluble-oil inhibitors are produced by the controlled reaction between sulfuric acid and selected petroleum distillates. The oleophilic sulfonic acids in the upper oil layer are converted to salts by neutralization with caustic soda or other alkali, removed from the oil, concentrated, and purified. A number of different molecular weight grades are available. The emulsification properties come about because the polar group (sulfonate) orients itself in the water phase and the hydrocarbon group orients itself in the oil phase.

The oils used vary widely but are generally those that are available in reasonable quantities at low prices. The more aromatic oils appear to be easier to work with but are also the oils that are the most prone to attack rubber hose, so that a careful balance between these two properties must be maintained.

At the present time the use of soluble oils for diesel locomotives is limited to a few railroad lines, due primarily to the rubber-hose problem. A solution to this problem would result in an inhibitor which would find widespread acceptance in the railroad industry.

Another major type of nonchromate corrosion inhibitor which is used in the railroad industry is the "boron-nitrite" type. This designation is somewhat misleading since formulations of this type contain a number of other inhibitors as well, but nitrite and borax are common to all of them. An interesting thing about these inhibitors is that they represent a case of "tailor-making" corrosion inhibitors to meet a specific industrial need. In contrast to the chromates and soluble oils, most of the other corrosion inhibitors are not universally applicable to all metals that are found in a diesel engine and consequently a proper combination of inhibitors must be formulated.

Borax is a common constituent of these formulations. There is considerable controversy as to whether its function in inhibitors is solely that of supplying buffering capacity or whether it has corrosion-inhibiting properties in its own right. It is generally present in an amount equal to about half or more of the total inhibitor concentration. It serves to maintain the pH in the range of about from 8 to 9.5 which is desirable. It is also very inexpensive, a characteristic which is of considerable importance in these formulations. Blaisdell[62] shows conclusively that the use of small quantities of borax in a recirculating water system inhibits rusting of steel and zinc. Thus, whether the inhibition is due to the pH developed by the borax or to the chemical itself, it is a fact that inhibition does occur. Newlin[63] also presents evidence of the inhibiting properties of borax. Mayne and Menter[64] as well as Hancock and Mayne[65] show that sodium borate behaves in a manner similar to that of sodium phosphate and carbonate in that the protective iron film is mainly of cubic oxide having the composition $Fe_3O_4 \cdot Fe_2O_3$ or an intermediate compound.

An extremely important component of the nitrite-boron formulations is sodium nitrite. This chemical is known to be an excellent corrosion inhibitor for iron and certain other metals. Wachter[66] studied the effectiveness of sodium nitrite as a function of the severity of the conditions and the pH and the composition of the water. He shows that nitrite is effective even in the presence of sodium chloride, 0.03 per cent sufficing for a 0.05 per cent sodium chloride solution. A graph is presented which shows that increasing dosages of sodium nitrite are effective for the protection of steel even at NaCl concentrations up to 10 per cent. He further shows that the effectiveness of sodium nitrite increases with increasing pH. Below a pH of 6, the nitrite is relatively ineffective. The inhibiting properties increase rapidly as the pH increases past that point and a pH of 9 to 10 appears to be optimum. The value of combining sodium nitrite with borax which will buffer the solution in this pH range thus becomes apparent. Wachter further shows that sodium nitrite is effective even when the test specimen has been prerusted, a condition which prevails in most industrial applications. He concludes that this effectiveness occurs because there is little or no depolarization at the cathodic areas. He also shows that sodium nitrite protects several other metals, such as Monel and aluminum, at high temperatures. Both Hoar[67] and Wachter point out that nitrite will not protect alloys which contain zinc. The result is actually deleterious in some cases.

Putilova, Balezin, and Barannik[68] point out that sodium nitrite is a dangerous inhibitor since it accelerates corrosion when present in insufficient dosages. This fact is further substantiated by the experiences of American railroads with the boron-nitrite inhibitors. Dosage control was shown to be critical; many cases of liner failure have been reported when inhibitor dosages were allowed to fall below minimum levels.

The mechanism by which sodium nitrite functions as an inhibitor is not yet the subject of complete agreement. Rozenfel'd[69] states that sodium nitrite is an anodic inhibitor. Putilova *et al.*[68] believe that the inhibition is due to the oxidation of corrosion products (e.g., ferrous, stannous, and cuprous) to higher salts by nitrite ions which are deposited on the metal surface and cause a rise in the electrode potential. Wachter and Smith[70] feel that nitrite functions as an oxidizing agent to produce a thin, very tenacious film of iron oxide on anodic areas. Cohen[71] sets forth the most widely accepted theory which postulates that the passive film is $\gamma\text{-}Fe_2O_2$ with a small amount of $\gamma\text{-}Fe_2O_3 \cdot H_2O$. The oxide film is formed by a reaction between nitrite, oxygen, and the metal at the liquid-metal interface with adsorption of the inhibitor as a probable intermediate step. The geometry of the nitrite ion is such as to lend itself to proper adsorption.

Most of the boron-nitrite formulations contain other inhibitors which are specific for some of the metals to be protected. Thus, for example, 2-mercaptobenzothiazole or else its sodium salt is a frequent ingredient for the protection of copper or its alloys. The alkaline pH values at which the treated system is maintained (generally about 8.5 to 9.5) ease its solubility problems and make it easy to get enough of the chemical into solution to provide adequate inhibition.

In a similar manner, sodium silicate is frequently included for protection of aluminum. The need for the silicate has diminished as the frequency of aluminum headers has diminished. Here again, the alkaline pH value generated by the borax proves to be fortuitous since the protection afforded by the silicate to the aluminum is much better at a pH of 9 to 9.5 than it is at neutral pH values.

Sodium nitrate is frequently used in these formulations. It appears to have some value for inhibiting iron, but its principal merit is for solder and aluminum. Rozenfel'd[69] believes that it functions by shifting the potential of the anodic solution to higher positive values. He states that effective protection with this type of inhibitor can only be attained when the anodic process is completely suppressed.

In addition to these inhibitors, formulations for diesel locomotives also contain chemicals to protect against foaming and possibly scaling, to color the treated water so that the presence of the inhibitor is apparent, to act as buffers, and to give simple analytical tests. Thus, the final formulation can have as many as five to 10 components in it. A typical formulation which is in widespread field use was patented by Green and Boies[72] and developed under the direction of the author of this book. The mixture contains 5.4 parts of Na_2CO_3, 65.4 parts of $Na_2B_4O_7 \cdot 5H_2O$, 6.5 parts of $Na_2SiO_3 \cdot 5H_2O$, 6.5 parts of $NaNO_3$, 5.5 parts of MBT, 0.7 parts of antifoam, and 5.0 parts of sodium alginate. The recommended dosage is 0.75 oz/gal with higher dosages recommended for more severe situations.

Field experience with these inhibitor formulations shows that when applied properly and kept at recommended dosages, they generally give satisfactory protection. They do not possess the toxicity problem of chromates and they are generally easy to apply. The dosage range over which they are effective appears to be less than that of chromates, so that there have been many more reported cases of failure with these materials than with chromates. A major disadvantage which they possess is that at the recommended dosage levels they are about twice as expensive as chromates. For a period of time, inhibitors of this type replaced chromates on most of the major railroad lines in the United States, but during the past few years chromates have begun to replace the boron-nitrite types and once again are the most commonly used inhibitors.

A major factor in the choice of corrosion inhibitors for diesel cooling systems is the behavior of the inhibitors with respect to cavitation-erosion. The general feeling appears to be that the chromate inhibitors are more satisfactory for this purpose than are the boron-nitrite inhibitors. Both treatments are used at twice the normal dosage when applied to engines which are subject to cavitation-erosion. Statistics gathered by many railroads which switched from chromates to boron-nitrites and back to chromates again appear to bear out the better protection against cavitation-erosion by the chromates. Leith and Thompson verified in the laboratory the effectiveness of chromates at dosages as low as 2,000 ppm.[34] Chromates apparently function by eliminating the corrosion which would weaken the metal and provide spots more susceptible to the cavitation. In addition, the protective iron oxide-chromic oxide surface film may be harder and more resistant to erosion than is the untreated metal.

A test of a soluble oil is reported by Leith and Thompson[34] which was developed by Bregman. In their evaluation, this soluble oil is even more effective against cavitation-corrosion-erosion than was the chromate inhibitor. In a discussion of the Leith-Thompson results, Bregman[73] postulates that this soluble oil functions in a twofold manner. (1) It reduces the surface tension of the liquid, which results in a reduction in cavitation-erosion probably due to a combination of several mechanisms, one of which being that more and smaller bubbles are formed due to the lower energy required for nucleation with reduced surface tension. (2) The inhibitor protects by means of a tough organic film formation. This formation means that it is relatively easy to keep the film in good repair once it is initially formed. It might also be postulated that the resilient nature of the film might "cushion" the attack on the surface from the shock waves due to the collapse of the bubbles.

AUTOMOTIVE COOLING SYSTEMS. Inhibitors used for automotive cooling systems which have not been treated with antifreeze solutions are generally purchased by the can at service stations. Traditionally, these solutions consist primarily of the soluble-oil variety. Generally, fair corrosion inhibition is obtained, but the disadvantages cited previously for the soluble-oil materials are applicable here. The attack on rubber hose and gaskets is especially severe and makes the corrosion-inhibition value questionable in view of rubber leakage problems. A number of authors have cited good corrosion-inhibition performance[55, 59, 74, 75] with Kempf and Daugherty[74] pointing out the value of this inhibitor for aluminum cylinder heads. They also found that at high chloride concentrations, steel-asbestos gaskets are associated with less corrosion than copper gaskets, but when soluble oil is present, complete inhibition is obtained in both cases.

Twiss and Guttenplan[75] report on a detailed study designed to develop corrosion inhibitors for No. 100 aluminum brazing sheet which is being used in aluminum radiators. They state that a soluble oil, either with or without the addition of Na_3PO_4 is effective under both static and agitated test conditions. Sodium silicate, sodium dichromate, and Na_2HPO_4 are also effective. Of these, however, all except the soluble oil are either incompatible or lose their effectiveness when used with antifreeze solutions. The corrosion inhibition of clad aluminum by soluble oil is less effective in waters of combined high pH and high chloride ion concentration than it is in waters of high chloride ion concentration alone. Addition of a buffer to the soluble oil to maintain the pH at or near 7.0 improves its effectiveness.

Uhlig's *Corrosion Handbook*,[57] in a section written by Eldredge and

Warner, states that 0.5 per cent of soluble oil is the recommended dosage for automotive cooling systems. Most commercial oils are sold with a 1 per cent recommendation today in order to insure that sufficient inhibitor is present.

Chromates are also used as inhibitors for automobile radiators. Their use is restricted, however, because of the question of compatibility with antifreeze materials and toxicity to humans. When chromates are used, however, they give excellent corrosion inhibition. Dosage levels vary, but generally 0.2 to 0.5 per cent gives excellent protection over a long period of time. Best and Roche[76] state that chromates are undesirable when small areas of aluminum are in contact with large areas of other metals. They suggest the use of borax as a buffering agent. A variation of the chromate treatment was patented by Michel.[77] Part of the chromate is replaced by alkali metal or ammonium nitrates. If the system has soldered joints which contain lead, then such compounds as phosphates, sulfates, or silicates are also added.

Inhibitor formulations similar to the boron-nitrite type previously described for diesel cooling systems are sold commercially for this purpose also. These formulations invariably contain mercaptobenzothiazole for protection of copper.

The corrosion inhibitor that is the subject of the greatest amount of discussion in the literature is *sodium benzoate*. Wormwell and his associates[78-81] wrote several papers on the subject of this inhibitor. They found that sodium benzoate is an effective inhibitor for the corrosion of steel in waters such as are found in automobile radiators. The potassium, lithium, zinc, and manganese salts also possess inhibitive properties. A combination of 1.5 per cent of sodium benzoate and 0.1 per cent of *sodium nitrite* appears to give better results than either inhibitor alone. In the absence of benzoate the nitrite protects cast iron but increases the attack on soldered joints. If benzoate is present, steel, cast iron, and solder are all protected, but aluminum is not. The problem insofar as commercial application of this combination is concerned is the prohibitive cost.

Wormwell[80] postulates that benzoate is more loosely held on the surface than is chromate, which explains the tendency of corrosion to spread out evenly if protection fails in benzoate solutions. The benzoate is thus categorized as a safe inhibitor. Brasher and Stover[82] conducted studies with radioactive benzoate which prove conclusively that the benzoate is directly involved in the protective surface film.

A number of chemically related materials were also evaluated as inhibitors. Bogatyreva and Balezin[83] compared sodium salicylate with sodium benzoate. They found that the salicylate is an effective inhibitor, but not as good as benzoate. The benzoate covers a wider temperature and pH range. The activity of both chemicals decreases as the carbon content of the steel increases and as the temperature increases. Stroud and Vernon[84] found the salts of methyl-, ethyl-, propyl-, and isopropyl-benzoic acids as well as the esters of p-hydroxybenzoic acid to be poor inhibitors. Evans[85] found that salts of cinnamic and nitrocinnamic acids are inhibitors. Putilova *et al.*[68] discovered that under certain pH conditions salts of phenylacetic acid are corrosion inhibitors, as are certain aminoalcohols and their benzoate and carbonate salts. They suggest combinations of ethanolamine benzoate and ethanolaminehexamine condensation products as inhibitors which inhibit steel but accelerate the corrosion of nonferrous metals. Weltman[86] patented an automobile-radiator corrosion inhibitor made by blending equal parts of p-tert-butylbenzoic acid with high-molecular-weight aliphatic carboxylic acids, and by neutralizing the free acids with an amine such as diethanolamine. He states that the inhibitor protects iron, gives residual protection, and does not harm other metals.

Rowe[35] conducted a series of evaluations of inhibitors under a variety of conditions. He compared six different corrosion inhibitors under four different conditions, two of which were in the presence of ethylene glycol and two in tap water such as might be found in a typical automobile radiator. The tests were run at 170° F for 14 days. He found that all the inhibitors—borate, nitrite, benzoate, dichromate, soluble oil, and MBT —protected steel. The soluble oil was the only one that did not protect brass. MBT was the best for copper, but benzoate and dichromate also gave satisfactory protection. Nitrite, benzoate, and dichromate protected aluminum. All except MBT and benzoate protected cast iron and all except soluble oil and nitrite protected solder. The potassium dichromate was the only inhibitor that was satisfactory for all of the metals. When 2 g/liter of NaCl and 1 g/liter of Na_2SO_4 were added to the tap water, the borate and MBT no longer protected steel, the benzoate dropped somewhat, only the MBT protected brass, the dichromate and the MBT protected copper, aluminum protection remained the same, borate no longer protected cast iron, and the solder remained the same. The dichromate was still the best over-all inhibitor. The results with ethylene glycol are discussed later in this chapter.

ANTIFREEZE. Borax is a common constituent of glycol antifreeze mixtures. It is used both alone and also as a member of inhibitor formulations. The mechanism by which borax protects was already discussed. Its buffering capacity is especially valuable in ethylene glycol, where the corrosive danger is the formation of acids. It is used at dosage levels as high as 3 per cent in glycol when used alone and 1 per cent when used as part of a formulation. Cutlip and Scheer[87] patented the use of 0.5 to 7.5 per cent of sodium metaborate as an inhibitor for ethylene glycol with the claim that it provides reserve alkalinity. Woodle, Howell, and Chandler[88] add H_3BO_3 to glycol and then pass the mixture through an ion-exchange resin bed in an alkaline-earth metal state to produce an alkaline-earth metal borate inhibitor which they claim to be superior to borax. Borax is generally used alone today in glycol which is sold at minimum prices and cannot support the cost which would be involved in utilizing any other inhibitor. In those cases the borax certainly gives better protection than would be obtained in the absence of an inhibitor altogether. It is desirable to check the pH frequently, however, to make certain that the buffering capacity is not all used.

An inhibitor combination which is frequently found in ethylene glycol antifreeze is one of *triethanolamine phosphate (TEP) and mercaptobenzothiazole.* Triethanolamine phosphate alone has good corrosion inhibiting properties[89] but attacks copper with the formation of blue cupramine complexes which break up at steel or aluminum surfaces, deposit, and cause localized corrosion. Evans[48] reports on work by Schlapfer and Bukowiecki[90] who found that this combination (using the Na salt of MBT) is the most effective of several inhibitors tested for glycol with several metals—iron, copper, soft solder, and aluminum. He also reports on a discussion by Squires[91] who found that the corrosion product of solder can remove TEP from the liquid and that cases are reported where old rust can remove MBT. This removal lends further reason to clean the system before adding inhibited solutions. He further points out that since the TEP is a weak base, the pH does not rise to a point where the aluminum is attacked. In a later report, Squires[92] states that the TEP-NaMBT combination protects both aircraft and road engines that contain aluminum alloys, brass, copper, solder-covered copper and brass, and plated steel. The only exception is nickel. An interesting sidelight is the report by Abramo and Banfi[93] that the use of amine phosphates produces masses of iron bacteria and hyphomycetes and concurrent action of reducing bacteria.

Patents on combinations of this type were issued to Kendall *et al.*[94] and Barker.[95] Kendall *et al.* also show the effectiveness of benzotriazole instead of MBT and cyclohexylamine instead of triethanolamine. Barker adds a small amount of nitrite as well to the TEP-MBT mixture. In another variation[96] he used 0.5 per cent of an alkali-metal nitrite, 0.5 per cent of triethanolamine, 0.25 per cent of an alkali-metal 2-ethylhexyl-3-methylbutyl orthophosphate, and 0.1 per cent of an alkali-metal mercaptobenzothiazole.

The *benzoate-nitrite* combination is widely used with antifreeze, especially in Great Britain. Mercer and Wormwell[97] show that the addition of 1.5 per cent sodium benzoate to 20 per cent ethylene glycol does not prevent corrosion of the cast-iron cylinder block and head in new engines, although it did arrest further corrosion in used engines. Addition of 0.1 per cent of sodium nitrite to the benzoate gives the required protection to both old and new engines. In a subsequent paper, however, these authors[98] state that protection occurs only if the system is initially heated. Otherwise dosage levels must be raised to 5 and 0.3 per cent. Mercer states[99] that the mixture protects cast iron, soldered joints, brass and copper, cadmium, lead, and tin-plated steels, but it does not always protect aluminum alloys.[81]

In view of their effectiveness in automobile radiator systems without antifreeze, there has been considerable reluctance to automatically discard the use of *chromates* when antifreeze is present. Best and Roche[76] show that chromates can be compatible with methanol antifreeze and can be used with them with considerable success. There is much field experience to support their contention. A Mutual Chemical Bulletin[100] states that pure ethyl alcohol does not reduce chromate to any appreciable extent, but that some of the common denaturants used in alcohol react with it quite rapidly. For this reason they recommend thorough flushing of radiators that were treated with chromates before introducing antifreeze.

Rowe[35] studied the use of sodium chromate with ethylene glycol in considerable detail. He conducted qualitative tests which show that the reaction between chromate and ethylene glycol is dependent upon heat, pH, and the catalyzing effect of light. In the presence of light, degradation begins within a few hours. In the absence of light, however, the solutions remain clear for weeks and after four months only a small amount of breakdown can be observed. On subsequent exposure to light, rapid breakdown occurred. He then ran field tests with automobiles using 2,000 ppm of chromate in ethylene glycol solutions. He found that when only an initial addition of chromate is made, the concentration is soon depleted, but that when chromate is added continually by means of a bypass filter, a concentration of about 450 ppm is maintained. He concludes that under certain conditions chromates could be used with ethylene glycol if light is excluded, but that their use with foreign materials or commercial antifreeze materials is not recommended. The rigid restrictions would appear to rule out chromates for routine use with ethylene glycol.

Other inhibitors which are suggested for glycol systems include hydroxyamines,[101] arsenate-borax mixtures,[102] and organic mixtures.[103-106] Antifoams are also frequently used and silicates can improve aluminum protection. In addition, boron-nitrite formulations discussed previously for diesel locomotives find considerable use with antifreeze materials.

A number of comparisons of performances of antifreeze inhibitors are reported in the literature. Rowe[35] in the tests previously discussed also considers the effect of ethylene glycol. He found that in the case of a 1:1 mixture of ethylene glycol and tap water, borate, nitrite, benzoate, dichromate, soluble oil, and MBT all protect steel; all except benzoate protect brass and copper; only borate fails to protect aluminum; benzoate fails to protect cast iron, while MBT shows only fair protection; and nitrite and soluble oil fail to protect solder. When the salts are added to the mixture, only nitrite, dichromate, and soluble oil protect steel and brass; only dichromate and soluble oil protect copper; borate and benzoate fail to protect aluminum; only dichromate and nitrite protect cast iron well; and only dichromate protects solder. Once again dichromate is the best inhibitor with the soluble oil as the next best. Dichromate is also best for protection of aluminum-copper couples. A number of other couples were evaluated where soluble oils appeared to have more merit. He concludes that nitrite is superior for ferrous metals but poor for solder; dichromate is excellent for most metals but cannot be used with glycols; MBT is excellent for brass and copper; soluble oil is good for most metals but poor for aluminum in coupled tests (it should be pointed out that there are many types of soluble oils, and some are quite good for coupled aluminum as established in tests by the author of this book); a combination inhibitor of soluble oil, MBT, and sodium nitrite proves to be very good for all metals.

Polarization characteristics of steel with various inhibitors have been studied. Borax, sodium nitrite, triethanolamine, chromate, silicate, and benzoate function primarily as anodic polarizers in both tap water and a 30 per cent solution of ethylene glycol. MBT is a cathodic polarizer, while citrate and hydroquinone accelerate corrosion by acting as anodic depolarizers.

Bregman and Boies,[23] in evaluating six different metals similar to those found in diesel cooling systems under both insulated and coupled conditions in a 50 per cent methanol-water mixture, found that a laboratory-developed *boron-nitrite* inhibitor gives excellent protection. This inhibitor is also effective for ethylene glycol solutions. By contrast, two commercially available inhibited glycol antifreezes give poor protection to most metals.

ONCE-THROUGH SYSTEMS

The term *once-through* is a literal description of a group of systems of corrosive waters. It deals with any system where the water is discharged to waste or else to some other purpose after it has passed through the metal piping or tubing, as contrasted to those systems where the water is recirculated for further use. The nature of such a system makes certain general characteristics implicit. These properties include large volumes of water, compositions usually corresponding to tap or river water, certain metals, flow rates and temperatures that are relatively moderate, and economics which severely restrict the type and dosage level of corrosion inhibitors.

The discussion in this section is limited to two basic types—home or municipal distribution systems and hot-water heaters. There are many other once-through systems, but it would be impractical to cover them all, and the principles applying to the systems described here also apply to the others to a great extent.

Literature

Eliassen and Lamb[107, 108] discuss the mechanism of the internal corrosion of water pipes in some detail. They go into detail about the variables affecting the rate and distribution of pipeline corrosion as well as the formation of corrosion cells. In another paper, Eliassen *et al.*[109] study the effects of pH and velocity on the corrosion of steel water pipes, while Klas[110] examines the effects of the other water constituents. Shuldener[111] and Dempster[112] discuss hot water piping in buildings. The British Non-Ferrous Metals Research Association[113] reports a detailed study of the behavior of copper pipes carrying supply water. Davy[114] examines "red water" and its prevention, while Kuhr and van der Vlugt[115] discuss both aerobic and anaerobic iron corrosion in water mains. Streicher,[116] LeClerc,[117] and Bombara and Gianni[118] all published detailed discussions of the factors which help make water corrosivity in these systems.

The corrosion of domestic galvanized hot-water storage tanks is discussed by Newell.[119] Haase[120] studies the effect of flow rates on scale and corrosion problems in hot-water heaters, while Dodson[121] examines bacterial influences. Corrosion studies on zinc which can be directly related to the water-heater problem are reported by Guest[122] and Grubitsch, Sinigo, and Illi.[123]

Economics

The economics for the once-through systems can be summed up in one word—minimum. The large volumes of water used make the allowable cost per unit volume very small. The result is that many inhibitors are ruled out on that basis alone, and others are used at extremely low concentrations. The choice rests between occasional equipment replacement, the cost of inhibitors, or the use of other approaches such as cathodic protection, protective coatings, more resistant materials or construction, or glass or plastic linings in the case of the hot-water heaters.

There are no figures or even crude estimates available as to the dollar volume of inhibitors sold today for once-through systems. One can say in all fairness that the figure is relatively small. An opportunity for an extremely large market exists here, but in all likelihood a major breakthrough in corrosion-inhibitor technology will be necessary to take advantage of it. The severity of this problem is shown by the fact that even the 2 or 3 ppm of polyphosphates that are used in some locations can be too expensive for widespread applications. Streicker[124] cites a cost of $1.00 per person per year for the use of sodium silicate as an inhibitor in apartment buildings. It was estimated in 1954 that the replacement cost of domestic hot-water heaters which were ruined by corrosion was $225 million per year.[125]

The Problem

DISTRIBUTION SYSTEMS. There are a number of different metals which can be present in water-distribution systems and which must therefore be protected from corrosion. An N.A.C.E. committee[126] which studied the service life of pipes exposed to domestic waters included the following metals as being the more common ones: galvanized iron, black steel, cast iron, wrought iron, red brass, copper, and aluminum. The metals can contain stressed areas, deposits, and mill scale depending upon the manufacture of the piping and the previous history of the system.

The temperature of the water to which the metal is exposed can be anywhere from just above freezing to just below boiling. The water composition varies anywhere from distilled water to brines, with tap water the most common. Table 4-1 shows the work of the N.A.C.E. committee on water analysis for the 39 domestic waters studied by them.

Other interesting analytical data from their study are that temperature varies from 33 to 190° F, pressure from 20 to 95 psi, pH from 4.2 to 10.1, and flow rate from intermittent to continuous.

Larson and Skold[127] report on laboratory studies relating water composition to the corrosion of cast iron and steel in connection with water-main problems. They found that the corrosive agents in domestic water, are chloride and sulfate ions. Inhibitive agents were bicarbonate, carbonate, hydroxide, and calcium ions. The relative effectiveness of each is affected by the presence of the others. Increasing velocity gives more protection when the ratio of corrosive agents to inhibitive agents is low. When it is high, the degree of corrosion increases as the velocity increases. Tuberculation of cast iron is most common when the concentration of the inhibitive agents is not sufficient to furnish complete

TABLE 4-1. Analysis of Domestic Waters[126]

ANALYSIS	CONCENTRATION (ppm)
Fe	0–1.4
Ca	2–300 as $CaCO_3$
Hardness	5–550 as $CaCO_3$
Alkalinity	0–350 as $CaCO_3$
Cl_2	0–1
SO_4	5–575
Cl	3–550
Dissolved O_2	Trace–saturated
F	0–2

protection. Effects of pH are peculiar, with the corrosion rates decreasing from 6 to 7, increasing sharply from 7 to 8, and then starting to decrease again as the pH continues to increase. Larson and King[128] earlier found similar results and cautioned that they are limited to the particular waters studied and might be different in other cases. Larson and King also show that after the amount of sodium chloride or sodium sulfate present reaches a given value, the corrosion rate is in direct ratio to the amount of oxygen present.

The results of the tests conducted by the N.A.C.E. committee are quite interesting insofar as the materials of construction are concerned. They show that black steel is not satisfactory for normal use; aluminum is not resistant to waters containing copper salts or with a pH less than about 6 to 6.5; galvanized iron is also affected in a detrimental manner by the presence of copper ions in the water, but was satisfactory otherwise. Copper gives good results consistently.

Klas[110] sums up the corrosive situations as follows. In waters free of O_2 and soluble salts, pH values are corrosion-rate determining. In soft waters or hard waters which have insufficient Ca and CO_2 to form protective scales, O_2 content is rate-determining. In waters close to equilibrium Ca/CO_2 values, it is the relation between O_2 content and the equilibrium level which determines whether the protective scale will form. Welty[129] describes the corrosion of carbon steel in 30-months' continuous service in a heat exchanger with raw Savannah River water. He states that the rate of pitting decreases with time until it reaches a constant value of 0.01 in./year after a year's service. A residual chlorine content of 0.1 to 0.5 ppm had no measurable effect on the corrosion rate at 10 to 30° C, but a greater proportion of the pipe surface is attacked when the temperature is raised to 55° C.

Shuldener[111] points out that in hot-water piping in buildings, faulty circulation causes fluctuating temperatures which lead to overheated areas, and consequently to accelerated corrosion and joint leaks. Dempster[112] points out the importance of realizing that treatment of water in building piping systems can lead to health hazards in the case of overtreatment or the use of the wrong chemicals. He recommends several alternatives, including treatment at the municipal plant.

One important factor to be considered in the case of distribution systems is that the main danger is due to pitting rather than to general corrosion. General corrosion can lead to rusty water nuisance and to loss of a few years of eventual service. The pitting, however, can result in failure by perforation with consequent inconvenience and expensive removal and replacement after only a small fraction of the normal life of the piping.

The phenomenon known as red water can be a serious problem in once-through systems. An excellent discussion of this problem is presented by Davy,[114] who attributes the formation of red water to one or more of the following three factors:

1. *Iron or manganese.*
2. *A corrosive water supply.*
3. *Iron- or sulfate-reducing bacteria.*

The presence of more than 0.3 ppm combined iron and manganese can lead to the formation of red water, especially if points of stagnation are present in the system. The factors causing corrosivity of the supply water were already discussed. Both sulfate-reducing bacteria (Desulfuricane) and iron-consuming bacteria (Crenothrix, Leptothrix, or Coccobacillus) are frequently found in stagnant areas. The sulfate reducers use the sulfate in the water as a source of nutrient, while the iron bacteria require dissolved iron and cannot make use of the metallic pipe. The presence of these bacteria in any quantity leads to pitting.

Because of its excellent resistance to corrosion in once-through systems, copper frequently is used as a material of construction. There was therefore a considerable amount of study of the corrosion of copper under these conditions. The British non-Ferrous Metals Research Association[114] found that pitting corrosion of copper cold-water pipes can occur because of carbonaceous films produced inside the tubes during manufacturing. "Green staining" of copper is experienced with waters containing a high proportion of carbon dioxide. Hot-water pitting seems to occur mostly with soft waters, while cold-water pitting occurs mostly with hard waters. Oxide scales can lead to pitting by providing large cathodic areas that localize attack at pores in the film or scale.

Robertson *et al.*[130] state that in the presence of excess oxygen the corrosion rate of copper is a linear function of pH for each of three anions—$SO_4^=$, Cl^-, and $C_2H_3O_2^-$. The rate is not a simple function of anion concentration, and the concentration dependence varies with pH. The effect of carbon dioxide is negligible. The temperature dependence of the rate, at constant oxygen concentration, for both chloride and sulfate solution is

$$\text{Rate} = Ae^{-9000/RT}, \qquad [4\text{-}1]$$

where A and R are constants and T is the temperature in $^\circ$ K. The corrosion rate for copper in solutions saturated with air goes through a maximum in the range of 71 to 77° C.

Hill[131] found three different rate processes for the corrosion of copper in aqueous systems, which he categorizes as initial (5 to 60 sec), intermediate (2 to 10 min), and long-term (10 to 40 min) corrosion periods. He postulates the following reaction sequence:

$$2Cu + O_2 + H^+ \rightleftharpoons 2Cu^+ + HO_2^- ; \qquad [4\text{-}2]$$

$$2Cu^+ + HO_2^- + 2Cu \rightleftharpoons 2Cu_2O + H^+ . \qquad [4\text{-}3]$$

In Reaction 4-2, the slow step, an oxygen molecule occupies a site consisting of a pair of copper atoms, removes two electrons from them, and becomes a peroxide ion at the same time, forming a biperoxide ion HO_2^-. In Reaction 4-3, a rapid reaction, a pair of electrons from an adjacent pair of copper atoms breaks the oxygen-oxygen bond in the biperoxide ion, allowing each $O^=$ to associate with a pair of the Cu^+ ions and releasing the proton to a water molecule in the solution.

First-order dependence on oxygen concentration was found for the flow reaction in the initial corrosion process. The rate constant for a period less than 60 sec was 1.90×10^2 liter/mol/sec. The corrosion rate increased with increasing pH. During the intermediate corrosion period, the reaction followed the parabolic rate law. The slow step is probably the diffusion of copper ions through the film of corrosion products newly formed on the surface. The rate of reaction varies inversely with film thickness. The rate law drops off rapidly to the log time dependence observed in the time interval for 5 to 60 sec. The rate constant K_2 for 2 to 10 min is $2.3 \times 10^5 A^2$ mol/sec. For the corrosion interval 10 to 40 min, the reaction rate is dependent on the log of the corrosion time, suggesting that the slow step in the reaction is a function of a process or surface, the nature of which is changing with time.

WATER HEATERS. Most water heaters today are galvanized or else have a glass lining or some other protective coating or cathodic control. For that reason, iron tanks are neglected here except to point out that the corrosive factors discussed would apply here and would be aggravated by high temperatures. This discussion is therefore concerned with galvanized systems.

The zinc coating becomes ineffective when it becomes cathodic to iron in the hot water tanks. Under certain conditions, the zinc can undergo rapid attack and expose bare iron. A principal cause of rapid zinc attack is the presence of as little as 0.1 ppm of copper in the water. The copper plates out on the zinc and local galvanic cells are set up. These cells cause rapid pitting and perforation. Newell[119] cites examples of corrosion of six galvanized tanks over test periods up to almost two years. He concludes that lower corrosion rates can be obtained by using all-galvanized systems, by removing carbon dioxide, by removing copper from the water, or by lowering the operating temperature. He traces several case histories of galvanized corrosion which were found to be attributable to copper piping.

Fischer[132] lists some of the factors significant in causing corrosion of domestic hot water heaters:

1. Composition of the water.
2. Temperature and pressure.
3. Flow rate.
4. Galvanic action from nonferrous fittings.
5. Kind and quality of the barrier coating inside the tank designed to prevent corrosion of the base metal.
6. Kind of base metal.
7. Design characteristics of tank.[132]

Grubitsch *et al.*[123] found that below 60° C the corrosion of zinc in hot water is limited by Reactions 4-4 and 4-5:

$$Zn + 2H_2O = Zn(OH)_2 + H_2 ; \qquad \text{[4-4]}$$

$$2H + \tfrac{1}{2}O_2 = H_2O . \qquad \text{[4-5]}$$

Above 60° C the limiting reaction is either Reaction 4-6 or 4-7:

$$Zn(OH)_2 = ZnO + H_2O ; \qquad \text{[4-6]}$$

$$Zn + \tfrac{1}{2}O_2 = ZnO . \qquad \text{[4-7]}$$

At low O_2 concentrations, the maximum corrosion velocity is displaced from 60° C to lower temperatures.

Guest[122] studied the conditions under which zinc becomes cathodic to steel. He made measurements at intervals of every ten degrees from 60° C to boiling and found that given time, potential reversals eventually occur at all those temperatures except for the boiling point. Reversal occurs more rapidly at 70° C than at any of the other temperatures.

Dodson[121] demonstrates the existence of bacterial growth in galvanized steel hot water tanks both in stored water (150° F) and in active rust tubercules in the tank walls. He was unable to identify the organisms.

Inhibition

DISTRIBUTION SYSTEMS. The earlier section on economics made it clear that the selection of inhibitors for once-through systems is severely limited by cost considerations. Only the cheapest inhibitors can be used and those only at the minimum dosages possible. In addition, health hazards must be considered when potable water is to be treated with inhibitors. For this reason most distribution systems have no inhibitors added to them or else they utilize relatively noncorrosive materials of construction or protective coatings.

The most inexpensive inhibitors are the *naturally occurring* ones. If the municipal treating plant is handled properly, it is frequently possible to send out the water in a relatively noncorrosive state. The *naturally occurring* inhibiting water constituents as mentioned by Larson and Skold[127] are bicarbonate, carbonate, hydroxide, and calcium ions. The ideal protective film is an eggshell thin layer of calcium carbonate on the pipe walls. The most common method for producing film consists of adding alkali or lime to adjust the pH for proper Langelier or Ryznar indices. Vincent and Carbonnel[133] patented a techinque for producing a protective film for potable water systems by treating the water with a soluble calcium salt after first passing it through a mass of $CaCO_3$ and $Mg(OH)_2$. When an inhibitor must be used, it is frequently one of the *slowly soluble polyphosphates*. The mechanism by which these inhibitors prevent scale and corrosion as well as red water was discussed previously. In the case of the once-through systems, the treatment level is always at the threshold-treatment level. Calgon and Micromet are representative of the polyphosphates that are used. Recently variations were introduced that contain appreciable quantities of divalent metals, such as calcium, magnesium, or zinc. The polyphosphate that contains zinc is much more effective than standard Calgon, requiring a smaller dosage, giving less reversion, having a lower solubility and rate of solution, and providing a more rapid protective film formation.

It should be remembered that for the polyphosphate to be effective, especially at those low dosages, it is necessary for the water to be in motion. Evans[48] points out that in one system a dosage of 1 ppm proved satisfactory, while in another system that had poor circulation as much as 20 ppm were required. The presence of iron can be beneficial for the protective film, in accordance with Seelmeyer's[134] theory of a protective layer of calcium iron double phosphate.

A major drawback of the polyphosphate treatment is the danger of pitting. Both Cohen[135] and Parham and Tod[136] found pitting can occur with city water, especially at alkaline pH values. For this reason, adjustment to a pH value of 7.0 or slightly less can be very important.

Another commonly used corrosion inhibitor for once-through systems is *sodium silicate.* Lehrman and Shuldener[137] state that the continuous addition of 8 to 12 ppm of silica is an effective method of controlling the corrosion of domestic water piping. A self-healing thin film forms over the surface of the pipe. A bulletin by the Philadelphia Quartz Company[138] claims that liquid sodium silicate is effective for corrosion control of water pipes of iron, steel, galvanized steel, brass, copper, lead, and systems made up of combinations of these and other metals. Wood, Beecher, and Laurence[139] describe the successful use of sodium silicate for this purpose during a 30-year period.

A method that was in use since the twenties is the treatment of hot water by bypassing a small part of it through a tank containing a highly insoluble glass with the composition $Na_2O:3.3SiO_2$.[124] This method found use in household installations because it is inexpensive and required little attention. A typical household unit might contain about 10 lb in the bypass tank which would be sufficient for one year. This technique appears to be applicable primarily to hot-water systems. For cold-water systems, where solubility problems limit this approach, feeding devices containing liquid solutions of the silicate are employed. Streicker[124] cites the successful application of silicate to the inhibition of the corrosive zeolite-softened waters in institutional laundries. This application illustrates the lack of dependence of silicates upon calcium or magnesium for action. A dosage level of at least 8 ppm is recommended for laundries, while 4 ppm is recommended for municipal systems.[124] While $Na_2O:3.3SiO_2$ is recommended for most waters, $Na_2O:2.1SiO_2$ is recommended for waters that have pH values of 6.0 or less. Streicker further states that while the dosage of silicate needed for protection increases with the chloride concentration, a level of 40 ppm is satisfactory even in brines. He further states that sodium silicate also protects yellow brass.

Wood, *et al.*,[139] list several advantages of the use of sodium silicate:

1. Ease of handling.
2. Nontoxic in normal use dosages.
3. Normal constituent of many waters.
4. Imparts no taste, color, or odor to the water.
5. No disposal problems.
6. Treatment is economical.[139]

Streicker[124] classifies the natural and synthetic forms of water-soluble silica in the following decreasing order of effectiveness.

1. *Stable hydrated colloidal silica.*
2. *Crystalloidal silica.*
3. *Unstable hydrated colloidal silica.*
4. *Unhydrated silica.*

Lehrman and Shuldener[137] in a study of the mechanism of protection in once-through systems found that solid iron corrosion products must be present before silica is taken up from the solution. This study corresponds to the findings of Wood, Beecher, and Laurence[139] for open recirculating systems. They found that the film formed on corrosion products is mostly amorphous silica which has small amounts of iron oxide and organic materials normally present in tap water enmeshed in it, as well as sodium and calcium. They postulate the following reaction mechanism. The zinc (from the galvanized pipe) reacts with water to form zinc hydroxide; the positively charged zinc hydroxide then removes negatively charged silica from the water to form the deposit. The silica takes along other materials from the water by an enmeshing procedure. They also show that the zinc hydroxide takes up the silica by adsorption and that more silica is removed as the temperature increases.

Eliassen[140] recommends an initial silica dosage of 12 to 16 ppm at a pH of 8 to 10.6 and then a reduction to 4 to 8 ppm after the film has formed at the far end of the system (usually about a month). He also states that good results are obtained with a combination of 2 to 4 ppm of polyphosphate together with 8 to 12 ppm of silica in corrosive waters that have not responded to either reagent alone.

Chromates are also used for once-through systems. They are effective inhibitors but are not used frequently because the economics are impractical. In addition, the danger of contamination of potable systems by the toxic chromates must be avoided. DeHalas[141] presents data to show that sodium dichromate can be an effective inhibitor for single-pass aluminum systems at dosages as low as 0.1 ppm.

An interesting observation which ties in with the good performance of copper lines in these systems was made by Campbell.[142] He presents evidence to show that many supply waters contain a natural inhibitory agent which suppresses expected pitting of copper cold-water piping. The inhibitor was not identified, but it appears to be a negatively charged colloid of *organic* origin. The cuprous oxide or chloride produced in anodic areas is converted from a loose nonprotective layer of coarse red crystals into an adherent protective film.

In his study of red water, Davy[114] states that the principal method of removal of iron and manganese that are the causative agents is by aeration followed by coagulation and filtration and cation exchange. Adjustment of pH is commonly employed, while use of polyphosphate inhibitors also minimizes red water. Since phosphate is a nutrient for iron bacteria, a low rate of chlorination is used. In the case of pitting of iron by sulfate-reducing or iron-consuming bacteria, control agents are chloramine or continuous or massive doses of chlorine.

WATER HEATERS. The situation here is very similar to that already described for distribution systems, and most of the comments made there apply here as well. Because of the frequency of galvanized coatings, the inhibitors for zinc deserve special mention.

A. D. Little (English Branch)[143] states that corrosion inhibitors for zinc include chromate, benzoate, picrate, and p-nitrosophenol. Blaisdell[66] says that borax is an excellent rust inhibitor for zinc. Gilbert and Hadden[144] studied the effect of sodium benzoate on galvanized steel. They found that exposed edges of steel under a zinc coating are severely attacked. Electrochemical determinations indicate that possible changes in the surface condition of steel in contact with zinc while the steel is the cathode can prevent the normal functioning of sodium benzoate when the steel becomes the anode.

Lariviere[145] found that *chromates* are the most effective inhibitors for heating systems. However, the problem of cross-connections enters here. He found evidence that suggests that 10 ppm for several days only causes marginal ill effects. However, the chance of toxic effects is enough to rule out the chromates. Evans[48] says that a mixture of a quickly dissolving *zinc* metaphosphate and a slowly dissolving *zinc-calcium metaphosphate* has given promising results for protecting galvanized tanks against very soft water in Australia.

Dodson[121] in his study of bacteria in water heaters evaluated several preventive measures. He found that the use of magnesium-aluminum anodes gives excellent protection. Use of zeolite-softened water eliminates most but not all of the bacteria. *Raising the* pH does not eliminate all organic activity. Corrosion is prevented only when the *p*H is raised so high that scale and sludge formation become excessive.

Mention of the use of zeolite-softened water brings to mind the fact that the tanks containing the softening zeolites are frequently themselves corroded by the high localized salt concentrations. Use of glass or plastic liners will minimize this condition. When galvanized metal or else plain steel, is used, it is customary to use *polyphosphates* as inhibitors. They are applied by adding a large mass in the form of a very slowly soluble polyphosphate and by letting the water entering the zeolite bed flow over it or else by letting it hang in the top of the water covering the zeolite. Both good and bad results are reported for such systems. Much of the effectiveness seems to depend upon finding the right polyphosphate as far as solubility rates are concerned and placing it in the proper position in the zeolite tank so that slow solubility is obtained, but phosphate precipitate build-up is precluded.

REFRIGERATING BRINES

The problem of refrigerating brine corrosion is an old one and is not elaborated in much detail in this book. The major purpose for its inclusion is to illustrate some of the problems that are encountered by inhibitors when the composition of the system changes from relatively dilute salt concentrations to a highly concentrated salt solution.

Economics and the Problem

Refrigerating brines are notably corrosive, and the cost of replacing ice cans and repairing pipes and pumps is high. Similarly, the use of brines in other industrial cooling systems can be prohibitively expensive if proper precautions are not taken. For this reason, their use for those purposes is limited. The refrigerating brines can generally be classified as either sodium chloride brines or calcium chloride brines. While the metal to be protected is frequently iron, it can also be brass, copper, bronze, tin, aluminum, zinc, and lead. There may be crevices, stagnant regions, old rust accumulations, and galvanic couples of dissimilar metals. Thus, for example, aluminum in contact with iron quickly becomes frosted and pitted in an uninhibited brine.

Brines containing free ammonia corrode brass cooler tubes. This attack consists of dezincification and solution of copper, which colors the brine light blue. Concentrations of 50 ppm of free ammonia can be found in calcium chloride brines. The brines can pick up carbon dioxide from the air during operation due to faulty agitation and become acidic, or else they can be unusually highly alkaline. The brine can become alkaline due to leakage of ammonia at a place where it is absorbed by the brine.

Another corrosive situation occurs when new cans are placed in service in an old freezing tank. The old cans are protected by a coating of corrosion product and the few new cans are attacked severely. This fact is particularly true for galvanized metal, where the galvanizing on the old cans is in poor condition and causes the new galvanizing to be severely attacked.

The temperature plays an important role in corrosion. A brine which would be relatively inactive at 15° F can strip much of the galvanizing from an ice can at 70° F.[146] For this reason, the brine should be cooled to at least 40° F by the addition of ice before pumping into the freezing tank. Calcium chloride especially must be cooled properly, as this salt evolves a great deal of heat when it goes into solution. No known treatment inhibits the corrosiveness of a heated brine. It is also important to keep the cans and the coils of the brine cooler from being exposed to air after they have been put into contact with the brine. Oxygen accelerates the corrosion and a very corrosive, highly concentrated corrosion cell develops on the surface.

On occasion, magnesium or lithium chloride or mixed chlorides may be present. These chlorides present the same problems as calcium or sodium brines. If ammonia gets into the system, its corrosive action in a closed absorption system results in clogging of small passages. It also causes formation of noncondensable gases which interfere with operation.

Work by Best and McGrew[147] led to some interesting conclusions concerning the relative corrosivity of brines. Examining the effect of concentration, they found that sodium and calcium chlorides in the vicinity of 2.5 per cent are more corrosive to steel than either more dilute or more concentrated brines. At this level, calcium chloride is more corrosive than sodium chloride. At 1 per cent of brine, the two exhibit the same strength. Above 2.5 per cent the corrosiveness of calcium chloride decreases more rapidly with increasing concentration than does sodium chloride. At 10 and 25 per cent strengths, sodium chloride brines are more corrosive than calcium chloride. Aluminum 2S and 3S are virtually unattacked by sodium chloride over the entire range of brine concentrations. Other grades of aluminum are attacked but to a much smaller extent than steel.

Riggs, Sudbury, and Hutchison[148] conducted some interesting studies on the effect of pH and oxygen on corrosion in brine. While this study was not designed for refrigerating brines, but for oil field brines, some of the principles are applicable. They measured corrosion rates for mild steel in brine over a wide range of oxygen pressures and pH values at room temperature. The rates generally increased with increasing oxygen content and decreasing pH; when the tests exceeded 6 hr an accelerated corrosion developed over a pH range of 8 to 12.

Inhibition

The use of *chromates* as corrosion inhibitors for refrigerating brines was known for a long time. Darrin, in 1930, stated that the American Society of Refrigerating Engineers recommended 2,000 ppm of sodium dichromate and enough sodium hydroxide to convert it to sodium chromate (pH 7.0 to 8.5) as a corrosion inhibitor for calcium chloride brines in steel equipment. A concentration of 3,200 ppm was recommended for sodium chloride brines. Uhlig states that for aluminum equipment, the Aluminum Research Laboratories recommends 1 per cent as much sodium dichromate as there is chloride ion present. For a concentrated brine, this concentration amounts to the same quantity of inhibitor as was recommended for the steel systems. Acidic or basic brines should again be neutralized or sodium chromate used for acidic brines and sodium dichromate for basic brines.

Darrin[149] reports that in tests with brass specimens fully submerged in a calcium chloride brine containing 50 ppm of free ammonia, 2,000 ppm of dichromate protected the specimens for five years and kept the brine clear. Darrin also shows that 500 ppm of chromate is sufficient to protect an all-galvanized system in a calcium chloride brine. In practice, a higher concentration is used in order to compensate for accidental loss, overflow, and drag-out of brine or to offset unusually aggressive conditions. Magnesium, lithium, or mixed chlorides are occasionally encountered and these can be inhibited by the same dosage levels of chromate as for sodium chloride. In the case of ammonia absorption systems, the practice today is to employ 2,000 to 4,000 ppm of sodium chromate which lasts for years and gives excellent protection during all that time.

Best and McGrew[147] studied the effect of intermittent exposure of various metals to sodium and calcium chloride brines. They found that the addition of 1 per cent sodium chromate—based on the sodium or calcium chloride solids—effectively minimizes corrosive attack. A like amount of sodium dichromate (i.e., lower pH) is less effective but still functions as an inhibitor. Also, less hexavalent chromate is consumed in the case of chromate. A solution of 0.5 per cent of chromate was adequate to protect 75S aluminum which was attacked by the brine. Addition of 0.5 per cent to either brine controls the corrosion of magnesium alloys.

Phosphates are also commonly used as corrosion inhibitors for refrigeration brines, especially in those cases where chromates cannot be employed. The American Society of Refrigerating Engineers recommends that 1.6 g/liter of disodium acid phosphate ($Na_2HPO_4 \cdot 12H_2O$) be used for sodium chloride brines. Darrin[38] states that some ice plants use 2 g/liter. Although the use of polyphosphates for refrigerating brines was not reported, Ismailov[150] shows that sodium hexametaphosphate is an effective corrosion inhibitor for flowing sea water under certain conditions and functions by increasing the cathodic polarization of steel. In a similar manner, Rogers[151] shows that aniline phosphate, pyridine phosphate, H_3PO_4, and alkylated pyridine phosphates at dosage levels of 20 to 150 ppm and pH values greater than 4.5 are inhibitors for sea water. Chen[152] shows that NaCl and Na_2SO_4 sharply increase the porosity of phosphate films, thus rendering them less protective. A formulation was reported which is successful in arresting 78 to 95 per cent of the corrosive action of brine and water in railway refrigerator cars.[153] Performance of this type in Canadian railroad cars (where the success was reported) would result in a savings in refrigerator car maintenance of $500,000 annually. The inhibitor is a mixture of sodium hexametaphosphate and powdered calcium chloride.

Silicates are also used as inhibitors for sodium chloride refrigerating brines. They are not effective against calcium chloride brines.[138] It is interesting to note that the addition of the divalent ions of zinc, nickel, or manganese were found to strengthen the inhibiting properties of sodium silicate against a 1 per cent NaCl solution.[154] Other inhibitors that were proposed for refrigerating brines include the *reaction products of a tetrahydroxaylkyl alkylene polyamine with phytic acid,*[155] and *lithium or sodium molybdate.*[156] The latter inhibitors were stated to be most effective in the *p*H range of 12.5 to 13.5.

REFERENCES

1. Hanson, M. A. Water problems in diesel locomotive operation. *J. Am. Water Works Assoc.,* **40,** 971, 1948.

2. Wise, R. S. Cooling-system corrosion problems. *Diesel Power,* **31,** 64–66, Dec. 1953.

3. American Locotomive Co., ed. *Symposium on Diesel Locomotive Engine Maintenance* (Schenectady, N.Y.: American Locomotive Co., 1953).

4. Talbot, L. E., *et al.* Treatment of water for cooling purposes. *Ry. Eng. Assoc. Bull.* 518, 347–55, Nov. 1954.

5. Crossett, J. W. Corrosion—a $400,000,000 millstone to the railroad industry. *Modern Railroads Ind.,* **10,** No. 12, 113–6, Dec. 1955.

6. Blackwood, A. K. Means of reducing coolant side corrosion of diesel. *Automotive Inds.,* **115,** No. 6, 164, 168, Sept. 15, 1956.

7. Benton, M. Corrosion in engine-cooling systems containing aluminum: a literature survey. Naval Research Laboratory, Washington, D.C., Bibliography No. 5, 1955.

8. Godfrey, D. J. Cavitation erosion—a review of present knowledge. Brit. Ministry of Supply, S. and T. Memo., No. 17/57, Sept. 1957.

9. Godfrey, D. J. Cavitation damage. A review of present knowledge. *Chem. and Ind.,* **23,** 686–91, June 6, 1959.

10. Piltz, H. A. Kavitation-Versuch einer Begreffsbestimmung und Beschreibring einiger Erscheinunger. *Metalloberflache,* **13,** No. 12, 285–88, Sept. 1959.

11. Nowotny, H. *The Destruction of Materials by Cavitation* (Berlin: V.D.I. Publishing Company, Ltd., 1942).

12. Joyner, J. A. Reduction of cavitation pitting of diesel engine cylinder liners. *Automotive Inds.,* **115,** No. 6, 162, 164, Sept. 15, 1956.

13. Wukman, A. S. Save that radiator. *World Oil,* **135,** No. 5, 136+, Oct. 1952.

14. Howard, F. L., Brooks, D. B., and Streets, R. E. Automotive antifreezes. U.S. Naval Bureau of Standards Circular No. 576, July 1956.

15. Ondrejcin, J. J. Automotive antifreezes. *Soap and Chemical Specialities,* **33,** No. 2, 91, 93, 95, 97, Feb. 1957.

16. Agnew, R. J., Truitt, J. K., and Robertson, W. D. Corrosion of metals by ethylene glycol solutions. *Ind. Eng. Chem.,* **50,** 649–56, 1958.

17. Collins, H. H., and Higgins, R. I. The corrosion of road vehicles by antifreeze solutions. *Brit. Cast Iron Research Assoc. J. Research and Develop.,* **7,** 667–91, 1959.

18. Anon. Sales of antifreeze. *Chem. Eng. News,* **31,** May 22, 1961.

19. Harbert, L. C. Engine cooling at elevated temperatures with vapor phase. A.S.M.E. Paper No. 52-OGP-9, 1952.

20. Copson, H. R. Effects of velocity on corrosion by water. *Ind. Eng. Chem.,* **44,** No. 8, 1745–52, Aug. 1952.

21. Schudlich, H. M., *et al.* M.B.M.A. covers steam and diesel subjects. Oil problems. Diesel cooling systems and boilers. *Ry. Locomotives and Cars,* **128,** No. 10, 65–6, Oct. 1954.

22. Tennyson, T. A. Hardness of diesel cooling water. *Ry. Track and Structures,* **130,** No. 1, 50, 1956.

23. Bregman, J. I., and Boies, D. B. Laboratory testing of railroad diesel cooling system corrosion inhibitors. *Corrosion,* **14,** No. 6, 275t–9t, June 19, 1958.

24. Wilkes, J. F. *Midwest Power Conf. Proc.,* **12,** 338–50, 1950.

25. Hanson, M. A. Water problems in diesel locomotive operation. Paper presented at the 114th Meeting, American Chemical Society, St. Louis, 1948.

26. Hold, P. Z. *Ver. Deut. Ing.,* **85,** 243–4, 1941.

27. Ramsay, W. Corrosion of bronze propeller blades. *Engineering,* **93,** 687–90, 1912.

28. Fittinger, H. Studies of cavitation and erosion in turbines. *Hydraulic Probl.* (Berlin), 14–64, 1926.

29. Richardson, E. G. Mechanism of cavitation. *Wear,* **2,** 97–106, Nov. 1958.

30. Crewdsen, E. Cavitation. *Engineer,* **195,** 122–3, Jan. 23, 1953.

31. Bogachev, I. N., and Mints, R. I. Cavitation damage of gray cast iron. *Trudy Ural Politekh. Inst. im. S. M. Korova,* No. 89, 71–8, 1959.

32. Glikman, L. A., Tekht, V. P., and Zobachev, Y. E. On the physical nature of cavitation erosion. *J. Tech. Phys., U.S.S.R.,* **25,** No. 2, 280–98, 1955.

33. Maraboe, E. C. Gas evolution from supersaturated liquids. *Chem. Eng. News,* **27,** 2198–2202, 1949.

34. Leith, W. C., and Thompson, A. L. Some corrosion effects in accelerated cavitation damage. *Trans. of A.S.M.E., Series D-J of Basic Eng.,* **82,** No. 4, 795–807, Dec. 1960.

35. Rowe, L. C. An evaluation of inhibitors for corrosion prevention in an engine cooling system. *Corrosion,* **13,** No. 11, 750t–6t, Nov. 1957. Lists reprinted by courtesy of L. C. Rowe and CORROSION.

36. A.S.T.M. Tentative method for glassware corrosion test for engine antifreezes. *A.S.T.M. D1384-55T,* June 1955.

37. Bregman, J. I., and Boies, D. B. (unpublished data).

38. Darrin, M. Chromate corrosion inhibitors in bimetallic systems. Technology under conditions encountered in practice. *Ind. Eng. Chem.,* **37,** No. 8, 741–8, Aug. 1945.

39. Darrin, M. Chromate corrosion inhibitors in bimetallic systems. *Ind. Eng. Chem. (Anal. Ed.),* **13,** 755–9, Nov. 15, 1941.

40. Anon. Solving the diesel water problems on a northern line. *Ry. Eng. and Maintenance,* **44,** No. 12, 1286, Dec. 1948.

41. Hanson, M. A. Developments in water conditioning for diesel locomotive cooling systems and steam generators. *Am. Ry. Eng. Assoc. Bull. 469,* 8–87, Nov. 1947.

42. Darrin, M. Chromate corrosion control for engine-jacket water. *Corrosion and Matl. Prot.,* **4,** No. 3, 6–11, May–June 1947.

43. Crane, L. S. Corrosion problems of the railroads. *Corrosion,* **8,** No. 4, 149–51, Apr. 1952.

44. Hatch, G. B. Protective film formation with phosphate glasses. *Steel,* **133,** 181–8, 194, Sept. 21, 1953.

45. Jacoby, A. L. Prevention of corrosion in aqueous systems. U.S. 2,582,129, Jan. 8, 1952.

46. Bardwell, R. C., and Dwyer, J. J. Progress in railroad water conditioning. *Ind. Eng. Chem.,* **40,** 1376–8, Aug. 1948.

47. Antinori, E. Protection of iron surfaces against corrosion. *Gas and Oil Power,* **47,** 112–7, 561, 1952.

48. Evans, U. R. *The Corrosion and Oxidation of Metals* (London: Edward Arnold Ltd., 1960; New York: St. Martin's Press, Inc., 1960).

49. Patterson, W. S., and Jones, A. W. A contribution to the study of the action of certain inhibitors upon corrosion in chlorine-polluted water. *J. Appl. Chem.,* **2,** No. 5, 273–80, May 1952.

50. Darrin, M. Chromate corrosion inhibitors in chloride systems. *Ind. Eng. Chem.,* **38,** 368, 1946.

51. Speller, F. N. *Corrosion Causes and Prevention,* 3rd ed. (New York: McGraw-Hill Book Company, Inc., 1951).

52. Eldredge, G. G., and Mears, R. B. Inhibitors of corrosion of aluminum. *Ind. Eng. Chem.,* **37,** 736–41, Aug. 1945.

53. Hancock, J. S. Discussion of paper by E. L. Streatfield before Diesel Engine Users Assoc., Feb. 17, 1955; cf. Ref. 5, p. 170.

54. Powers, R. A., and Cessna, J. C. How polar-type oils inhibit corrosion. *Ind. Eng. Chem.,* **51,** 891–2, 1959.

55. Hamer, P., Powell, L., and Colbeck, E. W. Emulsions of oil in water as corrosion inhibitors. *J. Iron St. Inst.,* **151,** 109P, 1945.

56. Ferri, A. Anticorrosive action of emulsifying oil. *Metalurg. ital.,* **42,** 261, 1950.

57. Eldredge, G. G., and Warner, J. C., quoted in Uhlig, H. H. *Corrosion Handbook* (New York: John Wiley & Sons, Inc., 1948), 905–15.

58. Bulow, C. L. Wrought copper and copper-base alloys. *Product Eng.,* **19,** No. 8, 43, Aug. 1948.

59. Evans, U. R. Corrosion problems arising from water in the chemical industry. *Chem. and Ind.,* No. 53, 1193–200, Dec. 31, 1951.

60. Bregman, J. I. Corrosion inhibitors. Paper presented at the 125th Meeting, American Chemical Society, Atlantic City, 1959.

61. Hanson, M. A., *et al.* New developments in water conditioning for diesel locomotive cooling systems. *Am. Ry. Eng. Assoc. Bull. 525,* 337, 1955.

62. Blaisdell, F. W. Borax solutions found to inhibit rusting. *Civil Eng.,* **24,** No. 8, 65–6, Aug. 1954.

63. Newlin, J. Borax as corrosion inhibitors. *Civil Eng.,* **22,** No. 4, 76, Apr. 1952.

64. Mayne, J. E. O., and Menter, J. W. The mechanism of inhibition of the corrosion of iron by solutions of sodium phosphate, borate, and carbonate. *J. Chem. Soc.,* 103–7, Jan. 1954.

65. Hancock, I. P., and Mayne, J. E. O. The inhibition of the corrosion of iron in neutral and alkaline solutions. *J. Appl. Chem.,* **9,** 345–52, 1959.

66. Wachter, A. Sodium nitrite as corrosion inhibitor for water. *Ind. Eng. Chem.,* **37,** No. 8, 749–51, Aug. 1945.

67. Hoar, T. P. Sodium nitrite as an inhibitor against the attack of sea water on steel. III. Inhibitor in sea water-distilled water mixtures. *J. Soc. Chem. Ind.,* **69,** No. 12, 356, 1950.

68. Putilova, I. N., Balezin, S. A., and Barannik, V. P. *Metallic Corrosion Inhibitors* (New York: Pergamon Press, 1960).

69. Rozenfel'd, I. L. Mechanism for protecting iron from corrosion with sodium nitrate. *Doklady Akad. Nauk S.S.S.R.*, **78**, No. 3, 523–6, May 21, 1951.

70. Wachter, A., and Smith, S. S. Preventing internal corrosion of pipe lines. *Ind. Eng. Chem.*, **35**, 358, 1943.

71. Cohen, M. An electron diffraction study of films formed by sodium nitrite solution on iron. *J. Phys. Chem.*, **56**, 451–3, Apr. 15, 1952.

72. Green, J., and Boies, D. B. Corrosion-inhibiting compositions. U.S. 2,815,328, Dec. 3, 1957.

73. Bregman, J. I. Discussion of paper on cavitation damage. *Trans. of A.S.M.E., Series D, J. of Basic Eng.*, **82**, No. 4, 802, Dec. 1960.

74. Kempf, L. W., and Daugherty, M. W. Corrosion resistance of aluminum cylinder heads. *Automotive Inds.*, **81**, 156–9, Aug. 15, 1939.

75. Twiss, S. B., and Guttenplan, J. D. Corrosion testing of aluminum. II. Development of a corrosion inhibitor. *Corrosion*, **12**, 311t–6t, 1956.

76. Best, G. E., and Roche, E. A. *Corrosion*, **10**, 217, 223, 1954.

77. Michel, J. M. Prevention of corrosion and deposition in aqueous cooling and heating systems. Ger. (East) 9,337, Mar. 18, 1955.

78. Vernon, W. H. J. Chemical research and corrosion control. *J. Soc. Chem. Ind.*, **66**, 137–8, 1947.

79. Wormwell, F., and Mercer, A. D. Sodium benzoate and other metal benzoates as corrosion inhibitors in water and in aqueous solutions. *J. Appl. Chem.*, **2**, Pt. 3, 150–60, Mar. 1952.

80. Wormwell, F. Corrosion inhibitors in neutral aqueous solutions. *Chem. and Ind.*, No. 23, 556–60, June 6, 1953.

81. Wormwell, F., Mercer, A. D., and Ison, H. S. K. Sodium benzoate and sodium nitrite as corrosion inhibitors in ethylene glycol antifreeze solutions. *J. Appl. Chem.*, **3**, Pt. 3, 22–7, 133, Mar. 1953.

82. Brasher, D. M., and Stove, E. R. The use of radioactive tracers in the study of the mechanism of action of corrosion inhibitors. *Chem. and Ind.* No. 8, 171–2, Feb. 23, 1952.

83. Bogatyreva, E. V., and Balezin, S. A. Sodium salicylate as an inhibitor of corrosion of steel in neutral media. *Zhur. Priklad. Khim.*, **32**, 1071–6, 1959.

84. Stroud, E., and Vernon, W. Prevention of corrosion in packaging. *J. Appl. Chem.*, **2**, 4, 1952.

85. Evans, U. R. Inhibition of corrosion. *Chem. and Ind.*, No. 22, 530–3, May 30, 1953.

86. Weltman, C. A. Water-soluble corrosion-inhibiting composition. U.S. 2,832,742, Apr. 29, 1958.

87. Cutlip, E. R., and Scheer, R. D. Antifreeze composition. U.S. 2,937,145, May 17, 1960.

88. Woodle, R. A., Howell, R. H., and Chandler, W. B. U.S. 2,834,735.

89. Thompson, P. F., and Lorking, K. F. Some aspects of the corrosion processes of iron, copper, and aluminum in ethylene glycol coolant fluids. *Corrosion*, **13**, No. 8, 531t–5t, Aug. 1957.

90. Schlapfer, P., and Bukowiecki, A. *Mitteilungen Uber Kuhl-und Frostschutz Mittel Fur Den Motorfahrzeugbetrieb Schweiz. Ges. Fur Das Studium Der Motorbrenstoffe* (Zurich). 1949.

91. Squires, A. T. B. P. Corrosion inhibitors for ethylene glycol water coolants for piston engines (Rolls-Royce). *Diesel Engine Users Assoc. Discussion*, Feb. 17, 1955.

92. Squires, A. T. B. P. Corrosion inhibitors for ethylene glycol-water for piston engines. *Soc. Chem. Ind. Monograph No. 4*, 51–68, 1958.

93. Abramo, F., and Banfi, G. Metallic corrosion and microbiological activities. Contribution to a hydrodynamic railway apparatus in presence of antifreeze substances. *Ing. Ferroviaria*, **11**, 677–92, 1956.

94. Kendall, J. D., Fry, D. J., and Lea, B. A. Ethylene glycol antifreeze solutions. Brit. 811,675, Apr. 8, 1959.

95. Barker, R. C. Rust inhibited permanent type antifreeze mixtures. U.S. 2,692,860, Oct. 26, 1954.

96. Barker, R. C. U.S. 2,817,626, Dec. 24, 1957.

97. Mercer, A. D., and Wormwell, F. Research and experience with sodium benzoate and sodium nitrate mixtures as corrosion inhibitors in engine coolants. *Soc. Chem. Ind. Monograph No. 4*, 69–78, 1958.

98. Mercer, A. D., and Wormwell, F. Corrosion inhibitors for cast iron and other metals in ethylene glycol solutions and in mains water. *J. Appl. Chem.*, **9**, 577–88, 1959.

99. Mercer, A. D., and Brasher, D. M. Corrosion inhibitors for ethylene glycol solutions, with particular reference to cadmium-plated and terne-plated steel. *J. Appl. Chem.*, **9**, 589–94, 1959.

100. Mutual Chemical Co. of America. *Chromate Corrosion Inhibitors for Internal Combustion Engines* (New York: Mutual Chemical Co. of America, 1945).

101. Kaputskaysa, V. A., Kofman, L. S., Mal'tsera, A. E., and Simkhovich, F. M. Preventing corrosion of metals resulting from the action of water, glycols, and aqueous glycol solutions. U.S.S.R. 123,824, Nov. 9, 1959.

102. White, C. M., and Ivancic, R. E. Mixtures of dibasic alkali metal arsenates and alkali tetraborates as corrosion inhibitors for aqueous glycols. U.S. 2,721,823, Oct. 18, 1955.

103. Fiser, W. O. U.S. 2,886,531, May 12, 1959.

104. Gaucher, E. Canada 469,632, Nov. 28, 1950.

105. Dixon, T. W., and Sproul, L. W. U.S. 2,637,703, May 5, 1953.

106. Burghart, L. M. U.S. 2,566,923, Sept. 4, 1951.

107. Eliassen, R., and Lamb, J. C., III. Mechanism of the internal corrosion of waterpipe. *J. Am. Water Works Assoc.*, **45**, 1281–94, Dec. 1953.

108. Eliassen, R., and Lamb, J. C., III. Mechanism of water-pipe corrosion. *Water and Sewage Works* (Reference and Data ed.), **103**, 99R–104R, June 1956.

109. Eliassen, R., Pereda, C., Romeo, A. J., and Skrinde, R. T. Effects of pH and velocity on corrosion of steel water pipes. *J. Am. Water Works Assoc.*, **48**, 1005–18, Aug. 1956.

110. Klas, H. Corrosion in pipes. *Tech. Mitt.*, **46**, 269–77, 1953; *Chim. and Ind.* (Paris), **71**, 318, 1954.

111. Shuldener, H. L. Effect of operating conditions on corrosion of hot water piping in buildings. *Corrosion*, **10**, No. 3, 85–90, Mar. 1954.

112. Dempster, A. T. Control of the treatment of water in building piping systems. *J. Am. Water Works Assoc.*, **45**, No. 1, 81, Jan. 1953.

113. British Non-Ferrous Metals Research Assoc. Copper water pipes. *Water and Water Eng.* (Gt. Brit.), **53**, 124, Mar. 1950.

114. Davy, P. S. Red water and its prevention. *J. Am. Water Works Assoc.*, **45**, No. 1, 10–8, Jan. 1953.

115. Kuhr, C. A. H. v. W., and van der Vlugt, L. S. Aerobic and anaerobic iron corrosion in water mains. *J. Am. Water Works Assoc.*, **45**, 33–46, Jan. 1953.

116. Streicher, L. Effects of water quality on various metals. *J. Am. Water Works Assoc.*, **48**, 219–38, Mar. 1956.

117. LeClerc, E. Measure of the corrosive activity of water. *Bull. Centre Belge Etude et Document. Eaux* (Liege), No. 92–3, 241–7, 1958.

118. Bombara, G., and Gianni, F. Factors in the evaluation of the corrosivity of waters. *Metalurg. ital.,* **48,** 503–12, Nov. 1956.

119. Newell, I. L. The corrosion of domestic galvanized hot-water storage tanks. *New England Water Works Assoc.,* **65,** No. 1, 71–87, Mar. 1951; *Corrosion,* **9,** No. 2, 46–51, Feb. 1953.

120. Haase, L. W. The effect of rate of flow on the precipitation of hardness-producing salts, and corrosion in hot-water heaters. *Werkstoffe u. Korrosion,* **6,** 81–4, 1955.

121. Dodson, R. E. Water heater corrosion studies, with especial consideration to possible bacterial influences. *Water and Sewage Works,* **99,** 345–9, Sept. 1952.

122. Guest, R. M. The potentials of zinc and steel in tap water. *Can. J. Technol.,* **34,** No. 5, 245–7, Sept. 1956.

123. Grubitsch, H., Sinigo, J., and Illi, O. Hot-water corrosion of zinc. I. Rapid testing by means of dithizone. II. Effect of temperature. *Korros. u. Metaleschutz,* **16,** 194–203, 1940.

124. Streicker, W. Protection of small water systems from corrosion. Discussion. *Ind. Eng. Chem.,* **37,** No. 8, 716–23, Aug. 1945.

125. Brinker, W. N. Mid-Year's Divisional Conference, Porcelain Enamel Institute, Chicago, May 12–14, 1954.

126. N.A.C.E. Unit Committee on Corrosion by Domestic Waters. Service life of pipe exposed to domestic waters. *Corrosion,* **16,** No. 9, 453t–6t, Sept. 1960. Table 4-1 reprinted by courtesy of CORROSION.

127. Larson, T. E., and Skold, R. V. Laboratory studies relating mineral quality of water to corrosion of steel and cast iron. *Corrosion,* **14,** No. 6, 258t–88t, June 1958.

128. Larson, T. E., and King, R. M. Corrosion by water at low flow velocity. *Corrosion,* **10,** No. 3, 110–4, Mar. 1954.

129. Welty, F. Corrosion of steel pipe by Savannah River water. *U.S. Atomic Energy Comm. Publication DP–170,* 1956.

130. Robertson, W. D., Nole, V. F., Davenport, W. H., and Talboom, F. P., Jr. An investigation of chemical variables affecting the corrosion of copper. *J. Electrochem. Soc.,* **105,** No. 10, 569–73, 1958.

131. Hill, G. R. Tech. Report 5. *Research Contract N7-onr-45163,* Feb. 1951.

132. Fischer, H. C. Solving design problems for cathodic protection of glass-lined domestic water heaters. *Corrosion,* **16,** No. 9, 9–17, Sept. 1960. List reprinted by courtesy of H. C. Fischer and CORROSION.

133. Vincent and Carbonnel. Corrosion inhibition of slightly mineralized water. Fr. 1,149,657, Dec. 30, 1957.

134. Seelmeyer, G. Rust and scale prevention in hot water plants. *Werkstoffe u. Korrosion,* **2,** 17, 1951.

135. Cohen, M. Sodium hexametaphosphate as a corrosion inhibitor for Ottawa tap water. *Trans. Electrochem. Soc.,* **89,** 109, 1946.

136. Parham, P. N., and Tod, C. W. Condensed phosphates in the treatment of corrosive waters. *Chem. and Ind.* (London), 628, 1953.

137. Lehrman, L., and Shuldener, H. L. Action of sodium salicylate as a corrosion inhibitor in water piping. *Ind. Eng. Chem.,* **44,** No. 8, 1765–9, Aug. 1952.

138. Philadelphia Quartz Co. *Soluble Silicates for Coagulation and Corrosion Control* (Philadelphia: Philadelphia Quartz Co., no date).

139. Wood, J. W., Beecher, J. S., and Laurence, P. S. Some experiences with sodium silicate as a corrosion inhibitor in industrial cooling waters. *Corrosion,* **113,** No. 11, 719t–24t, Nov. 1957. List reprinted by courtesy of the authors and CORROSION.

140. Eliassen, R. Corrosion control in potable water systems. *Water and Sewage Works (Ref. and Data Ed.)*, **99**, No. 4, R79–R81, 1952.

141. DeHalas, D. R. The use of minute amounts of sodium dichromate as a corrosion inhibitor in single-pass aluminum systems. *U.S. Atomic Energy Comm. Publication HW-33736*, No. 11, 1954.

142. Campbell, H. S. A natural inhibitor of pitting corrosion of copper in tap-waters. *J. Appl. Chem.*, **4**, No. 12, 633–47, Dec. 1954.

143. Little, A. D. Inhibitors for zinc. *Corrosion Tech.* (England), June 1960.

144. Gilbert, P. T., and Hadden, S. E. Behavior of galvanized steel in sodium benzoate solution. *J. Appl. Chem.* (London), **3**, No. 12, 545–8, Dec. 1953.

145. Lariviere, F. J. Cross-connections with heating systems containing corrosion inhibitors. *J. New England Water Works Assoc.*, **72**, 350–3, 1958.

146. Mutual Chemical Division, Allied Chemical and Dye Corp. *Corrosion Control in Refrigeration*, 2nd ed. (Publication No. 34) (New York: Mutual Chemical Division, Allied Chemical and Dye Corp., 1956).

147. Best, G. E., and McGrew, J. W. Inhibiting corrosion of steel, aluminum and magnesium intermittently exposed to brines. *Corrosion*, **12**, No. 6, 286t–92t, June 1956.

148. Riggs, O. L., Sudbury, J. D., and Hutchison, M. Effect of pH on oxygen corrosion at elevated pressures. *Corrosion*, **16**, 260t–4t, June 1960.

149. Darrin, M. Chromate corrosion inhibition in brine systems. *Am. Soc. Refrig. Engr., 1944 ASRED Corrosion Report*, 21, 1945.

150. Ismailov, A. G. Sodium hexametaphosphate as corrosion inhibitor for steel in running sea water. *Azerbaidzhan. Neft. Khoz.*, **38**, No. 1, 43–6, 1959.

151. Rogers, L. M. Corrosion inhibitors for ferrous metals in sea water. U.S. 2,901,438, Aug. 25, 1959.

152. Chen, N. G. Corrosive action of the chloride ion. *Izvest. Vysshikh Ucheb. Zavedenii, Khim. i. Khim. Tekhnol.*, **2**, 183–9, 1959.

153. Anon. Anti-corrosion compound developed by Canadian National. *Ry. Age*, **130**, No. 16, 42, Apr. 23, 1951.

154. Kobayashi, T., and Nagayama, M. An electrochemical testing method of corrosion inhibitors in neutral salt solution. *Boshoku Gijutsu*, **7**, 149–52, 1958.

155. Toekelt, W. G. Water-soluble corrosion inhibitors. U.S. 2,923,599, Feb. 2, 1960.

156. Stubblefield, E. M., and Cropper, W. V. Corrosion inhibitor. U.S. 2,755,170, July 17, 1956.

5

Petroleum—
Primary Production

The petroleum industry is perhaps the major user of corrosion inhibitors. It employs vast quantities of these materials in many different applications ranging from production at the wellhead to consumer use. This wide range of application is the result of the corrosive nature of the fluids and more generally of the water and gases that are associated with the hydrocarbons. A thorough discussion of the use of corrosion inhibitors in the petroleum industry requires a major portion of this book. The application of corrosion inhibitors in the petroleum industry can be conveniently categorized into a series of specific corrosion problems. Many of these problems arise in the production of petroleum at the well, and this chapter is therefore devoted to a discussion of the application of corrosion inhibitors in primary production. The next chapters discuss the use of inhibitors in other aspects of production, refining, transportation, and finished products.

LITERATURE

The literature with regard to the use of corrosion inhibitors in the primary production of petroleum is voluminous. Almost all of it was published during the past fifteen years when the advent of organic long-chain, high-molecular-weight corrosion inhibitors revolutionized the industry. Wells which previously were abandoned after a short time because of the destruction of pumping equipment were found to become amenable to continued use until such time as the ratio of water to oil being pumped made them economically unfeasible. The effect of the widespread use of these organic inhibitors on the total production of oil was remarkable and had a major effect upon the industry.

Two recent books discuss the problem of corrosion at the wellhead in considerable detail and are recommended to the reader. The first, which was co-sponsored by the National Association of Corrosion Engineers and the American Petroleum Institute, describes the problems of "sweet" corrosion, "sour" corrosion, oxygen corrosion, and electrochemical corrosion.[1] In each case a description of damage, methods of evaluation of extent of the problem, and a brief discussion of control measures are presented. The second book deals with a specific type of "sweet" corrosion, namely that of gas-condensate wells.[2] It discusses this particular problem in considerable detail and is the most comprehensive study that has yet been presented. Both of these books were written by committees of authorities in the field.

A general discussion of corrosion of production equipment and gathering lines and its prevention is presented by Lee and Haines.[3] Other general discussions of corrosion in primary production at oil and gas wells are presented by Stanton,[4] Cavallaro,[5] Uehara,[6] Greenwell,[7] Bilhartz,[8] Caldwell,[9] Moore,[10] and also by the N.A.C.E. Technical Unit Committee T-1.[11-13] Some of the more interesting general discussions of corrosion prevention were written by Shock,[14, 15] Bilhartz,[16] Bertness,[17] Bregman,[18] and Blair.[19] Articles in the literature which describe inhibition at specific locations are published by Biehl and Schnake,[20] who review the experiences of Ohio Oil in five years of processing crude oil at low pH values; Bradley,[21] who describes the experience of Shell Oil Company in the Trapp field of Kansas; Clements and Barrett,[22] who discuss Stanolind's experiences in the Midland Farms field of West Texas; and Koger,[23] who describes mitigation procedures used by Cities Service in connection with the Arbuckle production in Kansas. Many other worthwhile papers have been written on various aspects of the corrosion and inhibition problem. The papers mentioned here merely give the reader a representative scattering.

ECONOMICS

The number or the percentage of oil wells that are corrosive and require some protective measures are difficult to define. While practically all wells are corrosive to some extent, the point at which a well can be considered to need inhibitors varies depending upon the operator, the well production, the history of the well, and the techniques available for gauging the extent of the corrosion. Thus wells considered by some people to need corrosion inhibition can be considered as being trouble-free by others. In addition, the corrosivity of the well itself can vary as a function of time. As the well ages, a higher ratio of water to oil is produced and the corrosivity changes. Also, the corrosive effects of water in a new well may not show up in the way of failures until the well has been in operation for months or years. Thus a well which suddenly is found to be corrosive may have been corrosive for a long time but was just not recognized as such.

Caldwell[9] reports a survey of 8,215 sour crude wells and finds that 44 per cent were economically affected by corrosion. Bass,[24] writing in an English journal, estimates that 80 per cent of all sour crude producing wells need corrosion inhibitors. However, the N.A.C.E.-A.P.I. book on oil- and gas-well equipment corrosion[1] states that only 12 per cent of all sour production is considered corrosive. The difference between these two figures is obviously related to the definition of the term "corrosive." In the absence of protective measures, these corrosive sour wells can cost about $150 a month for equipment failure or a total annual cost of over $32 million. They further report that at least 20 per cent of all sweet oil production and 45 per cent of all condensate production are considered as corrosive. Approximately 16,000 existing gas-lift wells alone become corrosive annually and could cost the industry $16 million per year in corrosion damage. They present a map showing the location of corrosive gas and oil areas in the United States. It is of interest to note that they do not consider the Pennsylvania-Ohio-West Virginia area to be corrosive, nor East Kansas and almost all of Oklahoma. Most of the other oil- and gas-producing areas are labeled corrosive.

A figure of nine cents per barrel of oil produced and processed was recently cited as an average national cost of corrosion in oil and gas wells.[1] More specific figures are reported for the cost of condensate well corrosion. The N.G.A.A. book[2] estimates the cost in 1951 at $3.59 per

MMcf or $12,100,000 annually. The N.G.A.A. report points out that the $3.59/MMcf figure is an average, with the reported actual well costs ranging from a low of $0.71 to a high of $417. Costs of $1.00 to $22.00/MMcf are common. Caldwell[9] cites costs of sour crude corrosion to range from an average of $270 per well in the West Texas-New Mexico area to $2,000 per well in the Kansas area.

In nearly every oil field, scenes such as the piles of damaged equipment shown in Figure 5-1 are evidence of the tremendous ravage by corrosion. This picture was taken at an oil field in Illinois.

The use of inhibitors in primary production drastically reduced corrosion of subsurface equipment, resulted in savings of hundreds of dollars for each well protected, and lengthened the life of the average well considerably. Much data are accumulated in literature concerning

FIGURE 5-1. Damaged Equipment at an Illinois Producing Field

Photograph Courtesy of Petrolite Corporation

these savings. For example, Bradley[21] in discussing well-service costs due to corrosion failure of rods, tubing, and pumps states that Shell Oil saved about $110,000 in the Trapp field of Kansas between 1948 and 1951 primarily through the use of corrosion inhibitors. The N.G.A.A. estimates that $10 million of the $12,100,000 annual loss due to condensate well corrosion can be saved by presently known control measures.

Chemical treatment costs of 17, 18, and 53 cents/MMcf are cited by the N.G.A.A. for the use of chromates, neutralizers, and liquid organic inhibitors, respectively, in 1951 for treating condensate wells completed open-ended. Figures of 99, 80, and 82 cents are cited for neutralizers, liquid organic inhibitors, and stick organic inhibitors, respectively, for treating wells completed packed off that year. A comparison of these figures with the $3.59 for corrosion losses illustrates the value of using inhibitors. Uehara[6] reports that a survey of pumping wells in two oil fields shows that use of inhibitors resulted in a 50 per cent decrease in material replacements.

Blair[25] describes treatment of a typical highly corrosive condensate well in Louisiana. Corrosion costs before protective treatment was initiated are conservatively estimated at $5.50 per day. The cost of chemicals necessary to obtain complete protection is about $1.25 per day. Harper[26] points out that the use of an organic stick inhibitor in a Louisiana gas well costs about 25 cents per 1,000 cu ft of gas produced. He states that this amount is negligible compared to the cost of replacing the tubing or surface equipment, coupled with the loss of production as a result of shutdowns, possible fishing jobs, and even blowouts or loss of the well. Gross and Andrews[27] conducted a subsurface-corrosion cost analysis on a sour well. They found that prior to the use of an inhibitor, the total costs came to $768.00 for a 202-day period during which time 1,653 barrels of oil were produced. The average cost per barrel was thus 46.5 cents. Treatment for 248 days with an organic corrosion inhibitor resulted in a total of $100.50 of costs, of which $62.50 were for the inhibitor. For the 3,129 barrels produced the cost per barrel was 3.2 cents. Thus total cost was reduced by 93 per cent while production of oil was almost doubled.

Other examples of the economic value of inhibitors given by the N.A.C.E.-A.P.I.[1] book may be summarized as follows.

1. A Gulf Coast condensate well had to be plugged and abandoned at the end of two years' production because of perforation of one joint of tubing. Cost of the well and workover was $270,000. An offset well was drilled. The same corrosion was

*adequately controlled by the use of one quart of inhibitor per day over a period of
five years before these results were reported.*

*2. Use of organic inhibitors in sour wells in western Kansas has resulted in
significant reduction in maintenance expense. The cost of inhibition is approximately $13.50 per well per month.*

THE PROBLEM

The classification of oil and gas wells that is the most commonly
accepted is a breakdown into sweet and sour wells. The former term
denotes the absence of hydrogen sulfide and the latter its presence.
Within each category, a further breakdown can be made such as oil
versus gas and presence versus absence of oxygen. In this book, the problem is divided into the two categories of sweet and sour wells and the
discussion of the problem takes that form.

Sweet Wells

FLOWING OIL WELLS. Sweet wells can be further subdivided into flowing oil wells, pumping oil wells, gas-lift wells, and gas condensate wells.[4]
In considering sweet flowing wells first, Stanton[4] lists the types of possible corrosion as those which might be due to electrochemical attack,
galvanic attack, stress corrosion, electrolytic attack, and erosion-
corrosion. In the case of the pumping wells, he also adds oxygen corrosion to this list. Using this breakdown, the corrosive factors are examined
in each case.

The electrochemical attack is a function of the liquid and gas composition. It is related primarily to the water composition since this rather
than the oil phase is the corrosive part of the system. The amount of
water, its composition, the nature and amount of dissolved gases, the
pressure and the temperature can all vary widely and can have a major
effect upon the severity of the corrosion.

The water produced with the oil is generally a brine which is anywhere from 1 to 10 per cent NaCl. In addition, considerable amounts of
calcium, magnesium, barium, sulfate, and other normal constituents of
sea water may be present. The pH of this brine can be affected by the
presence of acetic acid, carbon dioxide, and dissolved acid gases and is
generally somewhat acidic. Because of the pressure gradient in wells,

gases become released from solution and the pH of the water at the well-head can be considerably higher than that downhole. A difference as great as 2.5 pH units is reported.[3] Therefore, wellhead pH measurements give no direct indication of the severity of downhole attack.

The relationship between bottom hole pH and corrosion is the subject of an intense study by an N.A.C.E. committee.[11] When examining 65 wells, this committee found that 26 had a bottom hole pH value of 6.0. A comparison of equipment failures versus downhole pH resulted in a finding that the bottom hole pH of 6.0 ± 0.2 appears to be critical in determining the expected tubing life. Only one well that had a higher pH had a tubing life of less than 20 years. Below 6.0 only three out of 26 showed tubing lives in excess of 12 years and only eight were in excess of nine years.

Below a pH of 5.5, the corrosion rate was generally high regardless of water concentration, but at least down to water values of 1 per cent. By contrast, wells above pH 6.6 appeared to be relatively noncorrosive even with 95 per cent water.

The ratio of oil to water in the produced fluid can vary from 1 per cent of water to 1 per cent of oil. That this ratio affects the corrosivity is shown by Greenwell[7] and other members of the N.A.C.E. TP-1 Committee who surveyed low-pressure sweet oil wells with the results shown in Table 5-1.

These findings are in agreement with the general pattern of corrosivity during the life of a typical oil well. At the beginning, the produced water is small and the corrosion is minor. As the well sees more service the produced water content rises and the system becomes more corrosive. Many oil wells are not treated with corrosion inhibitors until a few years after they have been placed in service.

TABLE 5-1. Relationship of Water Content to Corrosivity of Sweet Oil Wells[7]

WATER CONTENT (%)	CORROSIVE WELLS (%)		
	Field A	*Field B*	*Field C*
0–20	0	0	0
20–40	0	0	33
40–60	56	67	100
60–80	100	100	100
80–100	100	100	100

Carbon dioxide is a major cause of corrosion in sweet wells. The probable basic reactions are as follows:

$$CO_2 + H_2O \rightarrow H_2CO_3; \qquad [5\text{-}1]$$

$$Fe + H_2CO_3 \rightarrow FeCO_3 + H_2. \qquad [5\text{-}2]$$

The presence of carbon dioxide promotes the formation of hard black scales and deep, sharp-edged pits. Water must be present for the carbon dioxide to become corrosive, as is shown in a case history by McFaddin[28] of the Union Oil Company, Santa Maria Valley operation.

The N.A.C.E.-A.P.I. book[1] states that the important factors governing the solubility of carbon dioxide are pressure, temperature, and water composition. Pressure increases the solubility, temperature decreases it, and many dissolved minerals can buffer the water and prevent pH reduction.

Other dissolved acids which can be present include the short-chain aliphatic acids, such as formic and acetic. Although these acids are quite corrosive, their relatively small concentrations in comparison to carbon dioxide and brine make their contribution to the corrosion a minor one. In some cases, however, wells which are severely corroded have fatty acid contents as high as 1,000 to 1,500 ppm (as acetic acid).[7] These high concentrations are accompanied by low partial pressures of carbon dioxide. They appear to promote general corrosion rather than pitting. Unpublished data from our laboratory show that the presence of sufficient acetic acid with certain other pH and composition situations can promote hydrogen blistering of steel samples under conditions similar to some of those found in sweet oil wells.

Greenwell[7] shows that two distinct types of corrosion exist in sweet wells, depending upon whether they are low- or high-pressure wells. In the high-pressure wells, corrosion usually is present from the beginning of production. Severe attack occurs when as little as 0.1 per cent of water is produced and the corrosion rate stays constant as the percent of produced water increases. Conversely, low-pressure wells can be produced for years with little or no trouble. When corrosion does appear, it is very severe and tubing lives are as low as one year. It appears that the corrosion starts after some critical water to oil ratio is passed. The average corrosive well of this type is produced from a depth of 5,000 ft, has a bottom-hole pressure of 2,300 lb/in.^{2} and a bottom-hole temperature of 160° F.

The temperature of the fluid in the well varies widely and is a function of the depth of the well. Temperatures ranging from ambient to about 250° F must certainly be considered as common. Temperature has a profound effect upon the corrosion; dissolution rate increases very rapidly with temperature. It is important in another respect, since some of the organic corrosion inhibitors are ineffective above certain temperatures.

Another factor which must be considered, according to Greenwell,[7] is the wetting tendency of oil. The degree to which oil permits metal to come into contact with water varies and the protective film of oil is overcome at some critical oil to water ratio for each well.

The bulk of this discussion has dealt with electrochemical attack since this attack is the major reason for corrosion and since its effects are common to all types of wells. Galvanic and stress corrosion bring into consideration the nature of the metals that are being attacked. In a well, galvanic attack need not be the result of two different metals, but it can be associated with breaks in the mill scale and relationships between corrosion products and pure metal. The causes leading to stress corrosion have already been discussed. Electrolytic corrosion results from action by an externally impressed current and normally is confined to external attack upon the casing and flow lines. Since external casing corrosion is not treated with corrosion inhibitors, this subject is not discussed further here. Erosion-corrosion occurs in the lines where sudden changes in flow rate or direction are brought about by the nature of the equipment. This problem is best handled by physical methods.

A unique type of corrosion which occurs in some sweet wells is that which results from the deposition of scale or sludge on producing equipment. Stanton[29] says that the attack shows up as deep pits found under porous, dull-red scale deposits. Certain sweet crudes deposit scales consisting primarily of sparingly soluble sulfates as a matrix and containing significant quantities of chlorides. Case and Riggin[30] identified other components, such as cadmium, iron, magnesium, silica, barium, and strontium in this scale. The chlorides in the scale absorb water and hydrolyze to form an acidic, highly corrosive liquid entrapped in the scale.

PUMPING OIL WELLS. Sweet pumping wells are subject to the same causes of corrosive attack as are the flowing wells and in addition can have oxygen corrosion. The oxygen is introduced when the wells operate with open annulus and low fluid level. The oxygen leads to a corrosive situation which is very difficult to protect by the use of conventional corrosion inhibitors. It converts protective iron carbonate scales into nonadherent ferric hydroxide with rapid attack ensuing. The reason for the interference of oxygen with the protection by the long-chain organic nitrogenous inhibitors commonly used in wells is not clear. Perhaps the rapid development and flaking of the iron oxide or hydroxide prevents the tight adherence necessary for the film-forming nitrogenous inhibitors to function effectively.

GAS LIFT WELLS. These wells tend to be more corrosive than the pumping oil wells because of the high bottom-hole temperatures and the low bottom-hole pH values. In addition, they usually produce considerable quantities of water which also aggravates the corrosion problem. The partial pressure of carbon dioxide in these wells is generally quite high. To further accelerate the corrosion problem, the injected gas-lift gas may contain small quantities of oxygen. The nature of this system makes it difficult to get inhibitors down the annulus and below the gas-lift valves.

Stanton[29] states that electrochemical corrosion of the differential gas-concentration type can occur and is typified by the spongy, porous appearance of the affected area. Galvanic corrosion of the steel gas-lift mandrels in contact with Monel valves takes place, as does erosion of the interior of the mandrel. Oxygen corrosion can also occur if the lift-gas compressor pulls a suction on the well casings; air is introduced each time a well is pulled as well as when wells are lifted by air.

Shock and Sudbury[15] studied a severe corrosion problem in gas-lift wells in South Texas where producing pressures are not abnormally high. They found that top hole specimens do not reflect the severity of the corrosion taking place at the bottom of the hole. A considerable height of water column is present in the annular space. In general, the corrosion could be shown to be a function of pressure conditions at given depths and of temperatures and carbon dioxide content.

Surprising results for gas-lift wells were found by the N.A.C.E. T-1C Committee.[11] No correlation between tubing life and bottom-hole pH could be found. A distinction was found, however, in terms of water production. Those wells which produced over 300,000 barrels of water and over 50 per cent of water had tubing lives below 13 years, while those that produced less than the previous numbers had tubing lives in excess of 13 years.

GAS CONDENSATE WELLS. More has been written about corrosion and methods of its inhibition in gas condensate wells than in any other type of sweet well. The problem of controlling corrosion in these wells has been one of the major problems facing the producing industry. Extensive workover jobs, damage to the reservoir, and danger to operating personnel all contribute to make it a serious problem.[1] The book written by the N.G.A.A. Condensate Well Corrosion Committee[2] is recommended to the reader as a thorough and detailed discussion of the problem and its solutions.

Sudbury[2] defined a gas condensate well as a well which produces a vapor phase from a reservoir and which on reduction of temperature and pressure forms a condensate material from the saturated vapor. He also cites a more technical definition by Standing[31] as one which exhibits isothermal retrograde behavior in the temperature range that is of interest to petroleum engineering studies.

Corrosion in gas condensate wells usually takes the form of deep pitting. The tubing is attacked in sharp, well-defined pits that are caused by acidic gases dissolved in droplets of water condensed on the tubing wall. The tubing below the point of condensation may be completely free of corrosion damage since no aqueous phase exists. In line with this, corrosion of the Christmas Tree fittings is usually worse than in the producing string.

Other types of corrosion that can occur in gas condensate wells besides the electrochemical type are "ringworm" corrosion and erosion-corrosion. The former type occurs a few inches above and below tubing upsets. It has the appearance of a ring inside the tubing. The ring can consist of either very smooth or else deeply pitted attack. The cause of this attack is generally attributed to the upsetting process. The heat required in that process causes the heated end to have a different grain structure from the rest of the pipe. The transition zone thus formed allows the formation of potential differences which bring about galvanic corrosion.

The erosive process generally occurs near a restriction where velocities and turbulences are higher than normal. The turbulence, which brings about corrosion-product removal and thus promotes further corrosion, is most prevalent on the downstream side of chokes, valves, and producing string joints.

Condensate wells have high gas to oil ratios ranging from 5,000 to 100,000 cu ft per barrel of produced liquid hydrocarbon.[2] The systems that are the "wet" gases are those of the lower ratios. Pressures in wells are usually greater than 1,500 psi. The condensation of the hydrocarbons is accompanied by the formation of a few barrels per day of water, and this is where the corrosion problems come about. The water contains carbon dioxide and the lower-molecular weight fatty acids, primarily formic and acetic. This situation results in low pH and aggressive pitting.

In gas condensate wells, pressure is the controlling factor influencing carbon dioxide solubility, and the partial pressure of carbon dioxide can be used as a measure of the corrosivity of these wells. The N.A.C.E.-A.P.I. book[1] gives the following relationship between the partial pressure of carbon dioxide and the corrosivity of gas condensate wells.

  1. *A partial pressure above 30 psi usually indicates corrosion.*
  2. *A partial pressure between 7 and 30 psi may indicate corrosion.*
  3. *A partial pressure below 7 psi is considered noncorrosive.*

Shock and Sudbury[32] examine the relative efficiencies of carbon dioxide and the fatty acids in promoting corrosion in gas condensate wells. They show that the carbon dioxide is the primary causative agent. The organic acids produce general attack rather than the pitting type associated with carbon dioxide. The corrosion rate of steel due to attack by the organic acids decreases with time; the reaction is self-stifling. In addition and probably most important, the concentration of organic acids is quite low compared to that of the carbon dioxide. They also found that the presence of these fatty acids would cause carbon dioxide attack to occur at lower concentrations than in their absence.

Sour Wells

OIL WELLS. The problem of corrosion in wells producing hydrogen sulfide has been a serious one for many years. Approximately 40 per cent of the oil wells in the United States are producing hydrogen sulfide. In these wells, the corrosion generally starts slowly and then accelerates as the well ages. In some areas tubing leaks occur on an average of one every 30 days. Figure 5-2 shows a closeup of tubing that has been damaged in an Illinois field. Pumps may have to be pulled at frequent intervals either because of perforation or because of corrosion products from the pipe accumulating in the pump. Figure 5-3 shows the extensive destruction caused by corrosion in an oil treater at Rangely Field, Colorado after eight years of service.

FIGURE 5-2. Corroded Tubing from an Illinois Producing Field

Photograph Courtesy of Petrolite Corporation

Since many of the problems are similar to those already described for sweet wells and since the basic differences between wells can be thought of in terms of oil *vs.* gas wells, the sour wells are broken down into only two sections here—oil wells and gas wells. Using Stanton's[4] nomenclature for the different types of corrosion, one can expect to find any of the following corrosion processes in oil wells:

1. Electrochemical.
2. Sulfide—stress—corrosion—cracking.
3. Erosion-corrosion.
4. Embrittlement and blistering.
5. Microbiological.
6. Annular space condensation.
7. Galvanic.
8. Electrolytic.

FIGURE 5-3. Oil Treater After Eight Years of Uninhibited Service at Rangely Field, Colorado

Photograph Courtesy of Petrolite Corporation

The electrochemical type of corrosion is the one which shall concern us the most. It is due to the presence of sulfides and water and is accelerated by carbon dioxide, organic acids, and/or oxygen. The extent of the attack due to hydrogen sulfide and its corrosivity compared to sweet wells is shown in laboratory tests by Boies.[33] He found that the corrosion rate of mild steel went from about 10 mils per year in a synthetic oil well fluid to over 60 mils per year as the hydrogen sulfide fraction of the dissolved gas went from 0 to 100 per cent, the remainder being carbon dioxide.

The mechanism of the corrosion can be oversimplified in the following reaction:

$$H_2S + Fe \xrightarrow{H_2O} FeS + H_2. \qquad [5\text{-}3]$$

The iron sulfide produced in this reaction generally adheres to the steel surfaces as a black powder or scale. The scale then tends to cause a localized attack because it is cathodic to the steel. This attack brings about the deep pitting that is frequently noted on equipment.

In quiet water and in the absence of oxygen, iron sulfide can retard further corrosion if a uniform protective film is formed. In the presence of an air supply, however, the retardation effect is nullified by cathodic depolarization by oxygen.[34] Carbon dioxide appears to have some sort of a similar effect and it is rare that severe sulfide corrosion is found when either oxygen or carbon dioxide is not present as well, with air being the more severe of the two.

Rogers and Rowe[35] conducted a systematic study of various corrosive factors in oil-field brine. Corrosion in brines containing hydrogen sulfide starts out slowly and then accelerates as the steel became coated with iron sulfide and pitting takes place. Laboratory studies show the cathode to be an easily polarized hydrogen electrode of high potential during the first phase, but a difficultly polarized iron sulfide electrode of low potential during the second phase. Polarization measurements show that much smaller currents are required to change the potential of a steel cathode in brines containing carbon dioxide than in brines containing hydrogen sulfide. Protection currents depend somewhat on the pH, but more on the presence or absence of an iron sulfide film. The resistance of the iron sulfide electrode to polarization and the large corrosion current result in large cathodic areas, high corrosion rate, and low pitting. Easy polarization in carbon dioxide environments results in low corrosion rates when the cathode to anode ratio is small but in high corrosion rates and pitting when the ratio is high.

Negreev and Balayan[36] also found that the greatest corrosion is noted when both oxygen and hydrogen sulfide are present. They found that the corrosion drops as the salt concentration increases, presumably due to the decreasing solubility of the oxygen in the increasing salt content.

In the case of sucker rods of carbon-steel, sulfide stress corrosion usually appears as smooth pitting. Small cracks form at areas of surface damage, such as wrench marks, even when the damage is negligible. This cracking is caused by stress concentrations developed at the base of the pit and by embrittlement resulting from sulfide attack.[1] Erosion-corrosion can occur in sour oil wells for the same reasons that it occurs in sweet wells. For a detailed discussion of corrosion fatigue, the reader is referred to Morton.[37]

Embrittlement and blistering can develop occasionally in sour wells and is the cause of very rapid failure. Hydrogen atoms formed at the metal surface during the corrosion reaction do not recombine but instead they migrate into the metal lattice and separate at defects and dislocations. The atoms then recombine to form the diatomic gas at occlusions within the metal, and severe blistering and metal rupture can result. Alternately the hydrogen atoms can alloy with the steel to embrittle it. Balezin and Nikol'skii[38] postulate that this alloy occurs because sulfur atoms or ions reduce hydrogen and overvoltage, slow down the recombination of hydrogen atoms, and leave enough hydrogen atoms on the surface of the metal for diffusion.

Microorganisms, such as Desulfovibrio desulfuricans (sulfate reducers) or clostridia, can grow and cause corrosion in the absence of oxygen. The sulfate reducers, which are the major cause of concern, can bring about corrosion in one of two ways:

1. They can reduce sulfate to hydrogen sulfide, thus increasing the amount of this corrosive agent.

2. They can consume hydrogen (in production of the enzyme hydrogenase)[29] *formed at the cathodes in the corrosion cells. This formation is an efficient means of depolarization and leads to accelerated corrosion.*

In the interior of casing above the annular fluid level, attack by hydrogen sulfide can occur because the gas is saturated with water at reservoir conditions. As the gas diffuses up the hole, the water condenses on the surface of the casing at areas which are cooled below the dew point. Hydrogen sulfide then dissolves in the water droplet and corrosion takes place. Since there is little or no flow in the annulus, the iron sulfide scale is not removed and pitting develops.[1]

Galvanic and electrolytic corrosion can occur because stray currents enter the pumping unit and jump to the tubing somewhere downhole. This current jump usually occurs just above a high-resistance joint in the rod string. The thread lubricant in the joint presumably furnishes most of the resistance.[29]

GAS WELLS. Most of the problems encountered here are similar to those for sweet gas wells or for sour oil wells and therefore are not repeated at this time. In many deep high-pressure sour gas wells little pitting is seen, but rapid failure occurs due to stress cracking. A small initial crack, developed because of local stresses, extends across a rod in gradual stages and cracking is aided by corrosion. Ruptured members are characterized by the presence of a smooth plane on most of the rupture surface with an uneven torn portion on the other side. The crack works its way along a smooth plane through the steel until the stress on the uncracked portion of the plane exceeds the endurance limit and it tears apart.[29] No "necking down" of the metal member is evident in these fractures since the metal usually has lost much of its ductility prior to cracking.

INHIBITION

A wide variety of materials have been used as corrosion inhibitors for producing wells. Such things are included as formaldehyde, chromates, neutralizing agents, various types of organic compounds, and arsenates. Organic corrosion inhibitors are by far the most common ones used today and are generally considered to be most effective. Arsenate inhibitors are also used to a considerable extent, almost exclusively in sweet wells. This section of the book is broken down into a discussion of the various types of inhibitors used and other related factors, such as scale prevention and inhibitor application and techniques.

Formaldehyde

One of the earliest corrosion inhibitors used for producing oils was formaldehyde. It was first introduced in 1944[1] and enjoyed considerable use for the next few years. It is now utilized, however, only as an adjunct to other more complicated organic inhibitors.

Negreev and Balayan[36] state that very good results for preventing corrosion of subsurface pumps, pipes, pistons, and other equipment are observed by adding a 40 per cent aqueous solution of formaldehyde to sour wells. The amount of formaldehyde that was required for inhibition depended upon the composition of brine, the amount of hydrogen sulfide, and the daily flow of the well. The average consumption of formaldehyde varied between 15 and 80 mg/liter. The inhibitor was added every 24 hr.

Although formaldehyde is no longer of much use in the oil well industry, it is still an important corrosion inhibitor for commercial hydrochloric acid. Certain studies were conducted which are aimed at developing the mechanism by which formaldehyde and other aldehydes prevent corrosion. It is postulated[1] that a sulfide-iron formaldehyde film is formed on the surface of the metal in the well equipment and that this film reduces the corrosion rate. Kemkhadze and Balezin[39] point out the very interesting fact that aldehydes can act upon steel in acidic solutions in two opposing ways: they can either inhibit or accelerate the processes of dissolution. At a given aldehyde concentration the one or the other tendency is predominant. The inhibiting action of the aldehyde increases with rising concentration to a limiting value and then decreases. The speed of reduction of the aldehyde and the stimulation of corrosion increase in increased concentration, but they generally diminish with increasing molecular weight. Branched-chain aldehydes such as isobutyraldehyde, are generally better inhibitors than are their straight-chain analogues.

Chromates

The use of dichromates alone or in alkaline solutions for the prevention of corrosion in oil wells was known as far back as 1925.[40] The major use of chromates recently for petroleum production appears to be in controlling corrosion in gas condensate wells. Work was started in 1944 by the Bureau of Mines on this subject.[1] Among the earlier reported users were the Texas Company and the Lone Star Producing Company.[1] Since that time, sodium chromate or dichromate, either alone or in combination with other chemicals, has been used in many gas condensate wells with satisfactory results.

Fariss[41] patented the use of zinc chromate as a corrosion inhibitor for brines from the petroleum producing well. This technique would appear to be a logical improvement of the chromate inhibitor in a manner analogous to that already described in Chapter 3 on corrosion in cooling-tower systems. He states that at a dosage level of 13 ppm it gives steel essentially complete protection against corrosion from brine containing 52,000 ppm of sodium chloride and having a pH of 6.2 to 6.8. Even when the pH is reduced to 3.0 and oxygen is introduced into the system, the inhibitor is still effective. However, brines that contain sulfide precipitate zinc and eliminate its value.

An interesting discussion of the possible mechanism of inhibition of the corrosion of steel by dichromate ion in an air-free solution of acetic acid is presented by Hackerman and Hurd.[42] They believe that a high pH develops in a liquid film immediately adjacent to the metal and makes possible the precipitation of a protective coating in a solution which is acidic at other points. This film acts as a mechanical barrier between the metal and its environment.

Chromate inhibitors can be injected into the wells either as solids or liquids. If solid, the inhibitor is put into a stick form which can be coated or compounded with sodium silicate or some other material in such a manner that it dissolves slowly. Pellets can also be made from this combination.[1] The stick or pellets are dropped to the bottom of the well and dissolve slowly. The liquid can be injected through a string of "macaroni tubing" which brings it down to the bottom of the tubing that is to be protected.

In contrast to the low dosages of zinc chromate reported by Fariss, it is recommended that large dosages of dichromate be injected into gas condensate wells. At first, 3,000 to 6,000 ppm (based on the water contained) would be used, and then after protection is obtained, the chromate concentration can be cut down to a figure of 200 to 400 ppm.[2]

One of the drawbacks of the chromate treatment is that it can cause plugging by the formation of chromic oxide deposits. Alternatively, barium or strontium chromates can precipitate out. Another major drawback of chromate treatment is the toxic properties of the material and the handling problem. The cost is rather high at the dosage levels required and organic inhibitors are generally considered to be more effective.

Neutralization Inhibitors

The use of alkaline agents was successfully applied to gas condensate wells in the early days of inhibitors. The proposed mechanism involved the neutralization of the corrosive organic agents and the formation of bicarbonate salts by reaction with the carbon dioxide. This formation of bicarbonate salt gave a highly buffered solution. The application of this buffer system in practice is shown by the fact that samples of water taken from treated wells have pH values as high as 8.4. Alkaline inhibitors that were used included aqueous ammonia, sodium carbonate, sodium hydroxide, sodium bicarbonate, and sodium silicate.

It is pointed out[2] that the use of neutralizing agents must be limited to waters of low solids content, preferably below 2,000 ppm. The combined calcium and magnesium contents should be below 300 ppm; otherwise alkaline earth scales form and cause severe plugging problems. The use of sodium silicate became fairly widespread in 1949, and by the middle of 1950 about 150 wells were being treated with it. The following year its application dropped off almost completely, however. Other chemicals which were tested included sodium nitrite and magnesium. The use of neutralizing agents vanished with the development of the much more effective organic inhibitors.

Cyanamides

An unusual class of inhibitors was patented by Menaul.[43] He found that addition to the water of a water-soluble compound containing the cyanamide radical inhibits pump equipment against corrosion in sour oil wells. Typical inhibitors include cyanamide, calcium, barium, and magnesium cyanamide, dimethyl-, diethyl-, diisopropyl-, and diallyl-cyanamide, sodium, calcium, barium, and magnesium dicyanamide, and dicyandiamide. The trimers, such as melamine, are effective as inhibitors. The inhibiting effect is assumed to be due to film formation produced by attachment of one of the nitrogen atoms of the cyanamide radical to the ferrous metal surface.

Scale Preventatives

The formation of scale can lead to severe pitting corrosion underneath the deposit. Preventive measures for scale control and thus indirectly for corrosion control are taken occasionally in a manner reminiscent of those in common use in circulating-water systems. The major treatment used is polyphosphate, while chelating agents, such as ethylenediaminetetraacetic acid, EDTA, are used to some extent.

A number of application techniques for polyphosphates were devised. In one common procedure, which is described by Earlougher and Love,[44] a granular complex polyphosphate is mixed with sand injected during a fracturing operation. The phosphate granules dissolve slowly in the well fluids, sequester the ions in the brine, and prevent their precipitation. In another application procedure, wire baskets are filled with very slowly soluble polyphosphates and placed in a water supply tank near the inlet pipe or else in a water line.

The polyphosphates are generally effective for this purpose, but the organic chelating agents, such as EDTA, are generally ruled out. The latter materials are quite effective, but the cost of the considerable dosages required makes their use too expensive. One situation in which they are of use, however, is described by Kipps[45] who adds small quantities of an alkali metal salt of N,N-bis-(hydroxyethyl)glycine to the polyphosphates used for scale control. The chelating agent appears to be effective in preventing the reversion of the polyphosphate to the ortho form and thus maintains its effectiveness as a scale inhibitor.

Polyphosphates can be used in combination with more conventional corrosion inhibitors for this purpose. For example, Core and Jones[46] describe the beneficial effect of a mixture of a hexametaphosphate and an alkali metal arsenite. The hexametaphosphate acts as the scale inhibitor, while the arsenite is the corrosion inhibitor.

Arsenic Compounds

The use of arsenic compounds as corrosion inhibitors for sweet wells is second in volume today only to the use of the long-chain organic nitrogenous inhibitors. These materials find their greatest area of application in California. A series of patents covering their application were issued to Rohrback, McCloud, and Scott.[47]

Commonly used formulations include mixtures of arsenous oxide, sodium hydroxide, and water in varying proportions depending upon the desired physical properties of the final mixture. Thus, for example, hard, dense solids can be made from proper combinations of these chemicals, so that the inhibitor can be safely dropped down to the bottom of the well before much of it is dissolved in the surrounding fluid. Potassium hydroxide is occasionally used instead of sodium hydroxide, depending upon the resistance to softening desired at high temperatures so that the inhibitor will not spread on the hot tubing wall as it falls down the well. Pelleted corrosion-inhibitor formulations are also made which depend upon a combination of sodium arsenite and arsenous oxide for their inhibitive properties. The sodium arsenite dissolves relatively rapidly and provides the initial desirable high dosage, while the remaining arsenous oxide skeleton dissolves more slowly and gives the low, long-term inhibitor level. Weighting agents such as barium sulfate, powdered zinc, or iron metal can also be added.

The arsenic formulations are generally successful when they are used. They suffer from the handicap of toxicity. Under the acidic conditions encountered during their use, the formation of volatile and poisonous arsine is a danger. Recently, Frisius[48] extended the versatility of these materials by adding H_3BO_3 to the As_2O_3-NaOH combination. The H_3BO_3 enlarges the pH range over which the material can be used safely and provides greater resistance to precipitation of the As_2O_3 by the CO_2 in the well fluids.

In evaluating the effectiveness of arsenic inhibitors, Rohrback *et al.*[47] cite an example of a corrosive well that was protected for four days by 3 lb of inhibitor pellets. Inhibition was checked by frequent iron counts. Dosage requirements vary, of course, depending upon the nature of the well and the frequency of inhibitor application. Hill and Davie[49] state that the most popular method at present in the California area of feeding arsenic inhibitors is to introduce the inhibitor daily in a batch down the annulus between the casing and the tubing so that it is produced up the tubing with the well fluids. Usually 20 to 30 gal of fresh water are used to flush the inhibitor down the casing. The proper dosage is determined by trial starting with an average of 2 qt per day.

While very little was published concerning the protective mechanism of arsenates in oil well systems, there is a strong relationship to the accepted protective mechanism of cathodic inhibition of steel in aqueous acids, as set forth by Kraemer[50] and Chapel, Roetheli, and McCarthy.[51] Bailey[52] explains the protective mechanism as being due to the formation of a compact thin film of elementary arsenic on the steel surface. The presence of elementary arsenic on steel surfaces was verified. There is some question however as to the homogeneity of the film. Many authors believe that arsenic is present in certain spots only. It is also established that arsine is formed routinely at the surface. Furthermore, arsenic compounds tend to promote embrittlement or hydrogen blistering by preventing the recombination of hydrogen atoms at the surface.

A logical explanation of inhibition by arsenates could therefore be as follows. The elemental arsenic plates out at spots on the surface. As hydrogen atoms are formed they combine with the arsenic to form arsine. In addition, an unusually high concentration of hydrogen atoms build up on the surface because of the apparent negative effect of arsenic upon hydrogen molecule formation. This build-up suppresses the formation of more hydrogen atoms and thus leads to a possible classification of cathodic inhibition.

Long-Chain Nitrogenous Inhibitors

The great bulk of inhibitors used today in producing gas and oil wells are long-chain organic nitrogenous materials. The most common ones, all of which have long-chain hydrocarbons (usually C_{18}) as a part of the structure, include:

1. *Aliphatic fatty acid derivatives.*
2. *Imidazolines and derivatives.*
3. *Quaternaries.*
4. *Rosin derivatives.*

The first category, the aliphatic fatty acid derivatives, can be further broken down according to:

1. *Primary, secondary, or tertiary monoamines.*
2. *Diamines.*
3. *Amides.*
4. *Polyethoxylated amines, diamines, or amides.*
5. *Salts of these materials.*
6. *Amphoteric compounds.*

Examples of commercially available inhibitors used today which fall into these various classifications are as follows, where $R = C_{18}H_{37}$ unless otherwise specified:

1. *Monoamines:*
   a. *Primary:* $R-NH_2$.
   b. *Secondary:* R_2-NH.
   c. *Tertiary:* $R-N(CH_3)_2$.
2. *Diamines:* $R-NHCH_2CH_2CH_2NH_2$.
3. *Amides:* $R-CONH_2$.
4. *Polyethoxylated materials:*
   a. *Amines (where* x + y *varies from 2 to 50):*

$$R-N\begin{cases}(CH_2CH_2O)_xH \\ (CH_2CH_2O)_yH\end{cases}.$$

   b. *Diamines (where* x + y + z *varies from 3 to 10):*

$$R-NCH_2CH_2CH_2N\begin{cases}(CH_2CH_2O)_xH \\ (CH_2CH_2O)_yH\end{cases}$$
$$\underset{(CH_2CH_2O)_zH}{|} .$$

   c. *Amides (where* x + y *varies from 5 to 50):*

$$R-\overset{O}{\overset{\|}{C}}-N\begin{cases}(CH_2CH_2O)_xH \\ (CH_2CH_2O)_yH\end{cases}.$$

5. *Acetic, oleic, dimeric, naphthenic, or phosphate acid salts.*
6. *Amphoteric compounds:*

$$\underset{R-NH}{\underset{|}{CH_3CHCH_2COOH}}.$$

At this point, one might cite examples of the use of some of these materials in the primary production of petroleum. Many suppliers highly recommend salts of N-Tallow propylenediamine as being especially effective and economical. The most common salts of this material that are used are the oleic-acid or naphthenic-acid salts. The common dosage levels are 1 pint of the 50 per cent active material per 100 barrels of produced oil.

A number of fatty acid derivatives were patented as corrosion inhibitors for producing wells. Some of these derivatives include the following.

Pfohl and Gregory[53] patented the diamines $RNH(CH_2)_xNH_2$ in which R is an aliphatic or alicyclic carbon chain of 8 to 22 atoms and x is 2 to 10. The alicyclic or aliphatic group is preferably a resin acid or high fatty acid residue containing 14 to 18 carbon atoms which can be obtained from resin or tall oils, soybean, or coconut oil, or tallow. Pfohl and Gregory in the same patent state that oleic-acid salts of these diamines are still better inhibitors.

Jones[54, 55] patented the reaction of the diamines with acids obtained by partial oxidation of certain liquid hydrocarbons. A typical example is the salt of Duomeen-T and Alox 425. (The terms "Duomeen" and "Alox" are commercial designations for the diamines and the acids.)

Lindberg[56] patented a salt consisting of the aminopropyl tallow amine neutralized by a petroleum sulfonic acid. In this formulation he also places a small amount of a germicide for sulfate-reducing bacteria and then uses 1 to 50 pints of the formulation per 1,000 barrels of well fluid.

Gunderson and Kerst[57] have patented oleyltriacetoyltriethylenetetramine, oleyldistearoylpropylenediamine, naphthenoyltriacetoyltriethylenetetramine, and similar materials that are effective in sour crude oil at 60 ppm.

Case[58] patented a formulation based on a salt of Duomeen-T with a water-soluble petroleum sulfonic acid. To the inhibitor is added urea or hydrated sodium acetate as a carrier and also a wetting agent.

Oxford[59] patented a combination of a Duomeen-T inhibitor with naphthenic acids such as Sunaptic Acids A. Hughes[60] patented the N-octyl acid phosphate salt of Duomeen-T. Jolly[61] patented mononuclear aromatic monocarboxylic salts of diamines of the Duomeen-T type.

A British[62] patent covers the use of an oil-soluble fatty amide of an aliphatic diamine. An example of this type would be the oleic acid monoamide of ethylene diamine.

Straight-chain monoamines do not find too much application as corrosion inhibitors in producing wells in view of the greater effectiveness of the diamines. Amides are used occasionally but the more frequent usage is given to amides derived from imidazolines. The polyethoxylated materials have the great advantage of providing almost tailor-made solubility to corrosion inhibitors. The inhibitors differ among themselves in water and oil solubility and dispersibility. The proper degree of solubility or dispersibility in the right phase can be very important to the chances of the inhibitor reaching and adhering to the surface that it is supposed to protect. The degree of water solubility increases as the amount of ethylene oxide added to the molecule increases. The result is that inhibitors that might have great potential value but are ineffective in practice because of solubility problems can be given different solubility properties which insure that they reach the surface. The ethoxylated diamines are especially good corrosion inhibitors for a wide variety of applications.

A relatively new class of aliphatic fatty acid derivatives that is beginning to show considerable value as a corrosion inhibitor is amphoteric materials. Compounds with the structures $RNHCH_2CH_2COOM$ or $RN(CH_2CH_2COOM)_2$ where R is C_{18} and M is an alkali metal or hydrogen are found to be exceptionally good corrosion inhibitors. Andersen[63] patented materials of this type and also similar alkaline earth salts. Amidic acids were patented by Stromberg and Hughes.[64] These acids have the general composition

$$\begin{array}{c} \quad\quad \overset{O}{\overset{\|}{C}}\overset{R}{\overset{|}{-N-H}} \\ R' \diagup \\ \quad\diagdown\, \underset{\|}{\underset{O}{C}}-OH \end{array}$$

where R = 6 to 22 carbon atoms and R' = C. A relatively new type of inhibitor, the diamine salt of an acylsarcosine, was patented by Titsworth and Martin.[65] This material is shown to be extremely effective in laboratory testing and variations of it are under study by a number of laboratories. The diamine can be a material like Duomeen-T, while the acylsarcosine has the structure

$$RCON(CH_3)CH_2COOH.$$

Fujii and Uehara[66] report inhibition by the salt of a higher aliphatic amine and an unsaturated fatty acid. Hughes[60] reports the Duomeen-T salt of octyl acid phosphate. A new inhibitor which has great promise is the salt of a tetrahydroxyalkyl alkylene polyamine with phytic acid.[67] The phytic acid has shown unusually effective corrosion inhibition properties and it is quite likely that some of its derivatives may be far more effective inhibitors than those that are in conventional use today.

The second category of inhibitors, the imidazolines, are used as such, as salts, or as derivatives.

A large number of different imidazolines used as corrosion inhibitors are found in patent literature. Examples of relatively common imidazolines are the following:

$$C_{18}H_{37}-C{\overset{\displaystyle N}{\diagdown}}{\underset{\displaystyle N-CH_2}{\diagdown}}CH_2 \; ; \qquad C_{18}H_{37}-C{\overset{\displaystyle N}{\diagdown}}{\underset{\displaystyle N-CH_2}{\diagdown}}CH_2 \; .$$
$$\phantom{C_{18}H_{37}-C}C_2H_4OH \qquad\qquad\qquad\qquad C_2H_4NH_2$$

Prilleux[68] condensed 1-ethylamino-2-heptadecylimidazole with ethylene oxide. He can further modify this product by reacting it with P_2S_5 to get inhibitors which are effective at dosage levels of 5 ppm in his laboratory tests. In a similar manner, Hughes[69] reacted a polyamine with a dicarboxylic acid to make a bis-imidazoline and then added ethylene oxide to it. Sterlin[70] cites the preparation of effective imidazolines by the reaction of oleic acid with aminoethylethanolamine. Lytle[71] made inhibitors from the reaction product of triethanolamine and dimer acid. Hughes[72] made corrosion inhibitors containing both an imidazoline and an imidazoline ring by reacting a polyethylene amine, an aldehyde, and an acid. These inhibitors are reported to be effective in sour wells at dosages as low as 10 ppm.

Salts of imidazolines that are effective as corrosion inhibitors are described by Sterlin[70] and Luvisi.[73] Sterlin reports that the sebacic acid salt of imidazolines is effective, while Luvisi describes the use of the salicylic acid salt. Hughes[74] found that the oleic acid salt of an imidazoline is an effective inhibitor, while Riggs[75] prevented corrosion in oil wells by using an alkaryl sulfonic salt of an imidazoline. Imidazoline salts of acids similar to those for the straight-chain amines are frequently used. Mixed salts of imidazolines (e.g., oleic and dimeric) are also effective inhibitors.[76]

A number of interesting derivatives of imidazolines are reported in literature and are in use as corrosion inhibitors. Hughes[77] for example, prepared imidazolidinones and imidazolidinethiones by reacting tetra-ethylenepentamine with either urea or thiourea. The resultant product is then allowed to react again with either the urea or thiourea or else with a monocarboxylic acid or an aldehyde. The final product has the structure

$$\overline{C(:Y)NHCH_2CH_2N}CH_2CH_2NHCH_2CH_2R$$

in which Y is oxygen or sulfur and R is a substituted imidazolidinone, an acid salt of it, or a substituted imidazolindine. Other interesting derivatives prepared by Hughes[78, 79] are diimidazolines and diimidazoline-mono-(or di-) pyrrolinedione compounds. Hughes also mentions the use of imidazoline-oxalines as corrosion inhibitors,[80] as well as amide or imidazoline derivatives of diimidazolines.[81] He made effective inhibitors by reacting maleic anhydride with imidazolines[82] and also by preparing imidazolineimidazolidines.[83]

A number of effective sulfur-imidazoline derivatives are reported. Westlund and Rudel[84] reacted a phosphorus sulfide with an imidazoline, while Scott and Garner[85] made an inhibitor by mixing a 1-alkylimidazoline derivative or 1-(aminoalkyl)imidazoline with carbon disulfides. Leboucher and Prilleux[86] made inhibitors which are effective at 10 ppm by reacting the derivatives of imidazolines with a benzene solution of sulfur. Chesnel[87] has discovered a whole series of effective polysulfide derivatives of imidazolines. Hughes[88] made bisthiazolines of the structure

$$(\overline{SCH_2CH_2N}{=}C)_2R$$

in which R is the residue of a dicarboxylic acid and found that effective inhibitors could be produced by reacting the terminal NH_2 group of the side chain of the intermediate imidazolinone reaction product of diethylenetriamine with urea or thiourea with an acid anhydride, aldehyde, or acid.[89] Oxazoline corrosion inhibitors are described by Butter[90] and Hughes.[91] Hughes also found substituted triazines to be good inhibitors.[92]

Quaternaries that are good corrosion inhibitors are usually based on the materials described above. For example, the quaternary

$$\left[\begin{array}{cc} R_1 & CH_3 \\ & N \\ R_2 & CH_3 \end{array}\right]^+ \quad Cl^-$$

where R_1 and R_2 are long chains (C_{12} to C_{18}) is frequently used as an inhibitor. Imidazoline derivatives include the benzyl chloride quaternary of the imidazolines or of similar materials. Aliphatic quaternaries were patented by Esso[93] (such as dodecyldimethylbenzyl ammonium chloride or dioctadecyldimethylammonium chloride) as being effective at 10 ppm for crudes. In another patent[94] they say that these materials are effective in sour wells even at pH values of 2 to 5. Chiddix, Maxcy, and Sundberg[95] made quaternaries which had good inhibiting properties by reacting alkoxylated amino diamides with benzyl chloride. Lytle[96] prepared double long-chain quaternaries represented by the formula $(RNR'_2ANR'_2R)^{++} X_2$. Examples include decamethylenebis (dimethylhexadecyl ammonium bromide) and tetramethylenebis (nonbenzyl dimethyl ammonium chloride). These quaternaries are effective at 0.0001 per cent. Green[97] describes the use of a quaternary imidazolinium salt such as 1-(2-hydroxyethyl)-1-benzyl-2-tridecyl-2-imidazolinium nitrite or chloride as being effective over a wide range of applications. Whether or not the nitrite contributes to effectiveness is a matter of considerable speculation.

The rosin derivatives are complex amine mixtures based on abietic acid and containing long chains. They are used in many wells with varying degrees of success. A British patent[98] discusses the use of ethylene oxide condensation products of rosin amines as inhibitors. Most of the materials of this type are marketed today in the United States under the trade name of Rosin Amine D or derivatives thereof.

A wide variety of *other nitrogenous inhibitors* are reported as having merit as corrosion inhibitors. Some of these inhibitors include the pyrimidines, as typified by Hughes' hexahydropyrimidines;[99] biguanidine derivatives, such as those of Chenicek and Thompson;[100] esters, such as the trialkanolamine ester of a dimerized polyunsaturated fatty acid;[102] and the reaction products of vinyl esters of fatty acids with ethylene-polyamines.[102, 103] Hughes and Stromberg[104] report that partial esters of polymerized fatty acids are effective in low dosages and counteract oil in water emulsions. The use of amino acetylene compounds such as 4-dimethylamin-2-butyn-1-ol is suggested by Hertel.[105] While materials of this type are known to be effective for acid-well acidizing, there is, as yet, not much information available on their effectiveness for downhole inhibition. In any event, the use of a long-chain amine (C_{18}) with the acetylinic alcohol would probably be more effective.

There is no accepted theory for the exact mechanism by which the long-chain organic nitrogenous inhibitors function. The division of materials into cathodic and anodic inhibitors which serves for inorganic materials in all-aqueous systems cannot be employed here, although there is considerable belief that there is a certain degree of inhibitor ion orientation at the cathodes on the metal surface in the case of the nitrogen derivatives. Carboxylic acid and sulfur inhibitors, on the other hand, would tend more towards orientation at the anodic portion. Hackerman and Sudbury[106] in studying polarization phenomena of amine additives in water and sulfuric acid found indications that both anodic and cathodic areas might be affected by the amine inhibitor. The anodic inhibition is explained on the basis of migration of electrons from the metal to the positively charged inhibitor rather than towards the cathodic areas within the metal. It should be pointed out, however, that the organic compounds are generally regarded as giving cathodic inhibition with this additional anodic inhibition being supplementary but not major.

Hackerman and Makrides[107] point out that the cathodic inhibition is thought to be the result of both physical adsorption and chemisorption. Electrostatic bonding at the cathodic areas contributes to over-all inhibition. The inhibitor chemisorption occurs through the formation of coordinate covalent bonds with the surface atoms of the metal, whereby the inhibitor acts as an electron donor and the metal as an electron acceptor. This mechanism explains the dependence of inhibitive power on the electronic structure, solubility, and substituents of the inhibitor, allows for differences between various metals, and permits both positive and negative temperature coefficients. Antropov[108] also discussed the mechanism of cathodic protection by organic inhibitors, while Schram and Burns[109] interpret the effect of amine salts on the polarization of iron cathodes in terms of the apparent area changes brought about by adsorption of the amines on the surface of the cathodes. In the concentration ranges that they studied, the per cent inhibitor efficiency for each amine was a linear function of the apparent per cent surface area masked by the amine. The different amines showed considerable specificity, however, in the relationship between the per cent of efficiency and apparent per cent of area masked. This function leads to the conclusion that there is apparently more to the action of amines as corrosion inhibitors than just a simple masking of certain portions of the surface of the corroding metal.

Blair[19] derived the equation

$$\frac{d \log R}{d \log C} = -1, \qquad [5\text{-}4]$$

where R is the corrosion rate and C is the concentration of inhibitor. This equation is based on the assumption that a conventional adsorption theory could be applied to the reaction of inhibitor molecules with the surface and that the uncovered surface corrodes at its normal rate. He found that in a laboratory test using a typical naphtha, brine, and hydrogen sulfide, the slope of corrosion versus concentration line followed that predicted by this equation. In the cases of a condensate well and a pumping well, however, the corrosion rates diminished more rapidly with inhibitor concentration than would be predicted by the equation. These results were then used to develop a modified formula for field results as follows:

$$R = \frac{K}{C^n}. \qquad [5\text{-}5]$$

K is a constant for a given system and has a value of about 1.6. Blair postulates that a physical picture of this effect is that penetration of the adsorbed layer on the metal by the corrosive medium is opposed by an energy barrier even when the surface is only partially covered. This barrier increases rapidly as the adsorbed film becomes more closely packed and more highly organized in structure.

It is interesting to note that all of the effective long-chain organic compounds mentioned here have both polar and nonpolar ends. The polar end of the inhibitor molecule takes part in the adsorption process. Whether the initial adsorption is really chemisorption or physical adsorption by van der Waals forces followed by chemisorption has not been satisfactorily resolved. Breston[110] states that both probably occur simultaneously; the chemisorption takes place at the "active spots," and the remainder of the surface is covered by inhibitor held by weaker physical forces. However, after a short period there does exist a strong covalent bond between the polar group of the inhibitor and the metal surface.

The literature is replete with examples showing a direct relationship between the strength of this bond and the effectiveness of the inhibitor. Hackerman and Cook[111] show that a portion of the surface of steel powder is specific to the irreversible adsorption of alkyl carboxyl acids, amines, alcohols, and esters. Certain areas apparently will irreversibly adsorb either acid or amine, while other areas are specific to the acid or to the amine. Fuji and Aramaki[112] studied the relationship between the adsorption of certain polar organic compounds on metals and their ability to inhibit corrosion. Using straight-chain C_{16} hydrocarbons as the nonpolar end of the molecule in each case, they found that amides are more effective than amines and both are more effective than acids or alcohols. The amide group also gives the strongest adsorption effect, while the adsorption strengths of the other inhibitors are in direct proportion to their effectiveness as inhibitors. Daniel[113] compared acids, esters, and alcohols. He found that for a given chain length, the acid is the most strongly adsorbed, the ester the least, and the alcohol intermediate. Nathan[114] shows that corrosion of steel powder is inhibited the most by strongly adsorbed materials and the least by weakly adsorbed ones.

This strength of adsorption of the polar end of the inhibitor molecule represents the first step in a theory that was set forth to account for the inhibitive action of long-chain organic nitrogenous molecules in producing gas and oil wells.[18] This theory postulates that the protective action can be thought of in terms of a "sandwich" mechanism. The bottom part of the sandwich is the bond between the polar end of the molecule and the metal surface. The entire strength of the protective action of the sandwich is dependent upon the strength of this bond, which is influenced by the factors mentioned in the previous paragraphs. The center portion of the sandwich is the nonpolar end of the molecule and its contribution towards protection is the degree to which this portion of the molecule can cover or wet the surface. Finally, the outside layer of the protective sandwich is the hydrophobic layer of oil attached to the long hydrocarbon tail of the inhibitor. This oil layer is then believed to serve as still another protective film, which covers the original inhibitor film and creates a barrier to both diffusion out by Fe^{++} and diffusion in by the corrodents or by the water.

The wetting of the metal surface by the inhibitor is really a function of two factors: (1) the strength of the bond mentioned above and (2) the orientation of the long-chain portion of the molecule. Presumably, this part of the molecule can orient itself in any manner from lying flat on the surface and parallel to it, to sticking out absolutely perpendicular to the surface. The degree to which the surface is covered is obviously a direct function of this orientation, and affects the effectiveness of the protective film. Nathan[114, 115] shows that branching of the alkyl chain decreases inhibitor efficiency as it decreases the ease of adsorption from solution. He postulates that the geometrical nature of the nonpolar radical should be such that a close interlocking of the hydrocarbon chains can exist. Molecular models show that such interlocking of the hydrocarbon chains is possible but does not occur when the chains are branched, as is also shown by Bigelow *et al.*[116] Aramaki and Fujii[117, 118] also found that the presence of a hydrocarbon branch in the neighborhood of the functional radical decreases the inhibitive action, and it also interferes with regular orientation of inhibitor molecules and reduces the adhesive force of the functional group on the surface.

Fujii and Aramaki[119] also report that better corrosion inhibition can be obtained with secondary amine inhibitors than with primary amines. They found that when fully dispersed in corrosive media, the secondary amines can be more rapidly adsorbed on the metal surface than are primary amines. Nathan,[114] on the other hand, found that secondary amines are much less effective as inhibitors than primary amines with the same number of carbon atoms, while tertiary amines are even less effective and are adsorbed to a lesser degree than are either primary or secondary amines. An answer to this apparent anomaly can be found in a study of the effect of chain length on the effectiveness on inhibitors.

The length of the hydrocarbon chain appears to be critical. At C_{12}, the effectiveness becomes appreciable, while for the best protection, a C_{16} or C_{18} chain should be present. This length would also appear to tie in to the wetting and oil-layer phases of protection and is also in agreement with Traube's rule of adsorption in accordance with the decrease in the solubility in water as the chain length increases. This chain-length effect was found in this author's laboratories and is also reported by Fujii and Aramaki[119] as well as by Nathan.[114] It therefore becomes apparent that the longer chain length of the primary amine (when all the amines have the same total number of carbon atoms) is the predominant factor. However, it is also a fact that in accordance with the branching effect a secondary amine having two chains, one of which is as long as the chain in the primary amine, would be more effective than the primary amine.

Fujii and Aramaki[120] found that when oleyl radicals are contained in the inhibitor molecule, some corrosive materials are included in the closed spaces which are formed by the oleyl radical and the metal surface. Although corrosion proceeds rapidly in closed spaces, when the corrosives enclosed are exhausted, the reaction stops. Therefore, the corrosive materials from the outside are shut out. The same phenomenon might be expected when the two organic radicals of C_9 inhibitors that are not connected to each other are present. However, they do not give good protection. Therefore, there are spaces through which the corrosive agents can penetrate.

Continuing his detailed study of the effect of the structure on the inhibition properties of amine corrosion inhibitors, Fujii and his coworkers[121] found that "cis" inhibitors (consisting of secondary oleylamine and oleic acid) are more effective than "trans" inhibitors (consisting of secondary elaidylamine and claidic acid). As an interesting contrast, however, the trans inhibitors are the most effective as additives to rust preventive oils, because of preferential wetting of the metal surface by the oils containing the trans inhibitors.

Nathan[114] found that aromatic amines which contained more than one aryl group attached to the nitrogen are adsorbed only weakly and are poor corrosion inhibitors. The presence of multiple polar groups does not result in substantially greater adsorption as shown by adsorption isotherm data. Eisler[122] studied the effects of several variables on the adsorption of polar organic rust inhibitors. He found that in the case of stearic acid, the amount adsorbed increased with time of immersion, with agitation, and with increased stearic acid concentration. The amount adsorbed was surprisingly found to be independent of temperature.

As the third step in the protective mechanism, the hydrophobic branches of the inhibitor molecules bring along with them an oil layer which covers the entire surface and presents the external barrier to water in this sandwich mechanism. Many experiments by this author and others show that the degree of effectiveness of organic long-chain nitrogen inhibitors is markedly improved by the presence of sufficient oil (either in the system to be protected or by addition with the inhibitor) to form this protective layer. Bartonicek[123] shows that this barrier mechanism by the oil is very small in the absence of inhibitors. The so-called soluble oils that are effective inhibitors in all-water systems probably function because one component (the minor one also known as the emulsifier) functions as the inhibitor and the major component which consists of oil forms the protective barrier on the metal surface.

It is apparent that there is no simple mechanism available to explain the effectiveness of the polar nitrogenous inhibitors. Such factors as physical adsorption, chemisorption, cathodic and anodic polarization, molecular structure, and preferential oil wetting all enter the picture. The over-all effect, however, appears to be a series of layers consisting of the metal surface, the polar group, the hydrophobic organic chain, and finally the oil film.

Sulfur Derivatives

Inhibition by thiourea derivatives and by the reaction products of sulfur compounds with long-chain nitrogenous compounds was already mentioned. Fisher[124] patented a series of *thiourea derivatives* with their carbamyl nitrogen atoms attached to long chains containing amide groups. Nathan[125] used corrosion inhibitors that are symmetrical thiourea derivatives having the general formula $(RNH)_2CS$. Examples of successful inhibitors of this type include 1,3-dihexylthiourea and 1,3-diphenylthiourea. Pullig[126] describes inhibitors that are symmetrical disubstituted thioureas, such as $(2\text{-}PhC_2H_4NH)_2C:S$. An interesting inhibitor containing sulfur and used in gas condensate wells was patented by Treseder and Raifsnider,[127] who used an alkyl ammonium sulfate sludge prepared by addition of concentrated sulfuric acid to petroleum fractions, addition of a metallic nitrite, and heating.

A major category of corrosion inhibitors based on sulfur and used for downhole applications is that of the *sulfonates*. Petroleum sulfonates can be made by the controlled reaction between sulfuric acid and selected petroleum distillates. The oil-soluble sulfonates are removed from the oil by suitable extraction after neutralization and are then concentrated and purified. Those sulfonates with molecular weights above 400 are generally categorized as the oleophilic ones and have structures like $(C_nH_{(2n-10)}SO_3)_xA$ where A can be either a metal of valence x or else an amine.

Several examples of inhibition by sulfonates are cited in literature. Baker, Singleterry, and Solomon[128] evaluate neutral dinonylnaphthalene sulfonates and show their effectiveness, with special emphasis on the barium salts. When the test solutions are acidic, then basic Ba(OH)-dinonylnaphthalene sulfonate is an effective inhibitor, whereas neutral soaps are not. Wisherd[129] used an oil-soluble, ammonia-neutralized, sulfonated mixture of polyalkylated benzenes. The raw material is the bottom from the distillation of monododecylbenzene and is mainly didodecylbenzene. The inhibitor is easily handled, nontoxic, and readily miscible with kerosene. It is effective at dosages of from 0.4 to 40 parts per 1,000 barrels of combined crude and brines. Kronig, Seeles, and Burmeister[130] describe the manufacture of effective inhibitors by sulfonating naphthenic spindle oils and reacting them with metaphosphoric acid. They also add sodium diisopropylnaphthalenesulfonate.

A commonly used sulfonate is a neutralized mahogany petroleum sulfonic acid. Fisch[131] describes the preparation of highly effective inhibitors by fractionating commercial mahogany sulfonates. He found that the inhibition effectiveness of the fraction with the highest equivalent weight (548 calculated as the sodium salt) is about three times that of the original unfractionated material. All the fractions are alkylated benzene sulfonates, but vary in size and possibly configuration of alkyl side chains and in number of naphthenic rings. Snider[132] made an inhibitor by combining 0.1 to 10 parts of HCHO with 1 part of either neutralized mahogany petroleum sulfonic acid or sulfonated dodecylbenzene bottoms and found it to be effective at dosages of 1 to 50 pints of inhibitor per 1,000 barrels of well fluid.

At this point, it might also be mentioned that some oils have *naturally occurring inhibitors* in them. For example, Kalish, Rowe, and Rogers[133] state that some sour brines contain sulfur compounds which serve as inhibitors and that there is evidence that some of these compounds may be alkyl mercaptans and sulfides. In laboratory experiments designed to verify this, they found that a number of straight-chain and aromatic mercaptans had inhibitive properties at a concentration of 12.5 ppm.

In this connection, a project was conducted at the University of Texas[2] to determine which polar acids might be present in those wells that show relatively little corrosion. A number of straight-chain organic acids were identified in both water and oil phases, with those in the oil phase generally being of higher molecular weight. Phenols and ketones were also found. In earlier work, naphthenic acids having 6 to 20 carbon atoms were also found. Most observers believe, however, that the natural inhibitors are primarily the sulfides, and the bulk of the experimental and theoretical evidence appears to support that view.

The effectiveness of these naturally occurring materials and especially the *polysulfides* can well tie in with observations that were made by Karagounis and Rels.[134] In studying the protective action of certain inhibitors against acidic attack, they found that a lattice-like polysulfide of high protective action against acid corrosion develops. It is not an uncommon occurrence in the field for polysulfides to be added to oil wells or for chemicals to be added which will cause the formation of polysulfides *in situ.*

The protective mechanism of the sulfonates is the subject of a number of studies. Van Hong *et al.*[135] show that the adsorption of calcium dinonylnaphthalene sulfonate increases with the relative humidity, leading to the conclusion that water is necessary for good adsorption. On that basis, they conclude that the calcium sulfonate adsorption took place as chemisorption rather than as physical adsorption. The work previously referred to by Baker, Singleterry, and Solomon[128] proposes a mechanism of inhibition for sulfonates which involves the sequestration of corrosive acid by micelles in the oil.

Roebuck *et al.*[136] propose a protective mechanism for sulfonate inhibitors which is similar to that proposed earlier in this chapter for the long-chain nitrogenous compounds. They point out that the sulfonates are dependent upon oil for their effectiveness and postulate that the polar head of the inhibitor is attached to the metal surface, the lipophyllic chain extends out from the surface, and a layer of occluded oil is attached to the end of the inhibitor chain. In the course of this work, they found that effective sulfonate corrosion inhibitors are those made from sulfonic acids in the molecular weight range of 300 to 470; effective inhibition with certain amine sulfonates is obtained at concentrations as low as 5 ppm; the solubility in oil or the dispersibility in water can be controlled by selection of the proper molecular weight sulfonic acid and amine; and the reaction products of amine and polydodecylbenzene sulfonic acid are much more effective as inhibitors than either the amine or the acid alone.

Water-Displacing Agents

The effectiveness of corrosion inhibitors can often be improved by incorporating water-displacing agents in the inhibitor formulations. These agents can also have some beneficial action themselves. Thus,

Rudel and Seitz,[137] for example, used esters of glycols or polyglycols or monoethers thereof as the water-displacing agents. Stedt and Dolph[138] suggest mixtures of esters of di- or polyhydric esters with triethanolamine salts or organic acids as corrosion inhibitors. Caldwell and Lytle[139] report that polyalkylene glycols themselves are good inhibitors for producing wells. They use 0.01 to 0.2 per cent by volume of a polyalkylene glycol having a molecular weight in the range of 300 to 1,500. Examples are given of the results obtained with polyethylene glycol, polypropylene glycol, and Pluronic inhibitors.

Vapor Zone Corrosion Inhibition

Corrosion in the vapor zone of steel oil well casing and tubing and oil and gas storage vessels of crudes as well as prevention of corrosion in the annuli of oil and gas wells is prevented by somewhat different techniques. Here the approach is that of using a *volatile vapor phase inhibitor*. Lytle[140] accomplishes this technique by injection of mixtures of urea and urease into the liquid phase. The urease hydrolyzes the urea to form NH_3 and CO_2, the former preventing corrosion in the vapor phase. Marsh[141] uses solutions of NH_4NO_3 or NH_4CNS which release NH_3 slowly. Barrett and Jones[142] show that the addition of di- or triethylamine or methylpropylamine to conventional inhibitor compositions, such as a Duomeen-T - Alox 425 mixture, gives the desired protection in both the liquid and gas phases.

Inhibitor Application Techniques

The technique of inhibitor application is of considerable importance in protecting producing wells. It is desirable to apply a protective film as rapidly as possible since otherwise (1) considerable corrosion product can form which interferes with subsequent film formation and (2) if only part of the surface is protected, then attack on the balance can be intensified and pitting occurs. For this reason, initial well treatment should be with a large dosage of inhibitor. Once the film is in place, the inhibitor dosage can be cut down to a much lower level which is necessary to keep the film in repair.

Chemical inhibitors are of value in protecting subsurface equipment only to the extent that they can be placed where they are needed in the quantity and frequency required to do the job. Shock and Sudbury[15] point out that in gas-lift wells, a considerable height of water column is present in the annular space and that any successful inhibition method must be so designed that the inhibitor will mix in the water and fall through it to the bottom. Oil-soluble and emulsifiable inhibitors are unsatisfactory because they are blown through the gas-lift valves and never reach the bottom of the tubing. Elliott[143] and Bertness[17] discuss the design of inhibitor injection systems, the stick method, automatic slugging, continuous annulus injection, and inhibitor injection systems in gas lift wells[143] and in pumping wells.[17] The use of weighting agents to get the inhibitor down to the bottom of the well is a common technique. Riggs and Shock[144] describe a corrosion inhibitor heavy enough to sink through the liquid column in an oil well. The inhibitor formulation consists of an oil-soluble inhibitor, an immiscibilizing agent, and a mutual solvent, the mixture having a specific gravity of 1.1. A typical example consists of a dimeric acid (polymerized linoleic acid), polyethoxylated sorbitan monooleate, and $C_6H_4Cl_2$.

Most inhibitor manufacturers today sell corrosion-inhibiting compositions in the form of sticks as well as liquids. The sticks contain essentially the same inhibiting agents but have materials added to them which allow the sticks to fall to the bottom of the well and dissolve at a slow uniform rate. The danger of making the stick too insoluble must also be avoided. Nathan[145] describes such a stick whose inhibitor portion consisted of a symmetrical thiourea, such as bis(2-phenylethyl)-thiourea, and the binder was a solid amorphous synthetic wax, such as a high-molecular-weight polyethylene glycol fatty acid ester or a primary aliphatic amide with 6 to 18 carbon atoms.

Jones[146] uses a binder made from polyethylene polyterpene (Piccolyte S-125) melted with magnesium stearate. He adds monoethanol stearamide to act as a coupling agent between the binder and the inhibitor, which in this case is an aliphatic amine-carboxylic acid salt. To the mixture, he then adds a water-soluble nonionic emulsifying agent, such as polyethoxylated dodecyl alcohol, which acts as a dispersion agent for the complex in an aqueous solution. Finally, a weighting agent such as barytes is also added. A slurry of all these materials is then poured into a mold and converted to stick form.

It is evident that a great deal of trouble is taken to make certain that the inhibitor is available at the locations at which it is needed. Dramatic field results are obtained at wells which were not previously susceptible to protection by liquid inhibitors. Substitution of the same inhibitor in stick form resulted in a sharp reduction of well corrosion and a considerable savings in maintenance costs.

Shock and Woods[147] made solid weighted oil well inhibitors from barium oxide or sodium tripolyphosphate as weighting materials and polydodecyl benzene as the corrosion inhibitor and dispersant. This material can also have scale or sludge dispersing properties if needed. Caldwell and Lytle[148] made the interesting observation that much better protection can be obtained from a paraffin-oil-inhibitor mixture than from the same inhibitor in the absence of the paraffin. They relate this observation to the fact that the protective film on the metal surface is several times heavier and thicker in the presence of paraffin. In field tests, rapid injection of barrels of this mixture onto the tubing case annulus gave complete coverage of the outside of the tubing in the gas space, and the film remained intact for at least six months. It is probable that the inside of the casing in the gas space was also completely covered by the inhibitor.

Even the weighted inhibitor sticks do not always reach the bottom and some operators have resorted to pushing these sticks to the bottom with wire tools.[149] Some are trying bottom-hole injection, but because of gelling of diluents in wells with high bottom-hole temperatures problems are being encountered.

Another factor in connection with inhibitor application that can lead to difficulties is pointed out by Fincher.[150] He found that treatment of gas condensate wells with organic polar inhibitors frequently results in emulsification of the condensate with the small amount of connate water usually produced. This emulsification interferes with operations to such an extent that continued use of inhibitors would be impractical. It is necessary to utilize inhibitors which do not produce this emulsification.

A recent inhibitor application technique that has gained much favor in the field is known as the Inhibitor Squeeze Technique. In this method, a drum or more of an inhibitor formulation is squeezed into the formation in the hope that the chemical will adsorb upon the formation sand and gradually desorb. This process could lead to continuous formation feedbacks of anywhere from three months to one year each time a well is squeezed. An "overflush" of oil of a few to more than 50 barrels is used to insure that the inhibitor is moved back into the formation.[29] A primary advantage of this method is that it successfully treats many well types which are packed off or have high fluid levels and are difficult to treat by other methods. In addition, the frequency of treatment is reduced drastically and a steady supply of inhibitor is assured over a long period of time. This technique requires less manpower and renders the treating procedure more foolproof. The entire length of tubing is treated, treating and shut-in times are reduced, and wear and tear on equipment is minimized. These advantages are especially important in off-shore applications.[151]

This technique is not without its disadvantages. The economic risk is considerable. Costs are high and the operator runs a risk of losing a great deal of money at one time if something goes wrong. It is not always possible to obtain the desired life from a squeeze. Probably the major concern is the possibility of the development of emulsion-blocks or reverse-wetting in the formation which would decrease well production rates. This problem has not been as formidable as first anticipated although tight formations are still considered risky.[29] The plugging effects of amine-derived inhibitors on water-wet cores are directly proportional to the molecular weight of the amines.

Squeeze treatments can be completed in relatively short time periods. For example, 2 to 4 hr are reported as sufficient to treat a 10,000-ft gas condensate well at a pressure of 5,000 psi.[151] In that well, desorbed inhibitor gave protection for four to six months.

The squeeze technique is generally continued indefinitely, and the consensus of opinion is that the second squeeze and the succeeding treatments all give a longer treatment life than the first squeeze.[152] Possibly part of the chemical used in the first squeeze is trapped in the formation and cannot return to the well bore. During the treating process, some chemical could be squeezed or absorbed into low-permeability pores and fractures where the fluid does not pass while the well is working. These pores are saturated during the first treatment. The initial treatment can also alter the wettability of the formation to enhance adsorption on subsequent treatments. Poetker and Stone[153] describe how treating costs in the Placedo Field of Victoria County, Texas, were cut 49.9 per cent and the treating efficiency was increased 16.9 per cent.

Foaming Agents

Although the use of foaming agents in gas and oil wells is not directly related to the corrosion problem, a short discussion is included because these materials also contribute to the effective life of the producing well and can help to make the job of the corrosion inhibitors easier. Many gas wells suffer partial or complete loss of production because of the accumulation of water in the well bore. Whether this "drowning" results from casing leakage, condensation, or actual water production is immaterial since the result is the same in each case. Other problems which lend themselves to a cure by the use of foaming agents are the deposits of heavy oils on the sand face, casing, and tubing, deposits of scale, clays, muds, and solid particles on the well bore and pipe string, and brine accumulations in deep wells.

The principle involved in the use of foaming agents to cure these problems is that of the gas lift. The column of water is gradually lifted in the form of a light foam column by gas pressures too low to lift the water column itself. The foam also acts as a flotation medium allowing the removal of solid particles from the well bore. Two types of foam causing agents are proposed. Lissant and Samuelson[154] suggest the use of a calcium hydride unit that creates a gas-lift effect at the bottom of the well. The calcium hydride reacts with water to form calcium hydroxide and hydrogen, which lightens the entire fluid column as it makes its way to the surface. The aerated column then has a sufficiently reduced hydrostatic head to permit the well to flow again.

The other approach is the more conventional one of using surfactants. Dunning and Eakin[155] found polyoxyethylated alkyl phenols to be especially effective. They state that Triton X-102, a nonionic polyoxyethylated detergent was successful in extensive field tests. Lissant and Samuelson[154] advocate the use of foaming sticks. By making solids of the surfactants that Dunning and Eakin recommend, they were able to get them down to the proper locations in the wells and found that one stick per barrel of fluid to be lifted is a minimum figure.

REFERENCES

1. Division of Production, American Petroleum Institute. *Corrosion of Oil- and Gas-Well Equipment* (Dallas: American Petroleum Institute, 1958). Material from the book paraphrased by courtesy of the American Petroleum Institute.

2. Natural Gasoline Association of America. *Condensate Well Corrosion* (Tulsa: Natural Gasoline Association of America, 1953).

3. Lee, G. A., and Haines, G. A. Corrosion problems of the petroleum industry. *S.C.I. Monograph No. 10,* 7–29, 1960.

4. Stanton, J. P. A new guide to corrosion control in oil and gas wells. *N.A.C.E. T-1a Meeting,* Los Angeles, California, July 1959.

5. Cavallaro, L. The use of corrosion inhibitors in the petroleum industry. *Corrosion et Anticorrosion,* **7,** 417–33, Dec. 1959.

6. Uehara, I. Studies of corrosion control of pumping wells. *Corrosion Eng.,* **4,** No. 6, 266–9, Dec. 1955.

7. Greenwell, H. E. Studies on water-dependent corrosion in sweet oil wells. *Corrosion,* **9,** No. 9, 307–12, Sept. 1953. Table 5-1 reprinted by courtesy of CORROSION.

8. Bilhartz, H. L. Sweet oil well corrosion. *World Oil,* **134,** 208–16, Apr. 1952.

9. Caldwell, J. A. Sour oil well corrosion. *Corrosion,* **8,** No. 8, 292–4, Aug. 1952.

10. Moore, S. C. Drill stem corrosion in West Texas. *Corrosion,* **9,** No. 4, 112–3, Apr. 1953.

11. N.A.C.E. Task Group T-1C-2. Report on "sweet" oil well corrosion. *Corrosion,* **13,** No. 11, 747t–9t, Nov. 1957.

12. N.A.C.E. Task Group T-1C-5. Status of downhole corrosion in the East Texas field. *Corrosion,* **13,** No. 11, 743–6t, Nov. 1957.

13. N.A.C.E. Committee T-1C. Sweet oil corrosion. *Corrosion,* **11,** No. 10, 61–3, Oct. 1955.

14. Shock, D. A. Research on the control of corrosion in natural gas wells. *Oil Gas J.,* **46,** No. 33, 53, Dec. 20, 1947.

15. Shock, D. A., and Sudbury, J. D. Corrosion control in gas-lift wells. *Corrosion,* **8,** No. 9, 296–9, Sept. 1952.

16. Bilhartz, H. L. How to predict and control sweet-oil-well corrosion. *Oil Gas J.,* **50,** 116–8, 151, 153, Apr. 21, 1952.

17. Bertness, T. A. Reduction of failures caused by corrosion in pumping wells. *Proc. Am. Pet. Inst.,* **37,** No. 4, 129–35, 1957.

18. Bregman, J. I. Comptes Rendus du Symposium European sur les Inhibiteurs de Corrosion. *Annali dell' Universita di Ferrara,* N.S., Sez. V., 549–72, 1961.

19. Blair, C. M., Jr. Some applications of organic corrosion inhibitors in the petroleum industry. *Corrosion,* **7,** No. 6, 189–95, June 1951.

20. Biehl, J. A., and Schnake, E. A. What Ohio Oil learned in 5 years of processing crude oil at low pH. *Oil Gas J.,* **57,** No. 23, 125–8, 1959.

21. Bradley, B. W. Pumping wells service costs cut by corrosion control. *World Oil,* **135,** No. 7, 214, Dec. 1952.

22. Clements, F. H., and Barrett, J. P. Drastic cuts in corrosion costs in sour crude field. *World Oil,* **135,** No. 5, 264, Oct. 1952.

23. Koger, W. C. How to reduce corrosion in production operations. *World Oil,* **141,** No. 1, 182–98, July 1955.

24. Bass, D. Preventing corrosion by crude: the use of surface-active agents. *Petroleum,* **20,** 139–42, Apr. 1957.

25. Blair, C. M., Jr. Organic corrosion prevention. *World Oil,* **131,** 159–60, 163–4, 166, Nov. 1950.

26. Harper, G. M. *Pet. Engr.,* 531–5, Nov. 1950.

27. Gross, W. F., and Andrews, H. W. Prevention of corrosion in sour wells with organic inhibitors. *Oil Gas J.,* Oct. 28, 1948.

28. McFaddin, D. E. H₂S and CO₂ corrosion of carbon steel in natural gas processing plants. *Oil Gas J.,* **50,** No. 32, 97–8, Dec. 13, 1951.

29. Stanton, J. A digest of the proceedings of the corrosion control short course. *The University of Oklahoma,* Mar. 31 to Apr. 2, 1959.

30. Case, L. C., and Riggin, D. M. Rid production equipment of costly scale and sludge. *Oil Gas J.,* **52,** No. 15, 98–102, 145, Aug. 17, 1953.

31. Standing, M. B. *Volumetric and Phase Behavior of Oil Field Hydrocarbon Systems* (New York: Reinhold Publishing Corporation, 1952).

32. Shock, D. A., and Sudbury, J. D. Prediction of corrosion in oil and gas wells. *World Oil,* **133,** 180–92, Oct. 1951.

33. Boies, D. B. A laboratory method for the evaluation of oil production corrosion inhibitors. *Corrosion,* **12,** No. 8, 371t–5t, Aug. 1956.

34. Negreev, V. F., Manakhoua, T. K., and Alekperova, R. Y. Corrosion inhibitors for oil well tubing. *Trudy Azerbaidzhan Nauch.-Issledouatel. Inst. po Dobyohe Nefti,* No. 6, 226–39, 1957.

35. Rogers, W. F., and Rowe, J. A., Jr. Corrosion effects of hydrogen sulfide and carbon dioxide in oil production. *Proc. Fourth World Petroleum Congress,* Rome, Sect. II, 479–99, 1955.

36. Negreev, V., and Balayan, A. Corrosion of steel in water, occurring below petroleum deposits. *Novosti Neftyanoi Tekh., Neftepromyslovoe Delo,* No. 6, 46–7, 1950.

37. Morton, B. B. Corrosion fatigue in oil well equipment. *World Oil,* **127,** No. 13, 156–8, Apr. 1948.

38. Balezin, S. A., and Nikol'skii, I. V. The development of hydrogen embrittlement of steels in aqueous hydrogen sulfide solutions. *J. App. Chem., U.S.S.R.,* **31,** No. 8, 1181–4, 1958.

39. Kemkhadze, V. S., and Balezin, S. A. The inhibiting action of aldehydes. *J. Gen. Chem.* (U.S.S.R.), **22,** 1848–55, 1952.

40. Walker, J. C. Preventing corrosion in oil wells. U.S. 1,873,084, Aug. 23, 1932.

41. Fariss, R. E. Prevention of corrosion of iron by aqueous brines. U.S. 2,695,876, Nov. 30, 1954.

42. Hackerman, N., and Hurd, R. M. Dichromate reduction rate at a steel surface in air free acetic acid solution. *J. Electrochem. Soc.,* **98,** No. 2, 51–6, 1951.

43. Menaul, P. D. Inhibiting corrosion by sulfur compounds. U.S. 2,700,652, Jan. 25, 1955.

44. Earlougher, R. C., and Love, W. W. Sequestering agents for prevention of scale deposition in oil wells. *J. Petrol. Tech.,* **9,** No. 4, 17–20, 1957.

45. Kipps, H. J. Inhibiting the formation of scale deposits. U.S. 2,890,175, June 9, 1959.

46. Core, C. D., and Jones, E. H. Composition for preventing deposition and corrosion in oil well equipment. U.S. 2,658,036, Nov. 3, 1953.

47. Rohrback, G. H., McCloud, D. M., and Scott, W. R. Corrosion inhibitors for oil wells. U.S. 2,635,996–2,636,000, Apr. 21, 1953; U.S. 2,684,332–2,684,333, July 20, 1954.

48. Frisius, E. N. Oil well corrosion inhibitors. U.S. 2,885,359, May 5, 1959.

49. Hill, P. W., and Davie, F. E. Corrosion treatment of pumping wells in California. *Calif. Oil World,* **47,** No. 11, 12–8, 1954.

50. Kraemer, K. *Iron Trade Ber.,* **14,** 841, 1928.

51. Chapel, E. L., Roetheli, B. E., and McCarthy, B. Y. The electrochemical action of inhibitors in the acid solution of steel and iron. *Ind. Eng. Chem.,* **20,** No. 6, 582–7, June 1928.

52. Bailey, K. C., quoted in Putilova, I. N., Balezin, S. A., and Barannic, V. P. *Metallic Corrosion Inhibitors* (New York: Pergamon Press, 1960), Ref. 23, p. 119.

53. Pfohl, F. W., and Gregory, V. P. Corrosion inhibitors. U.S. 2,736,658, Feb. 28, 1956.

54. Jones, L. W. Corrosion inhibitors, especially for oil wells. U.S. 2,840,525, June 24, 1958.

55. Jones, L. W. Corrosion inhibitors for oil wells. U.S. 2,840,584, June 24, 1958.

56. Lindberg, R. I. Corrosion-inhibiting compositions for oil wells. U.S. 2,882,227, Apr. 14, 1959.

57. Gunderson, L. O., and Kerst, H. Corrosion inhibitors for petroleum products. U.S. 2,902,447, Sept. 1, 1959.

58. Case, E. N. Oil-well corrosion inhibitors. U.S. 2,891,009, June 16, 1959.

59. Oxford, W. F., Jr. Corrosion protection of ferrous metals. U.S. 2,914,475, Nov. 24, 1959.

60. Hughes, W. B. Corrosion inhibitors for oil-brine mixtures. U.S. 2,891,909, June 23, 1959.

61. Jolly, S. E. Oil well fluids (sour). U.S. 2,920,040, Jan. 5, 1960.

62. Esso Research and Engr. Co. Petroleum-base corrosion-preventing compositions. Brit. 812,149, Apr. 22, 1959.

63. Andersen, D. L. Inhibiting the corrosion of steel in aqueous media. U.S. 2,926,108, Feb. 23, 1960.

64. Stromberg, V. L., and Hughes, W. B. Inhibitor for hydrocarbons. U.S. 2,944,969, July 12, 1960.

65. Titsworth, A. R., and Martin, E. C. Inhibitor for mineral oil. U.S. 2,935,389, Feb. 3, 1960.

66. Fujii, S., and Uehara, I. Corrosion-inhibiting treatment. Japan 1,259, Mar. 11, 1954.

67. Toekelt, W. G. Water-soluble corrosion inhibitors. U.S. 2,923,599, Feb. 2, 1960.

68. Prilleux, M. Corrosion inhibitors for crude oil or hydrocarbons containing water. Fr. 1,158,594, June 17, 1958.

69. Hughes, W. B. Down-hole inhibitor. U.S. 2,940,927, June 14, 1960.

70. Sterlin, A. Glyoxalidine salts of dicarboxylic acids as corrosion inhibitors for liquid hydrocarbons. U.S. 2,773,879, Dec. 11, 1956.

71. Lytle, M. L. Corrosion inhibition. U.S. 2,723,233, Nov. 8, 1955.

72. Hughes, W. B. Corrosion inhibitors for oil-brine mixtures. U.S. 2,724,695, Nov. 22, 1955.

73. Luvisi, G. W. Corrosion inhibitor for liquid hydrocarbons. U.S. 2,668,100, Feb. 2, 1954.

74. Hughes, W. B. Inhibiting corrosion of metals. U.S. 2,727,003, Dec. 13, 1955.

75. Riggs, O. L., Jr. Inhibition of corrosion by crude oil. U.S. 2,856,358, Oct. 14, 1958.

76. Petrolite Corp. Inhibitors—oil wells. Brit. 809,001, Feb. 18, 1959.

77. Hughes, W. B. Corrosion inhibitors for oil-brine mixtures. U.S. 2,895,961, July 21, 1959.

78. Hughes, W. B. Corrosion inhibitors for oil-well brine. U.S. 2,918,474, Dec. 22, 1959.

79. Hughes, W. B. Corrosion inhibitor. U.S. 2,877,179, Mar. 10, 1959.

80. Hughes, W. B. Inhibiting corrosion by oil-brine mixtures. U.S. 2,865,856, Dec. 23, 1958.

81. Hughes, W. B. The use of heterocyclic compounds as corrosion inhibitors. U.S. 2,851,415, Sept. 9, 1958.

82. Hughes, W. B. Inhibition of corrosion by petroleum-brine mixtures. U.S. 2,793,997, May 28, 1957.

83. Hughes, W. B. Corrosion inhibitor for gas and oil wells. U.S. 2,846,440, Aug. 5, 1958.

84. Westlund, R. A., Jr., and Rudel, H. W. U.S. 2,927,080, June 30, 1959.

85. Scott, W. R., Jr., and Garner, B. L. Corrosion inhibitor for ferrous metals. U.S. 2,785,126, Mar. 12, 1957.

86. Leboucher, B., and Prilleux, M. Corrosion inhibitors for crude oil or hydrocarbons and water. Fr. 1,133,393, Mar. 26, 1957.

87. Chesnel, J. Corrosion-inhibiting compounds. Fr. 1,151,170, Jan. 24, 1958.

88. Hughes, W. B. Inhibiting corrosion of metals. U.S. 2,832,735, Apr. 29, 1958.

89. Hughes, W. B. Inhibition of corrosion by oil-brine mixtures. U.S. 2,868,727, Jan. 13, 1959.

90. Butter, G. N. Substituted oxazoline corrosion inhibitors. U.S. 2,905,644, Sept. 22, 1959.

91. Hughes, W. B. Inhibition of iron corrosion in oil-field equipment. U.S. 2,924,571, Feb. 9, 1960.

92. Hughes, W. B. Oil-well corrosion inhibitors. U.S. 2,889,277, June 2, 1959.

93. Esso Standard Societe anon. francaise. Corrosion inhibitors for petroleum fractions. Brit. 798,620, July 23, 1958.

94. Prilleux, M., Esso Standard Societe anon. francaise. Corrosion-inhibiting additives. Fr. 1,150,430, Jan. 22, 1958.

95. Chiddix, M. E., Maxcy, W. J., and Sundberg, R. L. Corrosion inhibitors for oil-brine mixtures. U.S. 2,901,430, Aug. 25, 1959.

96. Lytle, M. L. Preventing corrosion in oil and gas wells. U.S. 2,659,693, Nov. 17, 1953.

97. Green, J. Corrosion inhibitor. U.S. 2,888,400, May 26, 1959.

98. American Chemical Products, Inc. Corrosion inhibitors for use in oil well brines. Brit. 826,536, Jan. 13, 1960.

99. Hughes, W. Inhibiting corrosion by oil-brine mixtures. U.S. 2,836,558, May 27, 1958.

100. Chenicek, J. A., and Thompson, R. B. Biguanide derivatives as corrosion inhibitors. U.S. 2,734,807, Feb. 14, 1956.

101. Fischer, P. W. Corrosion prevention in oil wells. U.S. 2,805,201, Sept. 3, 1957.

102. Keller, H. F., Jr. Corrosion prevention. U.S. 2,824,835, Feb. 25, 1958.

103. Keller, H. F., Jr. Corrosion prevention. U.S. 2,840,526, June 24, 1958.

104. Hughes, W. B., and Stromberg, V. L. Prevention of rust and corrosion. U.S. 2,888,401, May 26, 1959.

105. Hertel, O. Anticorrosive compounds. Ger. 1,024,773, Feb. 20, 1958.

106. Hackerman, N., and Sudbury, J. D. Effect of amines on the electrode potential of mild steel in tap water and acid solutions. *J. Electrochem. Soc.,* **97,** 109, 1950.

107. Hackerman, N., and Makrides, A. C. The action of polar organic inhibitors in the acid dissolution of metals. *Technical Report to the Office of Naval Research* [Contract NONR-375(02)], 171, Oct. 1953.

108. Antropov, L. I. Simultaneous action of organic inhibitors and cathodic polarization on the corrosion of iron. *J. Sci. Ind. Research* (India), **18B,** 314–9, 1959.

109. Schram, A. F., and Burns, L. Effect of amines on polarization of iron electrodes. *J. Electrochem. Soc.,* **105,** No. 5, 241–5, May 1958.

110. Breston, J. N. Corrosion control with organic inhibitors. *Ind. Eng. Chem.,* **44,** No. 8, 1755–61, 1952.

111. Hackerman, N., and Cook, E. I. Dual adsorption of polar organic compounds on steel (powder). *J. Phys. Chem.,* **56,** No. 4, 524–6, 1952.

112. Fujii, S., and Aramaki, K. Studies on amine-type corrosion inhibitors. XII. Adsorption ability of some functional groups. *Corrosion Eng.* (Japan), **7,** No. 3, 37–41, May 1958.

113. Daniel, S. G. The adsorption on metal surfaces of long chain polar compounds from hydrocarbon solutions. *Trans. Faraday Soc.,* **47,** 1345–59, Dec. 1951.

114. Nathan, C. C. Corrosion investigations related to adsorption studies. *Corrosion,* **12,** No. 4, 161t–8t, Apr. 1956.

115. Nathan, C. C. Studies on the inhibition by amines of the corrosion of iron by solutions of high acidity. *Corrosion,* **9,** No. 6, 199–202, June 1953.

116. Bigelow, W. C., Pickett, S. C., and Zisman, W. A. Oleophobic monolayers. I. Films adsorbed from solution in nonpolar liquids. *J. Coll. Sci.,* **1,** 513, 1946.

117. Aramaki, K., and Fujii, S. Studies on amine-type corrosion inhibitors. XVI. Inhibitors with branched hydrocarbon radicals. *Boshoku Gijutsu,* **9,** 6–9, 1960.

118. Fujii, S., and Aramaki, K. Amine-type corrosion inhibitors. XV. Inhibitors with branched hydrocarbon radicals. *Boshoku Gijutsu,* **8,** 143–6, 1959.

119. Fujii, S., and Aramaki, K. Studies on amine-type corrosion inhibitors. VIII. Secondary-amine-type inhibitors in aqueous solution. *Corrosion Eng.* (Japan), **5,** No. 2, 85–9, Apr. 1956.

120. Fujii, S., and Aramaki, K. Studies on amine-type corrosion inhibitors. X. *Corrosion Eng.* (Japan), **6,** 336–40, Nov. 1957.

121. Fujii, S., Ishida, H., and Miyazawa, T. Studies on amine-type corrosion inhibitors. "Cis"—or "trans"—inhibitors in polar or nonpolar media. *Corrosion Eng.* (Japan), **5,** No. 6, 307–11, Dec. 1956.

122. Eisler, S. L. Radiometric study of the adsorption characteristics of stearic acid. *Corrosion,* **9,** No. 3, 91–4, Mar. 1953.

123. Bartonicek, R. Corrosion studies. XVI. Effect of the rate of penetration of water vapor through oily films on the corrosion of steel protected by layers of oil. *Chem. listy,* **52,** 190–5, 1958.

124. Fisher, P. Corrosion inhibitors for oil-well effluents. U.S. 2,925,781, Feb. 23, 1960.

125. Nathan, C. C. Inhibition of corrosion by brines and acids. U.S. 2,799,648, July 16, 1957.

126. Pullig, T. R. Corrosion inhibitors for oil wells. U.S. 2,840,610, June 24, 1958.

127. Treseder, R. S., and Raifsnider, P. J. Corrosion prevention in gas-condensate wells. U.S. 2,734,029, Feb. 7, 1956.

128. Baker, H. R., Singleterry, C. R., and Solomon, E. M. Neutral and basic sulfonates—corrosion-inhibiting and acid-deactivating properties. *Ind. Eng. Chem.,* **46,** 1035–42, 1954.

129. Wisherd, T. G. Prevention of corrosion. U.S. 2,671,757, Mar. 9, 1954.

130. Kronig, W., Seeles, H., and Burmeister, H. Oil-soluble petroleum sulfonates. U.S. 2,650,198, Aug. 25, 1953.

131. Fisch, K. R. The preparation of highly effective rust inhibitors by fractionation of mahogany sulfonates. *Frankford Arsenal, U.S. Army Ordnance Corps. (PB 131231),* Mar. 1957.

132. Snider, F.M. Oil-well corrosion inhibitor. U.S. 2,882,226, Apr. 14, 1959.

133. Kalish, P. J., Rowe, J. A., Jr., and Rogers, W. F. Laboratory apparatus for

studying oil well subsurface corrosion rates and some results. *Corrosion,* **9,** No. 1, 25–33, Jan. 1953.

134. Karagounis, G., and Rels, H. Z. The mechanism of action of corrosion inhibitors. The permeability of molecular layers for hydrogen ions. *Elektrochem.,* **62,** No. 8, 865–70, 1958.

135. Hong, V., Eisler, S. L., Bootzin, D., and Harrison, A. Radiometric study of the adsorption characteristics of a calcium sulfonate rust inhibitor. *Corrosion,* **10,** 343–8, Oct. 1954.

136. Roebuck, A. H., Gant, P. L., Riggs, O. L., and Sudbury, J. D. Corrosion and adsorption studies using sulfonate inhibitors. *Corrosion,* **13,** No. 11, 733t–8t, Nov. 1957.

137. Rudel, H. W., and Seitz, W. Corrosion inhibitors containing water-displacing agents. U.S. 2,911,309, Nov. 3, 1959.

138. Stedt, T. P. G., and Dolph, A. A. H. Rust-preventive compositions. Swed. 169,110, Oct. 27, 1959.

139. Caldwell, J. A., and Lytle, M. L. Inhibitors for corrosion by petroleum-well fluids. U.S. 2,799,649, July 16, 1957.

140. Lytle, M. L. Corrosion inhibitor for ferrous metals. U.S. 2,721,175, Oct. 18, 1955.

141. Marsh, G. A. Decreasing vapor-zone corrosion of containers for sour crude oil. U.S. 2,755,166, July 17, 1956.

142. Barrett, J. P., and Jones, L. W. Vapor-corrosion inhibitor for oil-well casing and tubing. U.S. 2,889,276, June 2, 1959.

143. Elliott, D. J. Mechanical aspects of corrosion inhibitor injection. *World Oil,* **135,** No. 6, 190–2, 154, Nov. 1952.

144. Riggs, O. L., and Shock, D. A. Oil-well-corrosion inhibitor. U.S. 2,822,330, Feb. 4, 1958.

145. Nathan, C. C. Stick-type corrosion inhibitors for oil wells. U.S. 2,805,202, Sept. 3, 1957.

146. Jones, L. W. Solid corrosion inhibitor for oil- and gas-processing equipment. U.S. 2,833,712, May 6, 1958.

147. Shock, D. A., and Woods, W. W. Corrosion inhibitor for oil wells. U.S. 2,853,452, Sept. 23, 1958.

148. Caldwell, J. A., and Lytle, M. L. Internal casing corrosion for sour oil wells. *Corrosion,* **12,** No. 2, 67t–70t, Feb. 1956.

149. Greenwell, H. E. Corrosion mitigation knowledge in sweet oil wells. *Corrosion,* **11,** No. 10, 61–3, Oct. 1955.

150. Fincher, D. R. Inhibitors checked at wellhead. *World Oil,* **139,** No. 7, 200, 202–3, Dec. 1954.

151. Poetker, R. H., Brock, P. C., and Huckleberry, S. A. *Pet. Engr.,* Dec. 1957.

152. Smith, R. L. Corrosion checked in West Texas by inhibitor squeeze. *Oil Gas J.,* **57,** No. 43, 117–20, 124–6, Oct. 1959.

153. Poetker, R. H., and Stone, J. D. Squeezing inhibitor into formation. *Pet. Engr.,* **28,** B29–34, May 1956.

154. Lissant, R., and Samuelson, G. J. Chemical application helps unload oil, gas wells. *Oil Gas J.,* **58,** 124–7, June 1960.

155. Dunning, H. N., and Eakin, J. L. Foaming agents are low cost treatment for tired gassers. *Oil Gas J.,* **57,** No. 6, 108–10, Feb. 1959.

6

Petroleum— Secondary Recovery

The use of water flooding for recovery of oil after primary production techniques are exhausted is now widespread. This procedure is dependent upon additives, especially bactericides and corrosion inhibitors, to a very great extent for its successful use. Unlike most of the other problems treated in this book, the corrosion is not especially harmful *per se,* but it is undesirable because it plugs sand formations, thus requiring excessive pressures for successful operation. In time this obstacle can shut down the secondary recovery system. The microbiological aspects are extremely important as much of the corrosion can be traced directly to sulfate-reducing bacteria.

In this chapter, corrosion, bacteria, and scaling are the main concern. The latter two have a direct influence on corrosion and are therefore examined. There are a number of other additives used in secondary production. Most of them are applied to ease the flow through the formation and to prevent water-locking. The additives which change interfacial tension, for example, are of utmost importance. Materials for this purpose are not considered in this book because they represent a problem completely separate from that of corrosion. For more information on this subject, the reader is referred to the magazine *Producers Monthly.*

LITERATURE

Although the problem of water flooding is a major one and is the subject of a major industrial effort, the technical literature has failed to keep pace with it. A great deal of the knowledge in this field rests with the operators or the treatment manufacturers and is not readily available in the open literature. This particular industrial process now appears to have reached the point where a number of good review articles or books dealing with the subject would be appropriate.

A number of reports dealing with conditioning of waters at specific water-flooding locations are available. Powell describes water flooding of oil sands in various places in Kansas[1, 2] and Oklahoma.[3] Jones[4, 5] discusses corrosion-control practices in the Wilmington (California) flood, while Sudbury *et al.*[6] report on the conditioning of Pacific Ocean water for water-flood injection purposes. Geiman[7] discusses the general subject of the use of sea water for secondary recovery, and Kwaciszewska and Szedaj[8] describe the conditioning of Polish water for water flooding. Doscher and Tuttle[9] discuss the preparation of a sour brine for sub-surface injection, while Wright[10] studies water quality control for subsurface injection.

The battle against corrosion in water flooding is described by Prange,[11] while Robinson[12] presents a discussion of the application of organic inhibitors for this purpose. Amstutz[13] reports on the detection of corrosion, its causes, and control measures.

Two good descriptions of microbiological problems in water-flooding operations are available. One is the book by Beerstecher[14] entitled *Petroleum Microbiology* and the other is a review by Wolfson[15] entitled "Microbiology in Secondary Recovery Systems." The problem of incompatible waters and their plugging effect in oil-well sands is presented by Bernard[16] and in an article in an English journal[17] which describes work on this subject that was conducted at the West Virginia School of Mines. Earlougher and Love[18] discuss methods of reducing production losses caused by precipitation of insoluble materials from native or injected brines. There are a considerable number of papers published on wettability and displacement of water in oil-bearing sands, but these are not reported here since this subject is only mentioned very briefly in this chapter.

ECONOMICS

In considering the economics of this problem, there are really two different phases one must consider: (1) the economics of the secondary recovery process itself and (2) the economics involved in the use of additives to this process. An excellent article on the former subject was written by Torrey[19] in a recent issue of *Producers Monthly*. He points out that the economic opportunities for secondary recovery are sometimes more attractive than they are for development of primary production. This is because of the increasing cost of finding new fields and developing them. He cites a total cost of $2.96 per barrel of primary production crude oil in 1959. This figure includes $1.40 for finding it. By contrast, the figure in several areas of the United States for producing and developing secondary recovery oil in recent years is $1.50 per barrel. He names the following factors as determining the economics of individual secondary recovery operations:

1. Availability or cost of the prospect.
2. Probable oil recovery.
3. Depth.
4. Demand and price for crude oil.
5. Condition of producing equipment.
6. Availability of gas and water.
7. Availability and cost of fuel and electric power.
8. Crude oil transportation facilities.
9. Location and size of prospect or property.
10. Existing lease terms.
11. Availability and cost of labor and field services.[19]

Because of the large volumes of water involved in secondary recovery, the unit cost of treatment per barrel of water injected must be very small. Frequently it is cheaper to operate without any water treatment than it is with water treatment. The major reason for treating the water is to prevent plugging of the formation. Corrosion which does not lead to plugging can often be tolerated without the use of inhibitors if the replacement costs are low or if the equipment will outlast the life of the flood.

A number of cost figures are cited in literature for specific systems. Amstutz[13] describes the use of corrosion inhibitors in a system whose dissolved solids content is 125,000 mg/liter. Reduction of the corrosion rate from 10.4 mpy to less than 0.5 mpy was accomplished at a cost of only 0.4 mils per barrel of water. Robinson[12] quotes the treating costs at inhibitor dosages of 10 to 15 ppm to be from 0.8 to 1.2 mils per barrel of injected water, ignoring the cost of any initial slugging required at the outset of the treatment. Jones[4] discusses the corrosion-control practices at the Wilmington, California, water flood and states that the inhibitor which was used at a concentration of 20 ppm gave an approximate treating cost of 1.55 mils per barrel of injected water.

The cost of other additives such as bactericides or scale preventives must also be taken into consideration. Generally, the total cost of all the water-treatment additives should not come to more than 1.0 to 1.5 mils per barrel of produced water. Any increase in the cost of one additive should be offset by a reduction in the cost of the others.

THE PROBLEM

The use of secondary recovery, or water flooding, as it is more commonly known, to recover additional oil after the pumping well is exhausted has increased manifoldly in the United States during the past ten years. It is estimated that if the primary pumping well produces one third of the available oil, then water flooding produces another one third. As much as 30 years may be added to the life of a well by shifting over to a water-flooding system.

Secondary-recovery methods were first employed in the older fields of the Eastern states. Today, at least one quarter of all the oil produced in Pennsylvania is the result of secondary-recovery operations.[19] In 1959, 62.6 per cent of all Illinois oil production came from water-flooding operations. In the same year, approximately one million barrels per day of oil was produced in Texas as a result of some form or combination of fluid injection. It thus becomes apparent that water flooding has become a major process in oil recovery, and it will increase rapidly with time as the recovery of oil by primary production drops off because of the depletion of oil available by that technique.

The nature of the secondary-recovery operation can be described as forcing water under pressure back down into the ground in a number of wells in a fixed pattern in order to force out the oil through a central well. This technique involves permeation of water through the formations and sets up a different treatment problem than in primary production. As a rule, the formations are fine-grained, tightly packed sands, which contain residual oil remaining after the primary phase of production is exhausted. The mechanics of flooding involves the formation of an oil bank ahead of the advancing water and its removal through the producing well. The key to the process is the prevention of the formations from becoming plugged with anything: corrosion product, bacteria, precipitated compounds, or turbidity in the water. This prevention would increase the needed applied pressure, and eventually a point would be reached when the system would become inoperable. Obviously, the economic aspects of corrosion are secondary here to the necessity of avoiding the creation of corrosion products that might plug the formation.

The source of the injection water is invariably the fluid that has been produced at the well. This fact is generally true because of (1) the economics, (2) the arid nature of the oil‚producing areas, and (3) the waste disposal problem. Consequently, this fluid is generally highly corrosive because it has a very high salt content, it may contain small amounts of oil, and bacteria of many types (especially sulfate reducers) as well as turbidity may be present. These contaminants can all lead to plugging of the formation by one mechanism or another. A brief analysis of each follows.

Precipitation Phenomena

In this category of materials which can plug the formation there are two major subgroups—turbidity and scale. *Turbidity* is defined as particulate or colloidal matter already present in the water before it is injected downhole and which gradually plugs the formation. *Scale* is defined as the plugging material which is formed during the course of the injection and then precipitates on or in the formation. The problems involved in each case as well as the methods of solving them are quite different.

Turbidity can be present in the water for a variety of reasons. The water may have accumulated considerable colloidal material on standing in reservoirs open to air. Even clarification by conventional techniques can fail to remove all of this material. Particulate matter which may be present can include clay, silt, or sand. Failure of sand-control measures in the water supply well can be a cause of this. Another cause of particulate matter can be air leakage into a closed system which yields iron oxide. Still another source of trouble can be poor operation of wash tanks or their overloading in the case when the produced water is also the injection water.

Colloidal matter can penetrate the sand formation to some extent before it begins to build up in size by binding to other colloidal material and thus can become a source of severe plugging problems. The particulate matter, on the other hand, generally settles out on the face of the formation and acts as a filter. Its plugging action is a function of the average particle size and the degree to which close-packing can take place.

Scaling can result either in the case of water which is injected back into the formation from which it has been produced or else as a result of the incompatibility of the foreign-injected water with the native-formation water. The scales are generally either carbonates or sulfates, although iron oxides or sulfides can also be placed in this category. In the case of the carbonate scales, the cation is invariably calcium, while the most common sulfates are barium, strontium, or calcium. Calcium carbonate occurs frequently in the case of the injected producing-water and can be caused by changes in the chemical equilibrium between carbonate, bicarbonate, and carbon dioxide. Temperature changes are the most common causative agents, although pressure and turbulence can also contribute. Bernard[20] in a laboratory investigation found that up to 60 ppm of calcium carbonate supersaturation could be carried without plugging injection wells in a floodwater entering the reservoir in the temperature range of 80 to 130° F. Further discussion of calcium carbonate scaling is not given here since it is adequately treated elsewhere in this book.

Magnesium is generally not much of a problem in injected waters. A study by Krejci-Graf, Hecht, and Pasler[21] of the oil-field waters of the Vienna basin shows that the calcium to magnesium ratios of the waters are generally very high. Interestingly enough, they also found no relation between water analysis and the bionomic environment of reservoir rocks. While the sodium and chlorine contents increase with decreasing depth, oxygen and alkaline earths decrease.

There is considerable dispute over the role of incompatible waters in causing plugging of reservoir rocks. Laird and Cogbill[22] show that under certain reservoir conditions the effective permeability of the rock can be adversely affected by the intermingling of incompatible waters. Bernard,[16] on the other hand, presents both laboratory and field data to indicate that under normal conditions no plugging occurs when a floodwater is injected which is incompatible with the interstitial water. He cites instances where floodwaters containing hydrogen sulfide or sulfates were successfully injected into oil reservoirs containing ferrous and barium ions. The actual situation appears to lie in between these two extremes as was shown by a detailed study of this problem that was conducted at the West Virginia School of Mines.[17] Researchers conclude that the amount of plugging of oil reservoirs due to this cause is directly dependent on the permeability profile of the reservoir, and that, as a general rule, water that is incompatible with the interstitial water present in the formation should not be used for flooding operations. Their studies take into consideration various combinations of calcium, sodium, and iron sulfates, chlorides and sulfides, oxygen, flow rates, and core density.

Scales that result from incompatible waters are most often barium or calcium sulfates. The term incompatibility indicates that when the two layers are mixed, the solubility limit of the scaling material is considerably exceeded. The precipitation can occur anywhere in the system depending upon the saturation excess, the flow rate, the water composition, and temperature. Sulfate scales are very difficult to remove from the system, unlike carbonates which are readily susceptible to acid cleaning. Therefore extreme care should be taken to prevent their formation.

Wright[10] and Case and Riggin[23] discuss the problem of scaling in some detail. Wright presents techniques for determining particulate matter by a membrane filter technique. Case and Riggin outline procedures for the determination of scale components as well as preventive methods.

Bacterial Problems

A major cause of plugging and corrosion problems in secondary-recovery systems is the growth of bacteria. It is only in recent years that the extent of this problem was realized and that steps were taken to combat it. While the role of microorganisms is important in some of the other systems described, there is no system in which the corrosion problems can be affected by the same order of magnitude as is the case in water flooding.

There are a number of types of bacteria that are harmful to water-flooding systems. They include the following:

1. *Algae.*
2. *Slime formers.*
3. *Iron bacteria.*
4. *Sulfate reducers.*
5. *Other types.*

The sulfate reducers are by far the most important of these insofar as water-flood systems are concerned. Bacteria are discussed in this section in terms of their action in either causing plugging by their own masses or by corrosion enhancement.

There was considerable disagreement for the past several years as to whether bacteria directly contribute to plugging problems. Present-day evidence appears to indicate that this directness can be the case, although the frequency and the importance of this action are small compared to the corrosion contribution. Bacteria are found to cause plugging of injection wells due to their masses and to other materials which become entrapped in these masses and build up an impermeable barrier. In a similar manner, capacities of flow lines and pumps can be reduced because of mass build-up of the organisms or their by-products. Plugging because of masses of bacteria is obviously related to the size of bacteria, their degree of aggregation, and the nature of the pores in the formation.

Wolfson[15] states that the *algae* which cause trouble are invariably the fresh-water variety. No evidence exists to indicate that marine algae are responsible for any plugging problems. The primary trouble with algae comes in the open-type water floods since they require sunlight for growth. Blue-green algae are shown by several authors including Plummer *et al.*[24, 25] and Merkt[26] to produce harmful precipitates in oil field waters. Plummer states that the activity of these bacteria probably starts in the surface settling tanks and in many cases continues when water is forced into the subsurface formations. Merkt states that the algae are originally found in the bottom of drainage ditches, on the edges of tanks, and mixed with the water in the skimming pits. Their oscillating, threadlike filaments form thick gelatinous masses. They not only plug the formation themselves, but they are also characterized by their ability to precipitate calcium carbonate. Wolfson[15] points out that the algae form a blanket over a pond or tank, which makes conditions ideal for the growth of sulfate-reducing bacteria in the deeper regions of the water. The algae growths then often slough off and plug filters and pipes.

Slime formers that are troublesome in floodwaters are characterized by Wolfson as including Pseudomonas, Flavobacterium, Escherichia, Aerobacter, and Bacillus. Many of these grow in both fresh and salt waters. They grow in dense slimy masses on almost any surface to which they can attach themselves in the water-flood system. This growth causes trouble in three ways. First, the slimy masses can slough off and then start growing again elsewhere in the system or else block the sand face or clog the filters. Second, they can grow to such masses that they plug the water pipelines. Third, and perhaps most important, their dense masses prevent penetration by oxygen to the metal surfaces beneath them. The result is that an oxygen-free location is created which is especially suited for the growth of sulfate-reducing bacteria. The slime formers thus act as protective hosts for the sulfate reducers, and rapid growth of the latter proceeds together with intense local corrosion.

Merkt[26] found that spring waters from the area of the Patschki peat bog of Lee County, Texas, contained large numbers of *iron bacteria* which produce a flocculent gelatinous scum that causes plugging when this water is used for water-flooding purposes. The limestone cores reduce permeability by as much as 75 per cent. The plugging agent appears to be a coating of yellowish-brown oxide. Pringsheims[27] points out that this color can range from pure yellow to near black depending upon the type of iron bacteria present. The deposit formation occurs because the iron bacteria derive at least part of their energy by oxidizing ferrous ion to ferric ion, leading to the development of a sheath of iron hydroxide around themselves as they grow. The ferrous ion comes from the soluble iron in the system.[15] Some of the various types of iron bacteria also have the power of oxidizing manganese as well as iron, leading to a much darker-colored deposit than in the case of those which act on iron alone and give a cleaner yellow color.

Recent developments indicate that these bacteria can live with only trace amounts of oxygen present, and so they are found throughout a water-flood system rather than just in the supply system. When they build up in the system, they can cause clogging of pipes, filters, and screens and can slough off and cause the deposits which will block the formation. In addition, they can act as hosts for the growth of sulfate-reducing bacteria in a manner similar to that described earlier for the slime formers. This is an especially good relationship for them because the sulfate reducers help supply the ferrous ions that they need for their growth.

By far the major troublemaking bacteria in water-flooding systems are the *sulfate reducers* or Desulfovibrio. These bacteria are anaerobic in nature; that is to say, they require the absence of oxygen before rapid growth can take place. For this reason they can thrive beneath a coating of slime formers or iron bacteria which prevent oxygen from diffusing through them.

There is some debate as to the exact mechanism by which these bacteria cause corrosion. There is general agreement that the first step in the process is their utilization of the sulfate in the water and its conversion to sulfide which forms hydrogen sulfide by reaction with the hydrogen produced by the corroding metal surface. The sulfate reducers thus function as cathodic depolarizers, removing the accumulated hydrogen from the cathode and permitting the corrosion reaction to continue. This concept was suggested by Caldwell and Lytle,[28] Kuznetsov,[29] and Deuber.[30] The original suggestion was probably made by von Wolzogen Kuhr and Van der Vlugt[31] in 1934 when they postulated that at one state in the metabolism of these bacteria, hydrogen atoms on the cathodic areas are consumed, aiding in the reduction of inorganic sulfates to sulfides. Wormwell and Farrer[32] are not in complete agreement with this and suggest that both anodic and cathodic polarization are reduced. Their suggested reduction of anodic polarization can be justified by the next step in the process which is the production of iron sulfide, presumably by reaction between the hydrogen sulfide and the ferrous ion that is being produced at the anodic areas. An interesting observation in this regard was made by Adams and Farrer[33] who found that the presence of ferrous ions markedly increases the corrosion rate of cast iron by sulfate reducers. The corrosion product in the presence of a supply of ferrous ions tends to be loose, porous, and flocculent; while in the absence of ferrous ions, except for those being produced by the corroding metal, the corrosion product is hard, crystalline, and very adherent. This fact appears to support the concept of the reaction between hydrogen sulfide and ferrous ion. The reaction product would be adherent when the ferrous ion is derived from corrosion at the anodic areas on the metal, whereas it would be loose and at some distance from the metal when derived from iron already in solution.

The results of the action of the sulfate reducers are: (1) severe local attack at various points on the metal surfaces, (2) a blackening of the floodwater, (3) unpleasant odors, and (4) accumulation of finely divided iron sulfide product which sharply reduces the permeability of the formation. Beerstecher[14] cites cases of the reduction in permeability of a number of cores from different fields due to the action of sulfate reducers. The presence of reducers and their iron sulfide derivatives is widespread in secondary recovery systems, and the deleterious effect upon metal life and formation permeability was verified again and again.

A number of other types of bacteria are identified as troublemakers in water-flood systems. Many of these are of concern only if their count becomes too high. Wolfson[15] says that if their counts are allowed to run into the millions, then blocking of the sand face can occur due to sheer numbers. He also cites a new development—the role of Clostridia in causing sulfide corrosion in water-flooding systems and says that they were shown to be present in several water floods. These bacteria are putrefactive in nature. Some of them obtain their sulfur for the formation of hydrogen sulfide from proteins and amino acids while others can reduce sulfates. Presumably they can cause corrosion and iron sulfide formation in a manner similar to the sulfate reducers. Ulanovskii and Nikitina[34] also found that putrefactive bacteria enhance corrosion of steel in sea water and the effect of this species deserves more study.

Corrosion

The injection water used in water flooding is by its very nature highly corrosive. Most of the time it is a brine which was produced either in the same field or in other locations and then collected at one central spot. On occasion, fresh water can be used, but the location of secondary-recovery operations generally keeps fresh water to a minimum. A new source of injection water is being developed in the California area where ocean water is being used more frequently for this purpose.

The sodium chloride content of injected brines can vary anywhere from 1 to 25 per cent. Calcium, magnesium, strontium, barium, sulfates, carbonates, and other common ingredients of sea water are found. The dissolved gases that can be present are oxygen, hydrogen sulfide, and carbon dioxide. Their presence or absence affects the corrosive nature of the water very markedly. The general temperature range encountered is from 80 to 120° F. Flow rates are moderate with average values of several feet per second and very few stagnant locations. The metals that must be protected are invariably ferrous with mild steel being the most common one. The pH values are generally around the neutral point, although waters can be encountered where the presence of dissolved acidic gases results in fairly low values.

The high salinity is an obvious cause of corrosion. In those cases when oxygen is absent, however, the attack is much less than would be expected. The lack of oxygen slows down the corrosion process considerably. It was shown in the field that many corrosion inhibitors that are very effective at low dosages in its absence are relatively ineffective even at high dosages when oxygen is present in any appreciable amount. The ferrous hydroxide remains fairly close to the steel surface in the absence of an oxidizing agent and eventually provides a protective coating. A detailed discussion of this phenomenon is presented by Purins and Liepina[35] who point out that the initial cathodic process involves oxygen, but that with the depletion of the oxygen in the vicinity of the metal the mechanism changes. Surface films then become effective in retarding corrosion. These films form by electrophoretic migration of positively charged γ-FeO(OH) colloid to the cathodic areas and a discharge of the stabilizing charges there. As the salt content increases, the oxygen solubility decreases. In addition, the higher charges on the colloid particles result in better adherence of deposits to the metal surface.

The decrease in corrosivity of the brine with increasing sodium chloride thus can be attributed to the decrease in oxygen concentration at higher salt levels. If the oxygen level is kept constant at a low level as the salt content increases, however, there appears to be little or no change in the corrosion rate. Newman[36] presents data to substantiate this fact for water-flood systems.

As is pointed out by Evans,[37] the presence of calcium ions in the brine is probably a major reason that it is not as corrosive as plain sodium chloride solution. The calcium and perhaps the magnesium lay down a chalky film at the cathode and halt the attack. This film is presumably calcium carbonate, and the theory here is similar to that for cooling-tower systems where a minimum calcium content must be maintained for effective protection.

A major source of corrosion difficulties in water-flood brines is the presence of three types of dissolved gases: oxygen, hydrogen sulfide, and carbon dioxide. The effect of oxygen was already mentioned. Oxygen causes rapid pitting of iron pipes and clogging of injection wells and sand formations with ferric hydroxide. This gas can be present in concentrations anywhere from practically zero to approximately 8 mg/liter. Its concentration is determined by two factors: the concentration of the dissolved brine and the type of water-flood system.

The first factor was already discussed. The second factor affecting the oxygen content is the nature of the water-flood system. There are two general types: open and closed. In an open system the injected brine is allowed to come into contact with the air and thus absorbs a considerable amount of oxygen. This absorption occurs especially when fresh waters are used or if a common reservoir is maintained for produced brines prior to their use for injection purposes. In a closed system the produced brine, which has little or no oxygen in it, is generally reinjected without an opportunity to pick up oxygen from the atmosphere. Even in these closed systems oxygen can enter with the source water or else because of leaks at the packing glands on pump suctions, nonfunctioning gas blankets, or other accidental means.

Newman[36] studied the effect of dissolved oxygen and found that the corrosion rate increased in a linear manner with the dissolved oxygen content in the range of 0 to 6 mg/liter of dissolved oxygen. This work, which was done under our direction, was conducted in a 3 per cent brine which contained 10 mg/liter of dissolved hydrogen sulfide. An interesting effect is observed when a conventional water-flood corrosion inhibitor is added. Inhibition is quite good until an oxygen level of about 4 mg/liter is reached. Beyond this point inhibition drops off rapidly. At 100 mg/liter of inhibitor, the protection is 90 per cent at an oxygen level of 1 mg/liter or less; at an oxygen level of 5 mg/liter the protection is down to 55 per cent; as the oxygen level begins to approach saturation, little or no protection is obtained. While this pattern may not necessarily hold for all inhibitors, it does point out the importance of oxygen.

Raifsnider and Wachter[38] recently published the results of a study on the effects of small traces of oxygen on pitting corrosion in water-flood systems. They were able to trace serious pitting attack to these trace quantities of oxygen (less than 0.4 ppm). They postulate that in the flood system differential oxygen concentration cells are set up under scale and dirt deposits. Even at dissolved oxygen levels as low as 0.1 ppm, it is theorized that the large volumes of brine moving through the lines would make significant amounts of oxygen available to large cathodic areas surrounding the very small anodic spots. This fact would account for the widely distributed pitting experienced in water-flood injection lines.

The hydrogen sulfide concentration can vary anywhere from trace quantities to around 600 mg/liter in extremely sour areas. It causes the formation of fine grained scales, shallow pitting, and embrittlement and blistering in steel. The produced iron sulfide colors the water black and rapidly plugs the formation. Newman's work[36] in a 10 per cent brine shows that increasing the level of dissolved hydrogen sulfide increases the corrosion rate, but not at a very rapid rate insofar as general corrosion is concerned. However, the situation is quite different with regard to pitting attack. In a high hydrogen sulfide environment localized attack proceeds very rapidly and a Corrosometer strip probe is perforated in several places in a one-week test. The inhibitor dosage required at a high hydrogen sulfide level is five times as high as at a low level.

Carbon dioxide levels can vary in a manner similar to those of hydrogen sulfide. Here also, the gas concentration is closely related to the type of primary production which had gone on previously. The type of corrosion attributable to carbon dioxide consists of hard black scales and deep pits. No published data are available relating the corrosion rate to the carbon dioxide concentration, but they would be expected to approximate the situation that is shown to prevail for hydrogen sulfide.

In water-flood systems, as in other industrial waters, an increase in pH from the slightly acidic to the slightly alkaline side results in a decrease in corrosivity. Newman[36] shows that under his test conditions the corrosion rate is cut in half when the pH is raised from 5 to 8. In those few systems where the waters are quite acidic, the corrosion rates are very high and the problem of inhibition is quite difficult.

INHIBITION

Precipitation

The prevention of precipitated material generally takes two different approaches depending upon whether the precipitated material consists of turbidity or colloidal material that was originally present in the water or whether it is the result of supersaturation under flood conditions or else due to the mixing of two incompatible waters. In the former case conventional clarification techniques are employed. These may include the use of settling tanks, coagulants, or filters of various types. For example, Kwaciszewska and Szedaj[8] mention the addition of 0.25 g/liter of $Al_2(SO_4)_3$ as the first step in conditioning floodwater, along with air-blowing at the rate of 0.5 m^3/min and using air bubbles of about 3 mm in diameter. Powell[3] describes the use of settling ponds and diatomaceous earth filters. Sudbury *et al.*[6] had the problem of preparing sea water for injection into a formation which had very low permeability. This system required water of exceptionally high quality. They obtained this water by a treating system consisting of a sand trap and a diatomaceous-earth filter.

Smith[39] describes a unique approach to the flocculation of argillaceous material. He uses an aqueous solution of a complex containing 1 to 3 moles of calcium chloride or magnesium chloride and 1,000 to 100,000 ppm of a nonionic surfactant of the general empirical formula $RO(CH_2CH_2O)_nCH_2CH_2OH$. In his preferred compound R is an isooctylphenyl group and n is 14. Bernard[40] proposes a novel method of controlling sulfate-reducing bacteria by a clarification technique. He removes their required sulfate ion by adding water-soluble salts of barium or lead to precipitate insoluble barium or lead sulfate. Clarifying agents, such as lime or alum, are also added to insure complete clarification of the precipitated sulfate.

The second precipitation case, that of supersaturation or precipitation due to incompatible waters, is generally treated by means of sequestering agents designed to keep the alkaline-earth metals in solution. Earlougher and Love[18] describe the use of hexametaphosphate briquets hung in baskets in the water supply tank near the inlet pipe for this purpose. They also discuss mixing a granular complex phosphate with the sand injected during a fracturing treatment. The phosphate granules dissolve slowly in the well fluids and sequester the appropriate cations in the brine.

Kwaciszewska and Szedaj[8] state that 10 mg of hexametaphosphate per liter of water is sufficient to stabilize a floodwater. Kipps[41] prevents the reversion of the added polyphosphates by the addition of small amounts of an alkali metal salt of N,N-bis(hydroxyethyl)-glycine. Bell and Shaw[42] describe the results of a large-scale field program which show citric acid is an efficient agent for sequestering iron dissolved in 354 oil-field water-flood projects and 92 salt water disposal projects. Nowak and Keller[43] patented the use of compounds like $C_{12}H_{25}NH(CH_2CH_2NH)_2CH_2CO_2H \cdot HCl$ as sequestrants, detergents, bactericides, and corrosion inhibitors all at one time.

Bacterial Control

The use of bactericides is discussed in some detail in the chapter on cooling towers. Many of the same bacteria must be treated in water-flooding systems, but their amounts and importance will be quite different. Thus, for example, *sodium pentachlorophenate* is still as effective against algae and slime formers in water-floods as it was in cooling waters, but only rarely are these microorganisms the major problems. Therefore, the pentachlorophenates are rarely used along in water-flood systems, but they are more often found as ingredients in a blended formulation.

Chlorine is an obvious bactericide to be examined for application to water-flood systems. Use of this material is not very widespread, however. One disadvantage is that it will oxidize ferrous iron to insoluble ferric iron. Another disadvantage is the fact that sulfate reducers can build up a tolerance to chlorine when it is applied continuously.[13] It also increases the acidity of the water and causes it to become more corrosive. When it can be used successfully, however, chlorine provides protection at costs as low as 1 mil per barrel of water, a figure considerably lower than the usual cost for organic bactericides. A detailed study of the use of chlorine for this application is presented by Beck.[44] He found that while chlorine-treated waters remain clear, injection rates gradually decrease in most cases. Bacterial counts increase with increasing distance from the treating plant, because of the reactivity of chlorine with other materials. Barton *et al.*[45] found that an effective technique consisted of periodic slug feeding of sodium hypochlorite.

Aldehydes are also used in water floods. Plummer and Walling[24] found that formaldehyde is effective at 40 ppm. Beck[44] found it is effective at 10 ppm against sulfate-reducing bacteria. A recent advance in this type of treatment was made by Yoder and Torgeson.[46] They found that saturated dialdehydes with 2 to 6 carbon atoms, such as glyoxal, pyruvic aldehyde, malonaldehyde, glutaraldehyde, and adipaldehyde, are unusually effective against sulfate reducers in water floods.

The great bulk of bactericides used in water floods today are *long-chain organic nitrogenous materials* or *quaternaries* of them. These materials are excellent dispersing agents as well as killing agents. It is this dispersing ability that is believed to contribute heavily to their success in microbiological control, especially insofar as sulfate reducers are concerned. The bacterial count can vary over a wide range, and it can become so huge that it is economically unfeasible to attempt a complete kill. This may not have to be done, however, since preventing the sulfate-reducing bacteria from adhering to the metal surface accomplishes the same objective. If the bacteria cannot get to the surface and be covered by a layer of other bacteria which prevents oxygen from reaching them, then they do not multiply and attack the metal.

The use of a good dispersant which prevents either the sulfate reducers or their protective cover bacteria from adhering to the surface goes a long way toward controlling them effectively. For this reason, a good dispersant is a desirable ingredient in a water-flood bacterial control formulation. When materials such as the long-chain organic nitrogen compounds are found which are both good dispersants and bactericides, then the combination of the two properties makes these chemicals especially attractive for this purpose. A corollary of this theorem is that laboratory tests designed to evaluate the efficacy of chemicals for water-flood bacterial control must bear this in mind. Simple kill tests are not sufficient, as was proven by the fact that some of the best available commercial chemicals for this use today fare poorly in laboratory kill tests. The dispersant properties must also be considered. A laboratory test which duplicates the system that exists in the field of bacteria growth on a metal surface past which water is flowing is a more valid procedure.

One category of chemicals that functions efficiently for bacterial control is that of the *quaternary ammonium salts of fatty amines.* Some of the most frequently used members of this category include the following:

1. *Soya trimethyl ammonium chloride.*
2. *Tallow trimethyl ammonium chloride.*
3. *Dicoco dimethyl ammonium chloride.*
4. *Alkyl bis-2-hydroxyethyl methyl quaternary ammonium chloride.*

Bass[47] states that the water-soluble monoalkyl quaternaries are generally more effective bactericides than are the oil-soluble water-dispersible dialkyl dimethyl quats. The corrosion-inhibiting properties of these quaternaries follow the opposite pattern, however. He postulates that the killing properties of the cationic quaternaries occur because the agents are absorbed onto the surface of the bacteria, thus destroying the cell metabolism. This may be because a diffusion barrier is formed which interferes with the metabolism. In addition, the chemical having the ability to lower markedly the interfacial tension disrupts the metabolism through increasing the flow of liquids into and out of the organisms while keeping out solids. Finally, there is probably some inherent toxicity in these chemicals.

The sulfate-reducing bacteria have not displayed resistant strains when waters are treated with quaternaries as they have with other bactericides. These chemicals do not function as protein oxidants, like chlorine, or as systemic poisons, such as arsenicals.

Examples of the effectiveness of these quaternaries as microbiological control agents in water-flood systems are presented by LaSusa[48] and Sudbury *et al.*[6] The latter report states that 7.5 ppm of a quaternary ammonium chloride sufficed to kill aerobic and anaerobic bacteria. Reports by the manufacturers of these chemicals claim that they will control algae as well as sulfate reducers. Gregory *et al.*[49] and Breston[50] show the dicoco bactericide to be very effective against the genus Pseudomonas and the genus Serratia.

In view of the effectiveness of some of these quaternaries as microbiological control agents and others as corrosion inhibitors, combinations of different quaternaries are now more frequently used in water floods than are the individual chemicals. These combinations have been very effective. Corrosion protection greater than 95 per cent and complete inhibition of bacterial growth were obtained at concentrations as low as 6 ppm when used in fresh water systems. They have proven equally effective in controlling the growth of algae and Pseudomonas.

Certain long-chain amines are also shown to be effective for microbiological control in water-flood systems. These include N-tallow propylene diamine, N-coco propylene diamine, and coco amine acetate. The diamines and occasionally their ethoxylated derivatives are the preferred materials. There is considerable discussion about the effect of chain length. Many authorities in this field feel that the chemicals which have the shorter C_{12} chain length are more effective than those with the longer C_{18} chain length. The reverse holds true for corrosion inhibition. The N-coco propylene diamine is reported to be especially effective for algae and slime control, as well as for Pseudomonas organisms.

Imidazolines and quaternaries based on them are reported to show effectiveness comparable to those shown by their fatty amine analogues. Materials of this type that are reported to be useful include those based on 1-hydroxyethyl-2-heptadecenyl glyoxalidine, its salts, and quaternaries. Hutchison and Ries[51] report that a mixture of

$$R\overline{C:NCH_2CH_2N}(C_2H_4NH)_mC_2H_4NH_2$$

and

$$R\overline{C:NCH_2CH_2N}(C_2H_4NH)_nC_2H_4NHCOR',$$

where R and R' are long straight-chain hydrocarbons and n is 0 to 2, neutralized with 2 moles of a low-molecular-weight carboxylic acid of less than 6 carbon atoms per mole of imidazoline, is effective in controlling sulfate reducers in the presence of soluble ferrous salts in either fresh water or brine systems. As little as 2 to 8 ppm plus a small amount of a nonionic wetting agent (a nonylphenol-ethylene oxide adduct) is effective against both aerobic and anaerobic microorganisms, especially sulfate reducers.

There are a number of *other nitrogenous materials* that are reported to be effective. Pelcak and Dornbush[52] inhibited sulfate reducers with substituted guanidines or their salts. Dodecylguanidine acetate is stated to be especially effective. Wolf[53] inhibited the growth of many different types of bacteria found in water floods by use of 15 to 50 ppm of a condensation product of HCHO with an aliphatic polyamine having the general formula $H_2N(C_nH_{2n}NH)_xH$ where n is 2 or 3 and x is 1 to 4. Rosin amine acetates and ethylene oxide condensation products of them are also used with some success in these systems.

Hitzman[54] found that the addition of hydrogen peroxide will increase the bactericidal effect of certain phenols, amines, and quaternary ammonium salts against sulfate reducers. Cross[55] patented a combination of rosin amine acetate, a higher alkylbenzyldimethylammonium chloride, and a polyglycol ether to obtain a formulation which is very effective. In addition to its bactericidal properties, a formulation of this type is useful in that it is compatible with all types of waters. Many other formulations are being used today for the purpose of providing good protection against the various types of bacteria that can be present as well as to incorporate suitable physical stability and economic factors into the treatment.

There is considerable controversy as to the universality of application of bactericides in water flooding. Some of the treatment suppliers claim that these materials are effective in most floods and that this effectiveness especially applies to those formulations that have built-in corrosion inhibitors. Amstutz,[13] on the other hand, says that bactericides are even less universal than are corrosion inhibitors and that laboratory determinations should be made for each specific application to determine the most economical chemical. He presents evidence to also show the need for working out the proper dosage-level treating sequence.

A completely different and novel approach to the problem of killing bacteria in injection waters is suggested by Wainerdi.[56] He postulates that radiation sterilization of injection water can be a suitable technique in the future. Fission products either before or after separation from the fuel elements would be used to sterilize the waters. A dosage of about 250,000 roentgens would be required.

Corrosion Inhibition

Most operators agree that corrosion inhibitors are needed for the successful operation of the majority of water floods, but Doscher and Tuttle[9] present a unique approach to the problem of sour injection brines which does not require the use of inhibitors. They recommend removal of the hydrogen sulfide by a *stripping mixture of carbon monoxide and nitrogen,* along with the use of sequestering agents to keep in solution any corrosion products which do form. The finished brine contains no traces of hydrogen sulfide or oxygen and is insufficiently corrosive to warrant the use of inhibitors.

This technique is in contrast to the more common method of removing the hydrogen sulfide by *aeration.* That procedure replaces hydrogen sulfide with even more corrosive oxygen and results in corrosion further downstream. Unfortunately, the corrosive nature of most water-flood systems is such that merely removing the hydrogen sulfide does not eliminate the corrosion due to other causes.

Jones[5] describes a three-year program of an attempt to control corrosion in the Wilmington field when sea water is the injection medium. Inhibitors were found to be the most satisfactory solution after also evaluating cathodic protection and use of corrosion-resistant materials. Amstutz[13] points out that the corrosion can be derived from many causes and that the treatment technique depends upon them. For example, when oxygen is a major factor, the corrosion can be retarded by either eliminating the oxygen contamination mechanically, removing it chemically by use of a reducing agent, or else by adding inhibitors. The chemical removal is best accomplished by treating the water with sulfur dioxide gas at a cost of about 1 mil per barrel for each 2 to 3 mg/liter of oxygen. Sodium sulfite can also be used.

The use of *inorganic inhibitors* is evaluated thoroughly in the early stages of water flooding. A few are found to have some value. Thus, Fariss[57] found that zinc chromate at a dosage level of 13 ppm gives protection against a brine containing 52,000 ppm of sodium chloride and having a pH of 6.2 to 6.8. Even when the pH is dropped sharply and easy access to oxygen is allowed, the zinc chromate still gives protection. The presence of sulfide is harmful since it precipitates the zinc and eliminates its synergistic effect with the chromate. Similarly, the presence of organic materials is undesirable. Alderman and Stout[58] evaluated chromates for other types of brines and found that the addition of a non-ionic surfactant improves protection considerably. Jones[4] evaluated polyphosphates, sodium hydroxide, and sodium hypochlorite in the Wilmington flood and found them to be valueless. He did achieve protection with arsenic compounds, but he found that organic chemicals are the most effective. This preference for organic inhibitors in the Wilmington flood was also verified by Stormont[59] who found that corrosion could be controlled effectively by the addition of 20 ppm of amines.

The use of *organic inhibitors* is now widespread in controlling corrosion in both the injection side and the production side of secondary recovery units. There are at least three good reasons for this use: (1) the organic compounds provide good inhibition at very low cost, (2) the same materials can double as bactericides, or perhaps even function primarily in that manner and thus prevent corrosion by an indirect route, and (3) as Robinson[12] points out, practically all good organic inhibitors decrease interfacial tension, with higher injection rates resulting from that fact alone.

Corrosion inhibitors which are effective in water-flooding operations are primarily of the *organic nitrogenous* types described earlier for the primary production wells. Generally, however, the most effective ones are the *quaternaries either of the fatty or imidazoline types*. There is some speculation that this effectiveness occurs because in addition to being good corrosion inhibitors, they are also excellent dispersants and thus prevent the formation of adherent deposits on the metal wall which would eventually break off and cause plugging problems. Interestingly, in water-flood systems these inhibitors are effective at dosages of 1 to 10 ppm, whereas much larger quantities may be required in producing wells. This concentration may be due to the much better opportunity for rapid inhibitor distribution in the water-flooding process. There is generally present sufficient oil in the injection water or else in the inhibitor formulation to provide for the two-layer protective mechanism.

In the selection of corrosion inhibitors for water-flood systems, the degree of water solubility becomes quite important. If the inhibitor is only slightly or poorly soluble, it can be lost at the filter or elsewhere in the system and never have an opportunity to display its protective mechanism. In addition, it can lead to plugging of the formation because of poor dispersion and solubility characteristics. On the other hand, if the inhibitor is too soluble, inhibition may be poor because film stability is reduced and the desorption of the inhibitor from the metal surfaces is rapid. As a general rule it can be stated that the solubility of many organic water-flood inhibitors is inversely proportional to the chloride content of the floodwater.

The previous section described a number of bactericides which also function as corrosion inhibitors. In addition to these, Fairweather[60] has shown the effectiveness of a quaternary ammonium polyoxyalkylated amino diamide material. The material is prepared by making an amino diamide from long-chain polyalkylene polyamines and unsaturated fatty acids, by reacting it with a polyalkylene oxide, and then by quaternizing it with an alkylating agent. Specific examples include the reaction product of soybean oil, diethylenetriamine, ethylene oxide, and benzyl chloride. Rydell[61] achieved excellent field results with imidazoline quaternaries such as 1-(2-hydroxyethyl)-1-benzyl-2-tridecylimidazolinium nitrite.

Breston[62] was able to protect water lines from corrosion by slightly acidic air-free floodwaters without having to raise the pH by using *rosin amine acetate*. Two to four ppm reduced the corrosion rate from 50 to 85 per cent. The use of *phytic acid* in water-flood systems is described by Toekelt[63] who made a good inhibitor from the reaction product of N,N,N′,N′-tetrakis-(2-hydroxyethyl)ethylenediamine with phytic acid. Another new category of inhibitor which is now beginning to receive considerable attention is that of *sarcosine* derivatives. These materials show considerable promise as inhibitors, but they suffer at present from their relatively high cost. Pines and Spivack[64] conducted laboratory studies that indicate that N-oleoyl sarcosine in a hydrocarbon solution is an effective inhibitor in synthetic sea water. Jones[65] has shown that alkali or alkaline earth salts of sebacic or azelaic acid are effective inhibitors against synthetic sea water. In field practice, these inhibitors would not be expected to be effective for water floods, although their amine salts are useful for this purpose.

One of the most successful chemicals in use in water floods today is *coco amine acetate salt*. This material, especially when used in the distilled form, acts as a combination corrosion inhibitor and bactericide. Complete control of sulfate reducers and general bacteria, as well as 95 + per cent corrosion protection is claimed at 5 to 12.5 ppm on an active basis. The distilled coco aliphatic diamine is also stated to function in the same dual manner, giving the same degree of protection at dosage levels of 5 to 12.5 ppm on an active basis. The *adipic acid salt* of this material is stated to show the same effectiveness and is effective in the presence of appreciable oxygen concentrations.

There are a number of examples available of savings brought about as a result of use of some of these inhibitors. For example, one inhibitor supplier cited reduction in coupon weight loss from 6 per cent in two weeks using one inhibitor to 0.024 per cent during the next two weeks when using a tallow diamineoleic salt. Treatment costs for the inhibitor averaged 36 cents per day in the system where 20 to 30 barrels of sour crude were produced per day. Amstutz[13] has shown figures for a flood where the use of 12 ppm of inhibitor reduced the corrosion rate from about 7 mpy to about 1 mpy in a two-month period.

Wright[66] conducted a thorough evaluation of corrosion inhibitors for use with sea water taken near the surface for injection into the Wilmington flood. His test system involved treating with sodium sulfite to remove oxygen. He evaluated both filtered and unfiltered water. In both cases, use of a semipolar nitrogenous inhibitor at 5 and 10 ppm dosage levels reduced the corrosion rate (as measured in a variety of ways) from about 3 mpy to a few tenths of an mpy. By contrast, a polyphosphate-tannin mixture gave little protection. These results are important, since it appears that as much as 1,000,000 barrels per day of this water will be used for injection purposes in the near future. In an earlier paper[67] which describes the same test procedure, Wright showed that injection of 19 ppm of a corrosion inhibitor into oxygen-free Gaspur zone water from the Wilmington field reduced the 14-day corrosion rate from about 50 mpy to a few tenths of an mpy.

Newman's laboratory inhibitor evaluation[36] is of considerable interest. He makes the point, which is often neglected, that laboratory dosages required for protection are usually higher than those required for field use. Laboratory tests are generally more severe since results must be obtained in a short time. The inhibitor film does not have as much time to build up as it does in the field, and it is subjected to conditions which tend to remove it more easily. As an example of this, an inhibitor which required 25 ppm for efficient protection in the laboratory was effective at 10 ppm in the field. Nevertheless, with but few exceptions, the order of effectiveness of various inhibitors in the laboratory and in the field correspond. Newman also found that the relative slope of the curve of per cent protection *vs.* dosage is an important factor in comparing inhibitors. Many inhibitors were found that gave good protection at high dosages, but little or none at low levels. Others had a more gradual slope and retained a good part of their effectiveness at very low levels, even though their maximum effectiveness at higher levels was not especially impressive. He also cites the case of an inhibitor which has such a gradual slope and which has been very successful in the field.

As in the case of any other corrosion inhibitor application, the application method is of considerable importance. In water-flood systems, the inhibitor is applied in a batch, continuously, or in various combinations of these methods. The batch treatment is used in most supply wells where submerged pumps are installed.[12] The inhibitor is injected into the well, flushed, and recirculated properly. The recirculation procedure is very important since it insures proper distribution of inhibitor. In practice, at least three complete cycles are made. Slug treatments of as high as 10 to 15 gal of inhibitor per 100 to 200 gal of water are applied weekly or as often as conditions dictate. The location of the injection points is also important, since it is desirable to treat as far back as possible to insure protection of the entire system. On the other hand, care must be taken to see that the inhibitor does not disappear early in the system, e.g., by pickup on the filter.

REFERENCES

1. Powell, J. P. Water flooding of oil sands in Butler and Greenwood Counties, Kans. *U.S. Bur. Mines, Inform. Circ. 7750,* 1956.

2. Powell, J. P. Result of water flooding in Kansas oil sands containing viscous crude oils. *U.S. Bur. Mines, Inform. Circ. 7873,* 1959.

3. Powell, J. P. Some recent developments in water flooding in Washington County, Okla., 1956–57. *U.S. Bur. Mines, Inform. Circ. 7787,* 1957.

4. Jones, C. H. Corrosion control practices in the Wilmington Water-Flood Operation. *Corrosion,* **15,** No. 12, 99–102, Dec. 1959.

5. Jones, C. H. Battle against ocean-water corrosion. *Oil Gas J.,* **54,** No. 82, 76–9, Nov. 26, 1956.

6. Sudbury, J. D., Knutson, C. F., Felsenthal, M., and Lung, J. D. Conditioning of Pacific Ocean water for water flood injection. *J. Petrol. Technol.,* **8,** No. 9, 85–9, 1956.

7. Geiman, M. A. Use of water in water flooding. *Materialy po Geol. i Razrabotke Neft. Mestorozhdenii Azerbaidzhana,* 35–50, 1959.

8. Kwaciszewska, A., and Szedaj, Z. Conditioning of water for water flooding. *Prace Inst. Naft., Ser. A,* No. 58, 3–7, 1958.

9. Doscher, T. M., and Tuttle, R. N. How to prepare a sour brine for subsurface injection. *World Oil,* **140,** No. 4, 160, 162, 167, Mar. 1955.

10. Wright, C. C. How to evaluate corrosion inhibitors used in seawater flood projects. *Producers Monthly,* **58,** No. 10, 30–4, Oct. 1960.

11. Prange, F. A. New light on how to combat corrosion in water-flood operations. *Oil Gas J.,* **50,** No. 49, 148, Apr. 14, 1952.

12. Robinson, J. B. Application of organic inhibitors in water flooding. *World Oil,* **142,** No. 2, 156, 159–60, 162, Feb. 1, 1956.

13. Amstutz, R. W. Corrosion problems in water flooding. *Corrosion,* **14,** No. 5, 255t–9t, May 1958.

14. Beerstecher, E., Jr. *Petroleum Microbiology* (Houston: Elsevier Press, 1959).

15. Wolfson, L. L. Microbiology in secondary recovery systems. *Corrosion,* **16,** No. 6, 298t–300t, June 1960.

16. Bernard, G. G. A survey on the use of incompatible floodwaters. *Producers Monthly,* **21,** No. 4, 34–7, 1957.

17. Anon. Incompatible waters in porous media. *Mining Mag.* (London), **101,** No. 4, 170–5, 1959.

18. Earlougher, R. C., and Love, W. W. Sequestering agents for prevention of scale deposition in oil wells. *J. Petrol. Technol.,* **9,** No. 4, 17–20, 1957.

19. Torrey, P. D. Improving oil recovery. Lecture II. Part I. Economics of secondary recovery—often more attractive than primary. *Producers Monthly,* **25,** No. 4, 14–8, Apr. 1961. List reprinted by courtesy of P. D. Torrey and PRODUCERS MONTHLY.

20. Bernard, G. G. Effect of calcium carbonate supersaturation of floodwater on rock permeability. *Producers Monthly,* **21,** No. 9, 32–6, 1957.

21. Krejci-Graf, K., Hecht, F., and Pasler, W. Oil-field waters of the Vienna basin. *Geol. Jahrb.,* **74,** 161–210, 1957.

22. Laird, R. W., and Cogbill, A. F. Incompatible waters can plug oil sands. *World Oil,* **146,** 188–90, 1958.

23. Case, L. C., and Riggin, D. M. Rid production equipment of costly scale and sludge. *Oil Gas J.,* **52,** No. 15, 98–102, 145, Aug. 17, 1953.

24. Plummer, F. B., and Walling, I. W. Chemical changes in East Texas waters affecting its injections into subsurface sands. *Petroleum Technol.,* **9** (2), 2019, 1946; *Trans. Am. Inst. Mining Met. Engrs., Petroleum Div.,* **165,** 64–77, 1946.

25. Plummer, F. B., Merkt, E. E., Jr., Power, H. H., Sawin, H. J., and Tapp, P. Effect of certain microorganisms on the injection of water into sand. *Am. Inst. Mining Met. Engrs. Tech. Pub. No. 1678,* 1943; *Petroleum Technol.,* **7,** 1678, 1944.

26. Merkt, E. E. Thesis. The University of Texas, 1943.

27. Pringsheims, E. G. Iron organisms. *Endeavour,* **11,** No. 44, 208–14, 1952.

28. Caldwell, J. A., and Lytle, M. L. Bacterial corrosion of offshore structures. *Corrosion,* **9,** No. 6, 192–6, June 1953.

29. Kuznetsov, S. I. Role of sulfate-reducing bacteria in corrosion of metal structures. Teoriya i Praktika Protivokorrozion. *Zashchity Podzemnykh Sooruzhenii. Inst. Fiz. Khim., Trudy 6-go Vsesóyuz. Soveshchaniya* (Moscow), 246–51, 1956 (pub. 1958).

30. Deuber, C. G. The present status of bacterial corrosion investigations in the United States. *Corrosion,* **9,** No. 3, 95–9, Mar. 1953.

31. von Wolzogen Kuhr, C. A. H., and Van der Vlugt, I. S. *Water,* **18,** 147–65, 1934.

32. Wormwell, F., and Farrer, T. W. Electrochemical studies of anaerobic corrosion in presence of sulfate-reducing bacteria. *Chem. and Ind.,* No. 5, 108–9, Feb. 2, 1952.

33. Adams, M. E., and Farrer, T. W. The influence of ferrous iron on bacterial corrosion. *J. Appl. Chem.,* **3,** Pt. 3, 117–20, Mar. 1953.

34. Ulanovskii, I. B., and Nikitina, N. S. The effect of putrefactive aerobic bacteria on the corrosion of steel in sea water. *Mikrobiologiya,* **25,** No. 1, 66–71, 1956.

35. Purins, B., and Liepina, L. Electrochemical and corrosion behavior of iron in aqueous solutions of electrolytes. I. Electrode potential and corrosion rate of iron in aqueous solutions of chlorides of alkali and alkaline earth metals. *Latvijas PSR Zinatnu Akad. Vestis,* No. 5, 83–92, 1956.

36. Newman, T. R. A laboratory method for evaluating corrosion inhibitors for secondary recovery. *Corrosion,* **15,** No. 5, 307t–10t, June 1959.

37. Evans, U. R. *The Corrosion and Oxidation of Metals* (London: Edward Arnold, Ltd., 1960; New York: St. Martin's Press, Inc., 1960).

38. Raifsnider, P. J., and Wachter, A. Pitting corrosion by water-flood brines. *Corrosion,* **17,** No. 7, 325t–8t, July 1961.

39. Smith, G. H. Oil-treating process. U.S. 2,841,222, July 1, 1958.

40. Bernard, G. G. Control of bacteria in oil-well-flooding waters. U.S. 2,912,378, Nov. 10, 1959.

41. Kipps, H. J. Inhibiting the formation of scale deposits. U.S. 2,890,175, June 9, 1959.

42. Bell, W. E., and Shaw, J. K. Pfizer's Program 20 yields flood data. *Oil Gas J.,* **57,** No. 2, 84–6, 1959.

43. Nowak, T. J., and Keller, H. F., Jr. Water flooding of subterranean formations. U.S. 2,802,784, Aug. 13, 1957.

44. Beck, J. U. Use of bacteria for releasing oil from sands. *Producers Monthly,* **11,** 21–6, 1947.

45. Barton, J. K., Brown, C. F., and Heck, E. T. Slug feeding of sodium hypochlorite on water flood leases. *Producers Monthly,* **12,** 24–6, 1948.

46. Yoder, D. M., and Torgeson, D. C. Control of sulfate-reducing bacteria in water. U.S. 2,801,216, July 30, 1957.

47. Bass, D. Preventing corrosion by crude: the use of surface-active agents. *Petroleum,* **20,** 139–42, Apr. 1957.

48. LaSusa, C. D. Corrosion in water flood and disposal systems. *World Oil,* **140,** No. 5, 242–5, 1955.

49. Gregory, V. P., Groninger, C. R., and Prusick, J. H. Treatment of floodwaters used in secondary oil recovery. *Producers Monthly,* **14,** No. 7, 27–31, 1950.

50. Breston, J. N. Chemical treatment of floodwater for bacteria and corrosion control. *Producers Monthly,* **13,** No. 7, 16–26, 1949; *Oil Gas J.,* **48,** 96–100, 124–7, 1949.

51. Hutchison, C. B., and Ries, W. J. Bactericidal compositions for use in secondary recovery of petroleum. U.S. 2,839,467, June 17, 1958.

52. Pelcak, E. J., and Dornbush, A. C. Bactericides for water for industrial use. U.S. 2,906,595, Sept. 29, 1959.

53. Wolf, P. A. Inhibition of bacterial growth in water used for flooding in secondary oil recovery. U.S. 2,843,545, July 15, 1958.

54. Hitzman, D. O. Bactericidal compositions from tetraalkyl quaternary ammonium halides and hydrogen peroxide. U.S. 2,917,428, Dec. 15, 1959.

55. Cross, J. M. Water-soluble compositions containing water-insoluble organic amines. U.S. 2,779,741, Jan. 29, 1957.

56. Wainerdi, R. E. Radiation sterilization of injection water. *Producers Monthly,* **24,** No. 14, 20, Dec. 1960.

57. Farriss, R. E. Prevention of corrosion of iron by aqueous brines. U.S. 2,695,876, Nov. 30, 1954.

58. Alderman, E. N., Jr., and Stout, C. M. Corrosion inhibition of brine. U.S. 2,913,420, Nov. 17, 1959.

59. Stormont, D. H. Wilmington flood operators tackle sand plugging and corrosion. *Oil Gas J.,* **58,** No. 3, 98–9, 102, 1960.

60. Fairweather, H. G. C. Quaternary ammonium polyoxyalkylenated amino diamide corrosion inhibitors and surface-active agents. Brit. 816,617, July 15, 1959.

61. Rydell, R. G. Corrosion inhibitors for water for secondary recovery. U.S. 2,738,325, Mar. 13, 1956.

62. Breston, J. N., and Barton, K. Field test of corrosion inhibitor for low-pH floodwater. *Oil Gas J.,* **46,** 91–2, 95–6, Dec. 6, 1947; *Producers Monthly,* **12,** 13–7, Nov. 1947.

63. Toekelt, W. G. Water-soluble corrosion inhibitors. U.S. 2,923,599, Feb. 2, 1960.

64. Pines, R. M., and Spivack, J. D. A laboratory study of N-oleoyl sarcosine as a rust inhibitor in some petroleum products. *Corrosion,* **13,** No. 10, 690t–4t, Oct. 1957.

65. Jones, D. T. Rust inhibitors for aqueous systems. U.S. 2,726,215, Dec. 6, 1955.

66. Wright, C. C. Field testing of corrosion inhibitors in sea water. *Producers Monthly,* **25,** No. 1, 18–9, 27, Jan. 1961.

67. Wright, C. C. Screening inhibitors for prevention of water flood corrosion. *Corrosion,* **15,** No. 7, 97–8, 1959.

7

Petroleum—
Refinery Product
Problems

There are a greater variety of systems with corrosive conditions in the product side of a refinery than in any other phase of the petroleum industry. Corrosion problems exist from the point where the crude oil reaches the refinery to the location where the finished products are shipped out. Some of the pieces of equipment which must be protected include crude distillation units, alkylation units, gas plants, cracking units, straight run deisobutanizers, furfural refiners, reformers, hydrogen sulfide water-absorption plants, and many others. The problems may involve heat exchangers, reboilers, overhead systems, and distillation units. The scope of this problem and the possible uses of inhibitors are so great that a lengthy book could be written on those topics alone. In this section, we present a brief but comprehensive review of the problem and the present use of inhibitors. Refineries represent one location where the potential large-scale use of inhibitors for corrosion problems is only now beginning to be understood, and the use of inhibitors is starting to expand rapidly.

LITERATURE

The general problem of corrosion in refineries appears to have been the subject of more surveys abroad than in the United States, where the emphasis in literature is on discussions of specific problems and control measures for them. One of the earlier reviews was written by Daino[1] and involves a general discussion of refinery corrosion problems and protective measures. Robb[2] outlines basic mechanisms of corrosion in oil refining with metallurgical factors influencing corrosion rates, corrosive media, evaluation of corrosion rates and patterns, and solutions for the problems. Similar reviews were written by Tait,[3] Hijikata,[4] and Tourret.[5, 6] Cavallaro[7] gives a detailed treatment of the various types of inhibitors, the mechanisms by which they protect, and the required application techniques. The November 1959 issue of *Corrosion Technology*[8] presents an English abstract of a lengthy article by Zakharochkin *et al.*[9] describing Russian problems in processing, with emphasis on sulfur oils in the low-temperature equipment used for dealing with gasoline distillates. American reviews include one by Skinner, Mason, and Moran[10] closely examining the problems of high-temperature corrosion and another by Bennett[11] presenting a detailed discussion of the use of high-molecular-weight corrosion inhibitors in petroleum refineries.

A number of very good articles were published dealing with specific problems and solutions in refineries. Mason[12, 13] discusses fifteen case records of actual corrosion problems involving gas oil, spent sulfuric acid alkylate, depropanized naphtha, crude oil, naphthenic-base crudes, caustic soda and sodium plumbite, furfural, reduced crude vapors, and cracked propane distillate. Connors and Seyer[14, 15] discuss practical aspects of six commonly occurring corrosion problems and remedies for each one. Easton[16, 17] outlines corrosion problems encountered in refineries processing western Canadian crude oils and the methods used to overcome them. The problem units include crude distillation units, catalytic cracking light ends equipment, and catalytic reforming units. *Petroleum Processing Magazine*[18] describes the experience of six plants in cutting their corrosion rates by 95 per cent through the use of an organic inhibitor. Garner and Hale[19] review corrosion problems arising in the distillation and cracking of petroleum and those arising from the use of chemicals either for the refining of petroleum products or for the synthesis of hydrocarbons. Equipment described includes pipe-still heaters, fractionators, reactors, condensing equipment, catalytic cracking, and isomerization units. An excellent description of the entire group of corrosion problems for Tidewater's Delaware refinery is presented in a lengthy review article by the *Oil and Gas Journal*.[20] Brooke[21] gathered together a group of reports on unusual corrosion problems in a refinery and their subsequent solutions.

Individual units have been the subjects of a number of papers. Corrosion problems in amine gas treating plants were examined by Lang and Mason[22] as well as by Riesenfeld and Blohm.[23] Corrosion prevention in a Thermofor Catalytic Cracking (TCC) plant is described by Murray and Furth,[24, 25] while Backensto et al.[26] discuss similar problems in Thermofor Catalytic Reformers (TCR). McFaddin[27] presents a study by the Union Oil Company at its Santa Maria natural gas processing plants, and Swerdloff[28] reviews the problems in glycol-absorption and solid-dessicant gas dehydration systems. Phillips[29] examines high-temperature sulfide corrosion in catalytic reforming of light naphthas. Prange[30] gives a detailed analysis of corrosion problems in a butane dehydrogenation process at the Plains Plant of the Phillips Petroleum Company. Mason and Schillmoller[31] review corrosion in sour water strippers and an N.A.C.E. Task Group[32] reports on the nature and extent of corrosion problems in hydrofluoric acid alkylation units. Moore[33] describes various corrosion problems that occurred in a large diethanolamine (DEA) system that removes hydrogen sulfide from refinery gas streams and a liquid propane-butane stream. These problems include reboiler corrosion, rich DEA corrosion, stress corrosion cracking, and corrosion-erosion. A recent article by Ehmke[34] gives an account of corrosion problems in a fluid catalytic cracker and gas plant following a 19,000-hr run. Specific places where corrosion damage occurred and was examined included the carbon-moly reactor, the regenerator, the catalyst lines, and the gas plant.

ECONOMICS

The economics involved in corrosion and corrosion inhibition in refinery problems must be considered in a somewhat different light than for the other corrosive situations described in this book. In most other cases the cost of corrosion has a direct value involving primarily equipment replacement problems, and therefore the cost of inhibition and the degree of protection obtained can be related directly to the cost of the corrosion. The refinery, on the other hand, presents another type of problem insofar as corrosion costs are concerned. Here, in most cases, the cost of the equipment that must be replaced and even the manpower involved in the replacement are minor factors. The major reason for corrosion inhibition is the need for prevention of downtime. The unit involved generally is such that a delay in the production process can be very damaging to the economics of the entire operation. In addition, in a modern refinery, the equipment and processes are so complicated and interrelated, that the corrosive failure of a minor part can shut down a substantial portion of the entire refinery operation. The resultant nonoperational financial loss is considerable and far outweighs the cost of equipment replacement. It is for this reason that in considering the effect of corrosion in a refinery it is much more common to talk about a particular piece of equipment in terms of its length of service rather than in terms of the replacement costs. It is therefore difficult to place limiting values upon inhibitor costs within reasonable amounts. The section dealing with inhibition gives a number of examples of extension of the life of equipment as a result of inhibitor usage. In this section we analyze some of the few actual dollar corrosion figures that are available.

Sherwood[35] states that in the United States the annual damage to refinery equipment through corrosion is 14 to 18 cents per barrel, or about $400 million. Freedman and Dravnieks[36] estimate the total cost to be a somewhat lower figure, approaching $300 million annually, and they state that the cost would be considerably higher if inhibitors were not used to control corrosion rates in critical refinery equipment. Sherwood's estimate of the cost per barrel is fairly close to that which was estimated by the A.P.I. Subcommittee on Corrosion[37] in 1954 when they used a range of 11 to 19 cents per barrel of crude charge. Easton[16] approximates the cost of corrosion to Canadian refineries in 1957 to be $18.5 million based on the total product sold, including both domestic and imported supplies. The cost to Imperial Oil Limited is estimated at $6.8 million of that. Interestingly, Easton places the cost per barrel in Canada at only 7 cents.

Varying figures are given for the cost of corrosion inhibition. The cost of treating typical systems with inhibitors has been cited as 0.3 to

TABLE 7-1. Yearly Chemical Cost[16]

CRUDE UNIT SIZE (B/D)	AMMONIA COST ($/year)	INHIBITOR COST ($/year)
15,000	1,800	1,800
25,000	4,300	4,500
50,000	3,500	5,000

2.0 cents per barrel.[38] Hulbert and Rippetoe[39] state that the cost of organic inhibitor for crude fractionating units belonging to the Pure Oil Company is about 1.3 cents of crude. The savings for two crude topping towers amounted to an average of $46 per month. Easton's article[16] gives the breakdown shown in Table 7-1 for the costs in using a combination of ammonia and an organic inhibitor for typical crude unit overhead equipment.

These figures must be taken with considerable reservation since the cost of protection per barrel of crude processed varies appreciably from unit to unit. Factors influencing the cost include the type of crude being processed, the type and the age of equipment, the cost of chemicals at the location, the specifications to be followed, and many others.

A very detailed discussion of the estimation of the cost of corrosion in refinery crude units is presented by Landis.[40] He considers capital, maintenance, and operating costs. Twin crude units at Sohio's Cleveland refinery were studied. The direct cost of corrosion for the crude units was 1.36 cents per barrel. This cost included corrosion costs associated with maintenance, the capital cost of built-in corrosion protection, and operating costs consisting mainly of corrosion-control treatment. It did not include the cost of product volume or quality losses resulting from unscheduled shutdowns, nor did it include losses due to equipment fouling. Overheads and capital cost factors resulted in a total actual cost of 2.0 cents per barrel. The largest single corrosion cost in the crude units was repairs and retubing of exchangers. Furnace and vessel repairs were next in order; inhibitors followed.

THE PROBLEM

Consideration of the corrosion problems in refineries must follow a twofold approach, in view of the multitude and diversity of these problems. On the one hand, an examination of the problems as a whole reveals that the corrosive factors can be narrowed down to a reasonable number. While they may vary in intensity from location to location, it is possible to make generalizations concerning the corrosive factors. On the other hand, an examination of specific problems should also be undertaken to implement the generalizations concerning corrosion factors. This approach is undertaken here—an examination of generalized corrosive factors followed by specific problems.

Generalized Corrosive Factors

The major variables involved in refinery corrosion problems can be reduced to the following:

1. *Type of metal.*
2. *Liquid composition.*
3. *Temperature.*
4. *Fluid velocity.*
5. *Acidity.*
6. *Gas Content.*

The *metals* involved are most frequently iron and Admiralty. A fairly good portion of the metal in use for the lower and less severe conditions is carbon steel. Stainless steels of varying compositions are used at the higher temperatures, e.g., in trimming steel valves or in high-temperature furnace tubes. When stainless steel is used, it is especially important to remember that special care must be taken when an appreciable quantity of chloride is present. For example, acid cleaning with hydrochloric acid can leave chloride ions in crevices and if adequate flushing is not undertaken the metal can deteriorate rapidly after being put back into operation.

Admiralty metal is used mainly in overhead condenser systems. Its use minimizes corrosive attack to a great extent, but extreme care must be taken when ammonia is used as one of the inhibitors. In this case an overabundance of the ammonia raises the pH too high and causes severe attack of the metal. Admiralty is also found in many heat exchangers.

The *liquid composition* varies considerably depending upon the particular location in the refinery. It varies from the sour, acidic, crude oil-water mixture that enters the refinery to the final finished product (e.g., gasoline) practically water-free that leaves the refinery for shipment to the user. Overhead systems are unique in that they consist mainly of light hydrocarbons and water, in the case of the distillation systems at the input end of the refinery operation. Much of the light hydrocarbons are returned to the tower as reflux. This operation is probably the single largest application for corrosion inhibitors on the process side of refineries. The water is essentially distilled water that contains various corrosive dissolved gases. In the case of the crude heat exchangers, distillation units, and desalting units, considerable brine can also be present of composition similar to that in oil production. A strong effort is made to remove this brine at a very early point in the refinery so that not only corrosion from it is minimized, but also poisoning of catalysts is prevented. This latter problem can be quite serious, and corrosion inhibitors may be rejected for use in refinery systems if they contain small quantities of poisoning agents.

The *temperature* in the refinery systems varies widely, going anywhere from room temperature at the inlet points to over 1,000° F in the most severe cases. The temperature appears to apply a limit upon the nature of the metal problems and upon the use of inhibitors. Generally, whenever the temperature and pressure are such that water can exist in the liquid state, corrosion is possible and even probable. Thus in towers where water exists as a liquid in some sections and as a vapor in others, the corrosion occurs in the liquid areas. Below 300° F, the corrosion problems are fairly routine and readily susceptible to protection by the use of corrosion inhibitors. This protection includes heat exchangers, distillation units, reboilers, and overhead condensers. Above this temperature, however, many changes in the nature and intensity of the problem take place. Protection by inhibitors drops off rapidly, and 450° F appears to be the limit for effective inhibitor usage. Corrosion as apparent in the intermediate temperature units can drop off rapidly and be replaced by fouling of the equipment. This fouling due to product degradation becomes a very serious problem as it interferes markedly with heat transfer. Finally, at very high temperatures, very severe attack by hydrogen sulfide takes place and presents a problem that is still far from satisfactory solution. In general, one may say that above 450° F, corrosion inhibitors are replaced by either antifouling agents or else by the use of special alloys.

The *fluid velocity* varies greatly, again depending upon the particular process involved and the location in the system. There may be stagnant points where collection or storage tanks exist or else in crevices in some of the units. On the other hand, high-flow velocities (e.g., 20 ft/sec or more), impingement, or reflux conditions are not uncommon. In the case of the impingement attack, particularly severe corrosion can result in heat exchangers wherein partially vaporized streams of corrosive fluids strike hot exchanger tubes at high velocities, as, for example, in reboilers. This problem is discussed in some detail by Freedman and Dravnieks.[36] Laboratory procedures for reproducing this type of attack by duplicating temperature, pressure, velocity, geometry of the system, and stream composition are described by them. They present results obtained by using an oil containing unsaturated hydrocarbons from a petrochemical process. Small amounts of corrosive organic acids and peroxides were formed by oxidation during storage. At an oil temperature of 270° F, the corrosion rate is related to the temperature of the steel specimen tube.

Acidity and *gas content* should be examined together since dissolved gases are the prime cause of the solution acidity, which leads to very severe corrosion. The most common corrosive agents that are in this category are hydrochloric acid, acetic acid, other short-chain aliphatic acids, carbon dioxide, oxygen, naphthenic acids, and hydrogen sulfide. The hydrogen sulfide is the most troublesome member of this group and is the subject of considerable attention.

Hydrochloric acid, when present, is found in the early stages of refinery systems because of hydrolysis of chlorides. It is released when the crude oil is heated in the furnace prior to entering the tower or else when chloride salts are hydrolyzed in the distilling column and concentrate in the overhead condensers. The chlorides involved are calcium and magnesium with the latter having the most effect. Zakharochkin *et al.*[9] show that the calcium salt hydrolyzes to the extent of 3.5 to 10 per cent, the magnesium salt to 50 per cent, while the sodium salt is practically not hydrolyzed under the distillation conditions of atmospheric pressure and temperature. The joint action of hydrochloric acid and hydrogen sulfide is especially severe. The problem is a common one to most sour crudes and the widespread use of desalting units is designed to minimize it. The frequency of acetic acid and the other short-chain aliphatic acids is much greater, however, and a number of low-temperature corrosion problems in overhead systems are associated with their presence. It is not unusual for pH values of 3 or 4 to be present in the accumulators because of these acids. Carbon dioxide and oxygen can be present depending upon the nature of the crude and the particular refinery process. Their contributions to the corrosion problems are similar to those problems in petroleum systems described earlier, with the exception of carbon dioxide corrosion of steam reboilers. The attack appears on the steam side in the form of severe pitting on the lower portion of the steam tubes. The causes are similar to those of boiler corrosion. Typical reboilers on a deisobutanizer are described by Bennett[11] as operating at 250° F, heated by approximately 500,000 lb/day of 45 psig steam. These reboilers show corrosion rates as high as 67 mpy with intense pitting.

Air-oxidation problems are especially noted in high-temperature refinery situations. At these temperatures, the kinetics of the metal-gas reaction are very rapid, and considerable care must be taken in choosing materials of construction where this reaction can become a problem. Skinner, Mason, and Moran[10] describe the resistances of various alloys to this form of corrosion and point out that resistance of iron-nickel-chromium alloys appears to be largely a function of chromium content. If, however, cyclical temperature conditions prevail, then the role of the other elements becomes more important in determining the corrosion resistance. Thus, increasing the nickel content is beneficial since it reduces the difference in thermal expansion between the oxide and the base metal and correspondingly reduces the stress at the scale metal interface.[41] Silicon also improves the oxygen resistance markedly as does aluminum. A detailed knowledge of the proper choice of alloys exists, and therefore failures from simple oxidation are not very common.

Napthenic acids present a unique and severe corrosion problem. For some of the more detailed discussions of this problem the reader is referred to articles by Derungs,[42] Skinner, Mason, and Moran,[10] and Tandy.[43] Appreciable quantities of naphthenic acids are found in crude oils from certain regions, primarily Russia, Venezuela, and Southern California. The plural term acids is used because there are really a group of organic acids that are naphthenic in character, rather than only one. They vary over a wide molecular weight range and have a saturated acid ring structure such as the one given below:

$$
\begin{array}{c}
\quad\ \ CH_2 \\
\diagup \quad\ \diagdown \\
CH_2 \qquad CH_2 \\
| \qquad\quad | \\
CH_2 \!-\!\!-\!\!- CHCOOH .
\end{array}
$$

The type of corrosion caused by naphthenic acids is unique and appears as sharp-edged holes or, in cases where the stream is at high velocity, sharp-edged streamlined grooves. Such typical forms of attack are not observed when processing crudes free from naphthenic acids.[10, 42] Also, in the presence of naphthenic acids, the critical temperature at which severe corrosion can occur is considerably lower than when only sulfur is present. Finally, corrosion can become more active at elevated temperatures without the necessity of water being present.

For a long time, corrosion by naphthenic acids at high temperatures was an extremely serious problem. When mild-steel furnace tubes were used, tube bursts once a week were common. Cast iron-steel return bends had a service life of as short as 80 days and transfer lines of mild steel had to be replaced within 100 days to one year.[42] In recent times, however, alloys were developed that are resistant to naphthenic acids, and so the problem, while still serious, is no longer catastrophic.

The most common locations of naphthenic acid corrosion are in crude distilling plants and in high-vacuum distilling plants processing sour crudes. Equipment most commonly attacked includes hot-oil centrifugal pumps, furnaces, transfer lines, feed and reflux sections of columns, heat exchangers, condensers, bolts, and seams. The question of whether the acids are more corrosive in liquid or vapor phase is still unanswered. Tandy[43] and Derungs[42] found that the naphthenic acids are most active at their boiling points, but that the most severe corrosion generally occurs on condensation, whereas in the vapor state no corrosion takes place. Plant experiences, however, indicate that when a vapor phase exists, corrosion is invariably more serious than in a pure liquid phase. Derungs suggests that an explanation to this contradiction can be that the liquid velocity is considerably increased if vaporization occurs.

A major cause of corrosion in refinery systems is *hydrogen sulfide*. This acid can cause corrosion in low-temperature crude units or it can give serious and often unsolvable high-temperature attack at high-temperature locations in catalyst units. Finally, the phenomenon of hydrogen blistering which is associated with the presence of hydrogen sulfide is one which plagues the industry. Each of these problems is considered separately in the next few pages.

The presence of sulfur in crudes has long been known to be a corrosive factor. Sulfur itself is not the corrosive agent, but hydrogen sulfide is the troublemaker. This acidic gas can be present in the crude as it arrives at the refinery, or it may be created by thermal decomposition of sulfur compounds during processing. Piehl[44] studied this problem in crude distillation units and was able to correlate corrosion rates directly with the amount of hydrogen sulfide evolution in many parts of the crude unit. These parts include the furnace tubes, the atmospheric column, the vacuum column, and the atmospheric column overhead system.

While the corrosive properties of hydrogen sulfide by itself are not as severe in low temperature units as at higher temperature, the attack can become quite serious when the effect of hydrogen sulfide is reinforced by other acidic constituents, and especially hydrochloric acid. The simultaneous action of these two acids is extremely corrosive, with severe attack taking place throughout crude systems, and especially in the upper regions such as the overhead lines and condenser systems.

Of major consequence to the refining industry is high-temperature attack by hydrogen sulfide. This problem has warranted the creation of a special committee T-5B-2 by N.A.C.E. to study it. There have been a number of reports on the subject based on the work of this group, and the reader is referred to articles by Sorell and Hoyt,[45] Backensto *et al.*,[26] Bruns,[46] and Phillips.[29] The Sorrel and Hoyt article is especially valuable as it presents a thorough bibliography of sixty-nine published articles on this subject.

Not all of the hydrogen sulfide is removed in the low-temperature units or even produced there. Many of the sulfur compounds do not decompose to form hydrogen sulfide until high temperatures (400° F or more) are reached. Below these temperatures, intermediate sulfur compounds can be formed which carry through to the subsequent refinery units where they break down as the proper temperatures are reached.[43] Tandy[43] states that on carbon and low-alloy steels the corrosivity of hydrogen sulfide increases rapidly above 500° F and reaches a maximum at about 900° F, above which corrosion due to hydrogen sulfide then stops. Corrosion rates on carbon steel of 2 mils in 1,000 hr at 500° F and 250 mils in 1,000 hr at 900° F were observed.

Hydrogen sulfide attack of catalytic reforming and desulfurizing units differs from the attack on units processing sour crude in that severe attack takes place at much lower sulfur levels and also in that the chrome-moly steels effective in resisting attack at the lower temperatures are ineffective at the higher temperatures. Chrome-nickel stainless steels or aluminum coatings must be used instead. Typical sulfide scales formed in these units are brittle, permeable, lack adherence, and are ineffective as barriers against further attack. In addition, the poor resistance of nickel-rich alloys to hydrogen sulfide is connected with the low melting point of the nickel-nickel sulfide eutectic, while the excellent resistance of the iron-aluminum alloys occurs because of the high fusion point of the sulfide layer formed.[44]

Sorell and Hoyt[45] present a detailed discussion of chemical composition, physical properties, and mechanism of formation of sulfide scales. They reject the concepts of "corrosion catalyzer" or "trace impurity" reasons for the severe hydrogen sulfide attack, but they correlate it with environmental factors. Temperature is the most important variable and an equation derived by them to express its effect on the corrosion rate is as follows:

$$\text{Corrosion Rate (IPY)} = Ke^{0.007t}, \qquad [7\text{-}1]$$

where K is a constant and t is the temperature in degrees F. In correlating the corrosion rate with the hydrogen sulfide content they find that the partial pressure of the hydrogen sulfide in the gas mixture fits observed data better than more commonly used measures such as weight, volume, or mole per cent. High total pressures appear to have no effect on corrosion rates. The rate-time curve is quasiexponential in nature with rapid initial attack, a decrease until about 100 to 200 hr have passed and a constant rate of attack from then on. Cyclic conditions, such as alternate heating and cooling or exposure to alternate reducing and oxidizing atmospheres which are found in catalytic reforming, accelerate corrosion since they cause the sulfide scale to deteriorate. The nature of the diluent gas generally is unimportant, except that hydrogen can help promote attack. Surprisingly enough, contaminants such as small amounts of water, chlorides, or organic acids also have little or no effect on the high-temperature hydrogen sulfide attack.

Backensto *et al.*[26] made a detailed study of high-temperature hydrogen sulfide attack in Thermofor catalytic reformers. They find that it is extremely severe and is affected by both temperature and concentration. Carbon and low-chrome steels normally used as construction materials were attacked badly, and calorizing of carbon steel or use of aluminum coatings was necessary. Further information on the effect of hydrogen sulfide on various materials of construction is given by Bruns.[46] Phillips[29] cites a case of severe plugging of a catalytic reformer by over

600 lb of iron dust after only 50 days operation. The attack was in the first exchanger on the reactor effluent stream. A change in metal to aluminized steel solved the problem.

Blistering of refinery equipment due to hydrogen penetration through the steel has become a major problem in certain units of refinery equipment. Fractionating systems associated with catalytic cracking units are particularly prone to this type of attack. The point of greatest attack appears to be in the second and third stage high-pressure coolers and accumulator drums in the main fractionator gas-compression system. The overhead system from the stabilizer column also is susceptible. Overhead vapor-condensing systems in the absorption and fractionation section are also likely places of attack. Some attack has been observed in the main fractionator, low-pressure coolers and accumulators, and in the upper section of absorber columns. The mechanism of the formation of blisters was discussed earlier in this book in the chapter on boiler-water corrosion. The main change in this system is that the original corrosive attack is due to hydrogen sulfide. Aqueous hydrogen sulfide attacks the steel; atomic hydrogen is formed and passes into the steel leading to eventual blistering. In connection with this mechanism certain facts relating to blistering are generally accepted:

1. *Free water must be present at the spot where blistering occurs.*
2. *Hydrogen sulfide must be present in the process stream for most steels.*
3. *Attack can occur over a wide* pH *range, even in alkaline solutions.*

As a verification of item 2, Marsh,[47] in a study of hydrogen diffusion through steel in acidic solutions, found that the presence of sulfide increases the diffusion rate and that in the case of furnace-grade steel diffusion does not take place unless sulfide is present.

The role of the cyanide ion in hydrogen blistering is an important one. Frequently the presence of the cyanide ion accelerates blistering due to hydrogen sulfide, and an examination of the mechanism involved was conducted by Skei *et al.*[48] They found that the cyanide dissolves the iron sulfide coating and this coating in turn appears to permit blistering. When the cyanide is all used up, blistering ceases. Addition of more cyanide once more dissolves the protective iron sulfide coating and permits blistering. In examining other factors that influence blistering, they also found that it increases with decreasing pH, with increasing frequency of solution replacement, and with increasing air contamination. Under moderate conditions, the reaction is self-stifling by formation of an adherent insoluble coating of corrosion product. Effinger[49] also points out that a high nitrogen content in the feedstock appears to increase the probability of hydrogen attack in gas plants following catalytic cracking. Ciuffreda and Rowland[50] present case histories of three catalytic reactors that suffered permanent damage by hydrogen in one year. Attack varied in severity and location depending upon metal location. Ehmke[34] describes blistering in a gas plant and found it is a function of the *p*H downstream of the water wash tower.

Hydrofluoric acid is not mentioned in the list of corrosive factors, but it causes problems in a specialized application—that of hydrofluoric alkylation units. An N.A.C.E. task group recently reported on results of a questionaire on this problem.[32] The reaction involves isobutane, olefins, and 85 + per cent hydrofluoric at a temperature below 100° F. After the acid is separated out, it can come in contact with a recycler, regenerator, and acid stripper. The weak hydrofluoric is very corrosive to carbon steel, and many units become subject to corrosion when water enters the system from leaks or is concentrated by distillation during operation.

Specific Problems

At this point a brief look at a number of specific systems within a refinery would be of value. It is possible to see the corrosive effect of the variables that were just discussed.

The major problems that lend themselves to successful treatment with inhibitors are at the input end of the refinery. The handling and distillation of crude oil is probably the most common one. The crude can be pretreated to remove hydrogen sulfide and salt and the units in which these operations are conducted are subject to corrosion. The crude still containing some water is then put through a series of heat exchangers to bring it to the temperature needed for the first fractionation step. Corrosion takes place in these iron exchangers as well as in the lines leading to and from them. The temperature changes involved are from room temperature gradually to as high as 500° F. The fluid then enters the fractionator. Corrosion takes place within the tower itself, within the overhead condensing and accumulating system, and in the reboiler. While the material in the tower and reboiler is mostly crude or fractions, the liquid and gases in the overhead system consist of water, acid gases, and very light ends. An extremely corrosive system therefore arises, and if iron counts are measured in the condensed water they are very high, even though the temperature is relatively low. Admiralty metal is frequently used here for this reason and even then inhibiting techniques are usually required.

A number of high-temperature applications were already described in the discussion on hydrogen sulfide attack and are not mentioned here. Instead, some other refinery processes that were not yet discussed or else were barely touched on are examined.

The removal of hydrogen sulfide from such systems as gas that is to be processed, sour water strippers, or crudes presents a situation which is corrosive by its very nature and which must be protected by one means or another. A brief look at the corrosion problems in some of these systems might be of interest. We shall begin with the use of water only for the removal of hydrogen sulfide from refinery gas. Bradley and Dunne[51] describe the operation of a high-pressure water-absorption unit which is followed by simple low-pressure water flashing. The use of amines for systems that contain high acidic gas concentrations becomes undesirable because of high utility operating costs. Their system therefore consists of a high-pressure absorber column, low-pressure degassifying drum, water circulation pump, filter, heat exchanger, and gas scrubbers. Vessels are all constructed of stress-relieved carbon steel, piping of unrelieved carbon steel, and thermometer wells of type 304 stainless steel. Results may be summarized as follows.

1. Corrosion rates of steel are initially very high and then drop rapidly because of formation of a heavy layer of iron sulfide.

2. Hydrogen blistering can occur. Killed carbon steel must be used to reduce susceptibility to this type of attack.

3. Sulfide corrosion cracking can occur. Stress-relieving minimizes it.

Another all-water situation is found in the case of sour-water strippers. The problem here is to dispose of high sulfide waters without causing air or water pollution. For example, some areas call for a 1 ppm maximum of sulfide in the refinery effluent water.[31] Some of the procedures in use involve neutralization by sulfuric or hydrochloric acids, air oxidation processes,[52] biological treatment of phenol-containing water to supplement sulfide stripping,[53] or the use of various flue or fuel gases as stripping media. The process involves a feed tank, pump, pipelines, acid injection system and mixing plates, heat exchanger, tower, and overhead cooler and condenser. The principal water-soluble sulfides present are ammonium sulfides and ammonium hydrosulfides. The system is mostly carbon steel. The sulfides decompose in the tower bottom and significant corrosion can occur in the tower's top section, overhead transfer line, and condenser. Type and severity of corrosion depend on such factors as the pH of the sour-water feed, source of water (e.g., straight run, thermal, or catalytic cracking units), and severity of stripping.[31] Ingredients other than sulfides that can be present are ammonia, formic and acetic acids, cyanides, carbonic acids, and chlorides. Gas velocity and turbulence are also important factors.

Corrosion attack in these strippers is in the form of general attack, pitting, blistering, or combinations of these. Rates on the shell can be as high as 25 mpy, on the condenser tubes 45 mpy, and on the preheat exchanger 10 mpy. In addition, the acid injection point and area immediately downstream can be attacked by the sulfuric acid.

Amines are frequently used for removal of hydrogen sulfide or carbon dioxide from natural and refinery gases, and the amine-glycol process is used for the removal of gases and water from petroleum products. The liquid or gas charge is scrubbed with either monoethanol amine or diethanol amine. During the absorbing and stripping processes serious corrosion problems can arise. In the Girbotol process, for example, corrosion and/or hydrogen attack can occur either in the condensers and reflux accumulator of the ethanolamine reactivator, in the heat exchangers on the "acidic gas enriched" side, or the reactivator reboiler. In typical untreated units rapid hydrogen blistering can occur and corrosion rates of 5 mpy or more are not uncommon. Detailed discussions of amine gas treating-solution corrosion problems are presented by Lang and Mason[22] and Moore.[33]

Dravnieks and Samans[54] present a detailed picture of corrosion problems in ultraforming. They found that the corrosivity of the process streams increases with increasing total pressure and decreases with decreasing concentration of the hydrogen sulfide-hydrogen mixture in the total gas. The corrosion rate in gaseous mixtures containing hydrogen, hydrogen sulfide, and inert gases, including hydrocarbons, was roughly proportional to the 0.4th power of the sum of the sum of the partial pressures of hydrogen sulfide and hydrogen.

As mentioned earlier, corrosion in heat exchangers is prevalent up to temperatures of about 450° F and beyond that point fouling becomes the major problem in the exchangers. The fouling manifests itself in the form of adherent organic decomposition products which build up on the walls and seriously interfere with heat transfer. Even at very high temperatures, the deposits will invariably contain small quantities of iron sulfide or oxide mixed in with organic materials. This fouling strains the economics of the process involved, since the additional heat requirement can mean an appreciable increase in operating costs. In addition, the fouling creates conditions favorable for the development of localized hot spots and rapid metal perforation.

The nature of the deposit is such that it appears to be the breakdown product of unstable organic compounds in the hydrocarbon system. In addition, it is possible that small quantities of dispersed insoluble materials aggregate at these higher temperatures and precipitate on the hot metal walls. A considerable amount of work was conducted by various oil companies directed at locating the causes of these deposits so that they can be eliminated. These efforts were not successful thus far.

The main factor that makes the deposits undesirable is their tight adherence to the walls. On occasion, the deposits are soft, readily removed, and barely interfere with heat transfer. In this case, their presence is of no great consequence, except insofar as they may interfere with catalysts. The same holds true for deposits dispersed in the stream. The major problem therefore appears to be the prevention of the tight adherence to the metal walls rather than necessarily the prevention of deposit formation.

INHIBITION

As is the case with most of the other petroleum-water corrosion systems, the inhibitors used for refinery streams can be divided into the two general classes of inorganic and organic. They are considered according to that subdivision in this section.

Inorganic Inhibitors

The bulk of the inorganic inhibitors could more properly be classified as *neutralizers,* since most of them function almost solely by raising the pH of the system and especially the condensed vapors in the overhead units.

The pH of the water in the crude, the lines, the desalter, and the tower can be somewhat acidic, but the main problem is in the condensed over- head water which can be heavily loaded with hydrogen sulfide, carbon dioxide, acetic acid, and hydrochloric acid. Hafsten and Walston[55] present what is probably the most complete discussion available con- cerning the types of inorganic chemicals used as neutralizers, their methods of application, and advantages and disadvantages. We shall draw heavily upon this reference for the discussions of some of the nonammonia neutralizers.

Sodium hydroxide, as would be expected, is used to a considerable extent. It is generally injected in the hot crude-oil charge line just ahead of the flash drums or crude tower. The purpose at these points is to neutralize any hydrochloric acid that might have been formed by ther- mal hydrolysis of the magnesium or calcium chloride. Alternatively it is believed that the caustic functions by reacting with these salts before they can hydrolyze and by forming the alkaline earth hydroxides and stable sodium chloride. Care must be taken in choosing the point of addition and the amount of caustic to minimize the danger of caustic embrittlement in furnace tubes or excessive coking and fouling brought on by the caustic.

Caustic can also be used to protect desalters, to neutralize acidic oils after acid treatment and sulfur-dioxide extraction. Caustic washing of sulfide-bearing distillates from sour crudes is common. A major draw- back of caustic treatment is the inability to utilize it successfully for overhead streams. This disadvantage occurs because the neutralizing agent must be present at the point where condensation occurs, necessi- tating rather complicated injection devices and great care to choose the correct point of application.

Examples are cited by Hafsten and Walston of the successful applica- tion of caustic to various systems. Dosages used vary from 7 to 100 lb per barrel. Units protected included a pipe still, a crude-oil unit, a battery crude-oil still, and a phenol extraction unit. Equipment protected included vacuum heaters, lines, vacuum-tower internals, condenser coils, crude-oil preheat exchangers, and, in the case of the phenol extrac- tion unit, furnace tubes. In each of the first three cases excessive coking due to the caustic resulted, impairing its usefulness. When the caustic had been chosen for the purpose of neutralizing the naphthenic acids in the phenol extraction unit, increased corrosion at high temperatures resulted.

Sodium carbonate was mentioned by Leboucher and Larbre[56] as well as by Hafsten and Walston. It is frequently used instead of caustic, especially in desalting units where it exhibits easier emulsion-breaking properties. In addition, it will not cause the coking, fouling, or embrittlement that caustic does in furnaces. Disadvantages include the added special equipment needed for its use and the possibility of precipitation because of evaporation, with the consequent plugging of lines and equipment. Leboucher and Larbre cite its use to maintain the pH of a crude oil above 6.5. Hafsten and Walston used it in pipe stills and a battery crude still at dosages of from 7 to 30 lb per barrel. Equipment protected included furnace transfer lines, fractionator bottoms, overhead equipment, and the same equipment in the case of the battery crude still as was the case with caustic. Disadvantages were relatively minor and no coking occurred, although plugging took place in one instance.

The use of *calcium oxide* has been mentioned on one or two occasions. The disadvantages of this material are obvious. It raises a definite possibility of deposits and sludge formation and does not appear to be as effective on a dosage basis as is ammonia. Normally, lime is injected as a gas-oil slurry at a dosage level of 1.5 lb per gal of gas-oil. The principal protection is against high-temperature corrosion in thermal cracking units and viscosity breakers.

One application that is suitable for either lime or caustic soda is the neutralization of naphthenic acids during high-vacuum distillation of lubricating oil stocks.[42] The calcium or sodium naphthenates are then drawn off as side stream in the column above the feed inlet in order to prevent an increase in the ash content of the bottom product.

A new and novel approach to corrosion problems that is proposed by Hoover[57, 58] involves the use of an *ammoniacal copper carbonate* complex. This material added to crude oil in the liquid phase at ordinary temperatures reacts almost instantaneously with the corrosive agents present in the oil to form alkali metal salts and compounds that are stable at the ordinary distillation temperatures and which accumulate in the unvaporized residues. This leaves the vaporized hydrocarbons completely free of constituents which might corrode the distilling, cooling, and condensing equipment. Dosages used are about 2 gal of the ammoniacal copper carbonate containing 5 to 16 per cent by weight of copper to 1,000 barrels of crude oil.

By far the most common neutralizing agent in use today is *ammonia*.

It has a major advantage in that it may pass through part of the stream as a vapor and condense where the condensed acidic water is causing corrosion difficulties. It is volatile so that strongly alkaline solutions cannot be concentrated by evaporation. The ammonia can be injected either in the liquid form through pump techniques or else as the anhydrous gas. Strangely enough, it can, on occasion, be necessary to add water. This addition can occur when water is needed to wash away the deposited ammonium chloride and sulfide salts or else to prevent breakdown of anhydrous ammonium chloride which takes place readily in the presence of hydrochloric acid.

The efficiency of ammonia is a matter of some dispute. Hafsten and Walston[55] state that an excessive quantity of ammonia is needed for complete neutralization and protection. They attribute this requirement to the continuing breakdown of the ammonium sulfide and the subsequent reformation of hydrogen sulfide. On the other hand, Parker[59] claims that only small amounts of ammonia are needed to reduce sulfide corrosion to the vanishing point.

Faerman and Alekseev[60] describe the protection of equipment from corrosion by crude oil by a procedure involving desalting, water washing, and neutralization with ammonia. The severe hydrochloric acid corrosion problems in a large Indonesian refinery were solved by injection of ammonia to neutralize the acidic condensates.[61] Arunov and Barannik[62] mention the use of a saturated aqueous solution of ammonium hydroxide and ammonium benzoate to protect against corrosion caused by petroleum and petroleum products that contain sulfur.

The use of ammonia in overhead systems that contain Admiralty metal or other alloys containing copper can be dangerous. If too much ammonia is added inadvertently and the pH rises much above 7.0, severe corrosion and possibly stress cracking of the copper alloys can take place. This cracking happens in refineries from time to time when trouble is encountered with the automatic injection systems. This is one of the major reasons that an upper pH limit is placed on the use of ammonia and beyond that point the protection is completed by the use of organic corrosion inhibitors. Hafsten and Walston point out that the cracking danger may be overexaggerated since the presence of any one of a number of sulfur-containing compounds can inhibit it. The compounds include hydrogen sulfide, butyl mercaptan, and carbon disulfide. Since the hydrogen sulfide is also generally the corrosive agent, the stress cracking reaction may be considered to be self-stifling.

Organic Inhibitors

The use of *ammonia* today is frequently coupled *with* that of *organic corrosion inhibitors*. The ammonia is added to raise the pH value to a specific point, e.g., 7.0. The inhibitor then provides the remainder of the protection. The correct combination of the two materials provides the maximum degree of protection for the minimum cost.

Much work conducted under our direction indicates that organic inhibitors require constantly increasing dosages for overhead system applications as the pH of the system drops. When adequate inhibitor amounts are added at each pH, however, good protection can be obtained. The organic inhibitors vary among themselves in the rate of change of effectiveness as a function of the pH value. It thus is desirable to choose an optimum pH of operation for each system when combinations of ammonia and amines are used. Obviously the economics dictate a high ratio of ammonia to organic, but the presence of copper points in the other direction and a compromise must be reached.

A rather interesting variation of the ammonia approach is described by Biehl and Schnake.[63] They deliberately operated a crude-oil overhead water receiver at a low pH of 4.3 instead of 7.5 as was the case previously. The amount of ammonium ions and organic inhibitor used were increased, the former being raised from 6 to 10 ppm, and the latter from 10 to 15 ppm. Excellent corrosion control, cleaner equipment, and a reduction of ammonia contamination of the hydrocarbon stream were the results. This procedure was conducted for a five-year period. Maintenance costs were reduced and longer runs at increased charge rates became possible. This low pH operation represents an extreme case, but it proves that protection at even that low pH value (4.3) can be obtained. This low pH approach is now receiving a great deal of attention and may prove to be an effective mode of operation for many refinery situations.

Hur[64] presents another reason for the use of organic inhibitors in combination with ammonia. He discusses the case of alkaline waters bearing high concentrations of sulfides that must be processed for waste disposal. The use of ammonia in overhead systems, while minimizing the overhead corrosion problems, did not lower the sulfide content of the wastes. Use of organic film-forming inhibitors to replace a large portion of the ammonia did reduce the sulfide level in the wastes appreciably. Instead of being absorbed in the water and reacting with the ammonia, the hydrogen sulfide remained in the gas phase from which it was easily recovered. In this application also, sufficient concentrations of organic inhibitors give protection at a pH value as low as 3 and eliminate the need for ammonia completely.

Another interesting application of ammonia is described by Pollard and Lawson.[65] The corrosion problem was that encountered during the removal of Chlorex (bis-2-chloroethyl ether) from paraffinic and naphthenic fractions by distillation. Inhibitors evaluated included alcohols, organic phosphates, mercaptans, amines, and ammonia. Ammonia gave excellent protection but suffered from the formation of ammonium chloride which fouled condensers and lines. By contrast, a filming amine inhibitor did not quite give as good protection but was preferred because it eliminated fouling.

A number of other inhibitors are mentioned for special applications. Fierce and Sandner[66] used 0.4 per cent of *tributyl phosphite* to treat naphtha. The organic phosphite reacts with sulfides and mercaptan sulfur and leaves a distillate which is "doctor sweet" and free of sulfur. *Partially neutralized petroleum phenols* are used to neutralize sulfur dioxide in alkylate produced by the sulfuric acid process. The alkaline component must be soluble in the alkylate.

Naphthenic acids are also used to neutralize sulfur dioxide in cases where an oil-soluble neutralizer is required. The saponified acids are recirculated to the crude-oil towers where they react with the hydrochloric acid and form sodium chloride and regenerate the acid. *Triethanolamine* is also used to combat hydrochloric acid. It is highly alkaline, relatively nonvolatile, and completely miscible in water.

Filming amines that were found to be successful for some of the other petroleum applications also show excellent inhibiting properties in many refinery-stream applications. A few examples of this inhibition are cited here.

Mason and Schillmoller[31] found that filming amines counteracted corrosion on carbon steel in the tower and in the overhead condenser. Close control was necessary because turbulence, high velocities, and low pH values interfered with the formation of the protective films. In fact, they resulted in an increase of the corrosion to two or three times the normal rates. This increase was attributed to the detergent action of this inhibitor which serves to remove partially protective but not sufficiently adherent scales. The same inhibitors that gave good protection at dosage levels of 8 to 12 ppm actually appeared to increase corrosion when present at levels of 1 or 2 ppm.

Freedman and Dravnieks[36] evaluated a series of commercial high-molecular-weight organic inhibitors over a wide range of operating variables and obtained a number of very interesting results. The fact that no one inhibitor was best under all of the operating conditions stood out quite strongly. This fact shows that inhibitors should be chosen on the basis of the specific situation that is to be protected. For example, in studying the effect of pH on four inhibitors, it was found that the best inhibitors at pH of 8 are not nearly as effective at pH of 3 as is one of the poorer pH of 8 inhibitors. The effect of inhibitor concentration is an interesting one. Some inhibitors give a gradually increasing degree of protection as the concentration increases. Others are ineffective until a certain level is reached, at which point they become very effective. Their relative order of effectiveness in an air atmosphere is quite different than in the presence of hydrogen sulfide. The inhibitors also respond in different manners to the effects of temperature and velocity.

Easton[16] describes the successful application of organic film-forming inhibitors with ammonia for western Canadian crudes. Addition of inhibitor on a continuous basis in one tower eliminated both the severe attack in the overhead condenser tubes and shells and the hydrogen blistering in the reflex drums. The ammonia was injected into the tower while the inhibitor was injected into the overhead line. Following shutdowns, the inhibitor dosage was doubled during the first week to build up a protective film rapidly. The ammonia level was maintained to keep a pH value of 6.5 to 7.0 in the water drawoff from the overhead reflux drum. Inhibitor injection rates were closely controlled to minimize foaming. Inhibitor-ammonia combinations were also used to protect overhead systems in vacuum towers as well as in catalytic light ends equipment.

Other instances that are cited in literature for the prevention of corrosion by the film-forming or semipolar organic inhibitors include a discussion by Banta and Murray[67] of how an inhibitor of this type reduced fouling of a heat exchanger by corrosion products, with further improvements resulting from use of an inhibitor that also had demulsifying properties. Dravnieks and Samans[54] describe the use of inhibitors for the prevention of corrosion in ultraforming. They point out that corrosion mitigation must be considered from the viewpoint of the recycle gas itself, the mixture of the recycle gas and the naphtha, and also the naphtha alone. Feed desulfurization can eliminate sulfur corrosion, but it only shifts the problem to the desulfurizer section. In practice, satisfactory protection is obtained by the proper control of the ratio of hydrogen sulfide to hydrogen of the vapor stream by the separation of naphtha and hydrogen-bearing streams, and by the use of suitable inhibitors and alloys or coatings.

Wilcox and Watkins[68] describe the use of organic inhibitors to protect crude-still condenser systems with resistant alloys. Sudbury, Riggs, and Leterle[69] used an organic inhibitor to control diethanolamine attack. Leboucher[70] studied an organic inhibitor for corrosion inhibition of steel condensers used in primary crude distillation. Bradley and Dunne[51] in their discussion of corrosion in a hydrogen sulfide-water absorption plant state that a water-dispersible, amine inhibitor gives protection from sulfide stress corrosion cracking. Connors and Seyer[15] state that the Phillips Petroleum Corporation reduced corrosion in sour gasoline transfer lines by use of a film-forming organic inhibitor.

Fiske and Mernitz[71] give an account of the successful use of organic inhibitors in several applications in one plant. Ammonia injection to a pH of 8 in receiver waters was inadequate for crude and synthetic crude fractionators, Admiralty metal exchanger bundles, and depropanizer overhead lines. Corrosion was markedly reduced by adding 20 ppm of inhibitor to the crude input. The dosage was later reduced and the best injection point was found to be the overhead reflux lines. Ammonia was still used to give a pH of 6.5 to 7.5. Downtime for the pipe still due to restrictions from metallic sulfide accumulation was cut to 25 to 35 per cent of that when ammonia was used alone. The organic inhibitor extended the life of the tower several years beyond that expected with ammonia protection alone.

Dougherty[72] shows that by adding inhibitor to the reflux of a distillation column, much better protection is obtained than when it is added to the feed. Replacement of cooling coils is not needed for 10 years as compared to two to four years without inhibitor.

Prevention of hydrogen blistering can be accomplished by judicious use of inhibitors with other preventive measures. The *polysulfide* ion, which has value for some primary production applications, stops blistering that is encouraged by cyanide ion by reacting with the cyanide to form thiocyanate. Skei *et al.*[48] postulate the following control reaction:

$$CN^- + S_x^= \rightarrow SCN^- + S_{x-1}^=. \qquad [7\text{-}2]$$

Water washing and decreasing the pH also remove the effect of the cyanide. Ehmke,[34] on the other hand, presents data obtained in gas plants which prove that water washing alone does not completely remove the cyanides and is ineffective in preventing blistering. He describes control of hydrogen blistering in the absorber deethanizer by injection of a filming amine inhibitor. Effinger[49] also controls blistering by inhibitors, but he states that water washing and dehydration are also effective. Bonner[73] obtains protection by injecting air to form polysulfides and by maintaining the pH between 7.8 and 8.3. Alternatively, he shows the direct addition of polysulfide to be just as effective.[74]

The specific types of organic inhibitors that are effective in refinery applications are very similar to those used in primary production. This fact makes sense when one recalls that essentially the same corrosive agents are still causing trouble but they are transferred to different equipment and perhaps are concentrated. The major amounts of organic inhibitors in use for refinery process side-applications today are *imidazoline* compounds or derivatives of one type or another. *Rosin amines* and *sulfonates* are also used to a considerable extent, and some use is made of *straight-chain high-molecular-weight amines* and some of their *derivatives*. *Quaternaries* are used only sparingly.

Typical of the imidazoline compounds that are used for this application are the salicylic and sebacic acid salts of 1-(2-hydroxyethyl)-2-heptadecenyl-glyoxalidine that are patented by Luvisi[75] and Sterlin.[76] A wide variety of glyoxalidine derivatives for this purpose can be prepared by the reaction of acids, such as oleic, lauric, stearic, or palmitic, with aliphatic polyamines, such as aminoethylethanolamine, diethylenetriamine, or triethylenetetramine. Salts of these imidazolines are then made with almost any desired acid. The acid does not necessarily function as a corrosion inhibitor, but more likely it gives the product more desirable dispersing and solubility properties. Thompson[77] patented combinations of imidazolines with alkaline agents and long-chain carboxylic acid salts made from them for use in distillation and storage equipment in refineries. He also mentions the use of oil-soluble *alkyl amines* or *alkylene polyamines* instead of the imidazolines.

The formulation problem involved in the use of the imidazolines is typical of those encountered with the other inhibitors. The treatment can be added anywhere in the system. Therefore, it must be soluble or readily dispersible in either water or oil. Means of accomplishing this treatment include the making of various salts or the addition of certain dispersing agents. As an example of this, Rudel and Seitz[78] show that oil-soluble inhibitors can be improved by the addition of *water-displacing agents* such as the esters of a glycol or polyglycol or monoethers thereof. The additive is presumed to function by adhering to the protective film and repelling water from it.

The inhibitor cannot itself be corrosive. This would appear to be a ridiculous statement at first glance, but it is a fact that many inhibitors are corrosive in their concentrated form. It may be necessary to adjust pH, dilute, or even add a corrosion inhibitor to prevent corrosion from occurring at the point of application or in the inhibitor drum. The inhibitor must not promote foaming, even though it should be a good dispersant. For that reason another material may have to be added. Finally, a diluent may be required either because (1) the inhibitors are too viscous to pump in cold weather, (2) the dispersion of small inhibitor quantities requires costly pumps, or (3) the cost of normal spillage of the inhibitor is high.

Various derivatives of rosin amine are used in refineries, primarily in overhead systems. The well-known Rosin Amine D is probably used most often. A derivative made by Saukaitis and Gardner[79] has the structure $RN(CH_2CH_2Ac)_2 \cdot HCl$ in which R is abietyl, hydroabietyl, or dehydroabietyl. This inhibitor is good for acid corrosion and presumably might have value in many overhead systems.

Sulfonates are used in refinery overhead systems to a greater extent than in the production aspects of petroleum. Both commercial and plant prepared sulfonates are used. Many of these materials are available which differ from each other mainly in molecular weight and consequently in water and oil dispersibilty and solubility. In refinery applications, especially when the composition of the liquid being inhibited varies from system to system, a knowledge of the desired inhibitor properties allows an intelligent selection of the proper sulfonate.

A number of long-chain amines and their derivatives are recommended as inhibitors for refinery applications. Salts suggested include the Duomeen T-Sunaptic acid salt,[80] ortho- or pyrophosphate salts of

N-alkyldiaminoalkanes,[81] hexadecylamine-linoleic acid salt,[82] or the octadecylamine-lauric acid salt.[83] Prochinor[84] states that N-derivatives of polyglycols containing 2 to 12 $C_nH_{2n}O$ groups of lower aliphatic glycols, primary amines, and primary-secondary diamines of the aliphatic series containing 8 to 22 C atoms are useful as corrosion inhibitors for refinery equipment.

Many *other types* of inhibitors are advocated for refinery use. These inhibitors include such materials as the condensation product of polyethylene-amines and unsaturated alcohols that are especially effective in Girbitol units.[85] Oil-soluble fatty amides of aliphatic di-amines, such as the oleic acid monoamide of ethylenediamine, are suggested in Britain,[86] while a Japanese patent[87] covers the fusion product of itaconic acid and dodecylamine to give 1-dodecyl-5-oxo-3-pyrrolidinecarboxylic acid. Toekelt[88] describes the corrosion inhibitor made from the reaction of a tetrahydroxy alkyl polyamine with phytic acid. The advent of phytic acid into the corrosion inhibition field is a recent one and preliminary results look very encouraging. This acid and derivatives of it may some day play a large role in corrosion inhibition.

Lead soaps are used in some instances. Schiermeier and Poitz[89] use lead naphthenate as the base for a corrosion-inhibiting formulation, while Fischer[90] combines the lead soap of an oil-soluble petroleum sulfonic acid with the reaction products of fatty acids or oils and certain alkanolamines. This combination is effective in minimizing corrosion in systems where aliphatic or alkanol amines are used to purify gases, especially those with a high carbon dioxide and water content and small amounts of free oxygen.

The corrosion of metallic surfaces by acidic crude petroleum or its fractions is prevented by quaternaries such as dodecyldimethylbenzylammonium chloride.[91] The diphenylguanidine-hydrochloric acid salt halts corrosion of the top of crude distillation columns.[56] A surprising effect is that of certain *peroxides*. Thus, hydrogen peroxide, peracetic acid, performic acid, or tertiary butyl hydroperoxide, stop corrosion of stainless steel in contact with hot aliphatic acids containing appreciable amounts of acetic acid,[92] while benzoyl peroxide minimizes corrosion of certain oils.[93]

A new class of inhibitors which is described by Spivack and Kroll[94] is that of the *iminodiacetic acid derivatives*. The long-chain derivatives of this acid would be expected to have especially good inhibition properties in view of the increased strength of attachment of the polar end of the molecule to the metal surface because of the presence of the nitrogen and the two acid groups. In practice, this mechanism is exactly what happens. These materials were exceptionally effective in laboratory tests and a reduction in their costs and an increase in their ease of manufacture should result in a widespread use. Spivack and Kroll describe the preparation of stearolyiminodiacetic acid as well as the oleoyl and lauroyl acids. They also describe the preparation of other related and effective compounds including the following: stearoyl glycine, stearoyl sarcosine, stearoyl-α-alanine, and stearoyl-carbamoyl-methyl glycine.

A word about inhibitor application techniques is in order here. This particular point is extremely important since the mishandling of an inhibitor can cause it to appear to be ineffective, whereas more judicious application techniques would result in good protection. As in most of the other systems discussed, it is desirable to lay down a protective film as rapidly as possible. The use of a large dosage, e.g., 100 ppm of inhibitor for a few days, can result in the possibility of using a smaller dosage than usual in the normal application with a significant saving in costs over the long run. For example, in one Illinois refinery a corrosion problem existed in a heat exchanger that heated the gasoline feed obtained from a catalytic cracker charged to a debutanizer column. The temperature was 230° F, the pressure was 200 psi, and liquid water was present. Considerable quantities of hydrogen sulfide and chlorides were also present. Treatment was started at a level of 48 ppm of inhibitor for two days and gradually cut down, so that after about 45 days treatment could be maintained at a level of 3 ppm with perfect control.

In addition to dosage control, the selection of proper points of inhibitor injection can be very important. It is necessary to insure that the proper concentration of inhibitor reaches the points at which the corrosion is occurring. For example, if the corrosion is all in the overhead condenser system, then addition of a relatively nonvolatile inhibitor to the feed entering a tower may not be the proper application technique. Similarly, addition of concentrated inhibitor to a point in the system where the inhibitor does not disperse readily, but instead remains in one large accumulation, must be avoided. There may also be times when the corrosion is widespread and it is advantageous to add small amounts of inhibitor in a number of locations rather than to add it all in one place.

The development of corrosion inhibitors for application below 300° F in refineries appears to have progressed quite rapidly, and most of the corrosion problems in that category can be solved today by proper use and choice of inhibitors. Above 300° F, there are many problems that are far from solution by inhibitors. This fact becomes especially true as the temperature rises even higher. There would appear to be a considerable need for research for inhibitors that will function at the higher temperatures. The development of antifouling agents at elevated temperatures is proceeding at an accelerated rate, however, and great strides are being made in solving this vexing problem.

Antifouling agents in use today appear to be based on the principle of preventing the organic deposits from adhering to the walls of the heat exchangers and thus preventing adverse effects on heat transfer properties, rather than preventing the formation of the solid organic matter. For this reason, all of these materials are extremely strong dispersing agents. When possible, detergent materials are used which also have good corrosion-inhibiting properties. This use renders these materials more versatile and promotes their acceptance by the refiner.

Johnson and Thompson[95] patented a material for this purpose which is the salt of an organic aliphatic dicarboxylic acid and a glyoxalidine. An example of this salt is the sebacic acid salt of 1-(2-hydroxyethyl)-2-heptadecenyl-imidazoline. This material, which is also a very effective corrosion inhibitor, is used over a wide dosage range. In one example cited in the patent, 15 ppm of a diluted formulation which contained 12.5 per cent of active material was added to the crude feed to a heat exchanger that had been fouled to the extent that its operating outlet temperature was lowered from the regular range of 235 to 245° F to 210° F. After five weeks of treatment, the heat exchanger operated normally and all fouling deposits had been removed. A different approach was taken by DeChellis,[96] who reduced the formation of insulating deposits on heat-transfer surfaces in contact with straight run or cracked petroleum fractions by heating the oil with an aqueous alkaline solution of a salt of an organic acid. The treating agent together with the fouling material was then separated and the treating agent regenerated.

There are many other corrosion problems in refineries that are being treated successfully by corrosion inhibitors. These problems deal mainly with storage problems and are discussed in detail in the next chapter together with other storage and transportation problems involving both crude and refined products.

REFERENCES

1. Daino, P. Refinery corrosion problems and protective measures. *Metallurg. ital.*, **46**, Suppl. to No. 5, 47–50, 1953.

2. Robb, R. M. Corrosion problems in oil refining. *Australasian Engr.*, 48–53, Apr. 7, 1956.

3. Tait, E. J. M. The problem of corrosion in petroleum refining. Part I. *Corrosion Prevent. and Control*, **2**, 25–30, 44, Dec. 1955.

4. Hijikata, H. Corrosion problems and their solution in the refinery. *Shoseki Giho*, **3**, 1–9, 1959.

5. Tourret, J. Refinery corrosion problems. *Corrosion et Anti-Corrosion*, **4**, 389–99, Dec. 1956.

6. Tourret, J. Corrosion problems in refineries. *Corrosion et Anti-Corrosion*, **4**, 389–99, 1957.

7. Cavallaro, L. The use of corrosion inhibitors in the petroleum industry. *Corrosion et Anti-Corrosion*, **7**, 417–33, Dec. 1959.

8. Refinery problems in Russia. *Corrosion Technol.*, **6**, No. 11, 335–6, Nov. 1959.

9. Zakharochkin, L. D., *et al. Khim. i Tekhn. Topliva i Masel.*, **3**, 46–52, 1959.

10. Skinner, E. N., Mason, J. F., and Moran, J. J. High-temperature corrosion in refinery and petrochemical service. *Corrosion*, **16**, No. 12, 593t–600t, Dec. 1960.

11. Bennett, H. Use of high-molecular-weight inhibitors in petroleum refineries. *Corrosion*, **11**, No. 2, 19–27, Feb. 1955.

12. Mason, J. F., Jr. Analyses of some corrosion problems in petroleum refineries. *Petroleum Refiner*, **30**, 124, Oct. 1951.

13. Mason, J. F., Jr. Some corrosion problems in petroleum refineries. *Petroleum Engr.*, **24**, No. 2, C10, C13–C14, C16–C18, Feb. 1952.

14. Connors, J. S., and Seyer, C. L. How Phillips solved six gas plant corrosion problems. *Petroleum Refiner*, **37**, No. 5, 177–82, May 1958.

15. Connors, J. S., and Seyer, C. L. Solutions to corrosion problems in light-hydrocarbon liquids plants. *Proc. Am. Petrol. Inst.*, Sect. III, **38**, 39–50, 1958.

16. Easton, C. L. Corrosion control in petroleum refineries processing western Canadian crude oils. *Corrosion*, **16**, No. 6, 275t–80t, June 1960. Table 7-1 reprinted by courtesy of CORROSION.

17. Easton, C. L. Corrosion control in petroleum refineries processing western Canadian crude oils. *Oil in Can.*, **12**, No. 27, 76–80, 82, 84, 86, 1960.

18. Uhl, W. C. How six plants cut corrosion rates by 95 per cent. *Petroleum Processing*, **7**, No. 2, 190–7, Feb. 1952.

19. Garner, F. H., and Hale, A. R. Corrosion in the petroleum industry. Parts I, II, III. *Petroleum* (London), **17**, Nos. 11–12, 407–10, 440–2, 1954; **18**, No. 1, 12–4, 1955.

20. Anon. Tidewater's Delaware refinery. *Oil Gas J.,* **55,** No. 21, 159–98, May 27, 1957.

21. Brooke, M. Casebook of a corrosion chemist. *Petroleum Refiner,* **32,** No. 8, 131–2, Aug. 1953.

22. Lang, F. S., and Mason, J. F., Jr. Corrosion in amine gas treating solutions. *Corrosion,* **14,** No. 2, 105t–8t, Feb. 1958.

23. Riesenfeld, F. C., and Blohm, C. L. Corrosion in amine gas treating plants. *Petroleum Refiner,* **30,** 97–106, 1951.

24. Murray, C. A., and Furth, M. A. Corrosion-prevention in a T.C.C. gas plant. *Petroleum Engr.,* **23,** C3, C5–C8, July 15, 1951.

25. Murray, C. A., and Furth, M. A. Corrosion-prevention program for T.C.C. gas plant at its Smith's Bluff refinery. *Oil Gas J.,* **50,** 112, 115–6, May 24, 1951.

26. Backensto, E. B., Drew, R. D., Manuel, R. W., and Sjoberg, J. W. High-temperature hydrogen sulfide corrosion in Thermofor catalytic reformers. *Corrosion,* **12,** No. 5, 235t–44t, May 1956.

27. McFaddin, D. E. H_2S and CO_2 corrosion of carbon steel in natural-gas processing plants. *Oil Gas J.,* **50,** No. 32, 97–8, Dec. 13, 1951.

28. Swerdloff, W. What we've learned in 20 years about gas dehydrators. *Oil Gas J.,* **55,** No. 17, 122–9, Apr. 29, 1957.

29. Phillips, C., Jr. High-temperature sulfide corrosion in catalytic reforming of light naphthas. *Corrosion,* **13,** No. 1, 37t–42t, Jan. 1957.

30. Prange, F. A. Corrosion in a hydrocarbon conversion system. *Corrosion,* **15,** No. 12, 619t–21t, Dec. 1959.

31. Mason, J. F., Jr., and Schillmoller, C. M. Corrosion in sour water strippers. *Corrosion,* **15,** No. 7, 358t–62t, July 1959.

32. N.A.C.E. Task Group T-5A-6. Summary of questionnaire replies on corrosion in HF alkylation units. *Corrosion,* **15,** No. 5, 237t–40t, May 1959.

33. Moore, K. L. Corrosion problems in a refinery diethanolamine system. *Corrosion,* **16,** No. 10, 503t–6t, Oct. 1960.

34. Ehmke, E. F. Hydrogen diffusion corrosion problems in a fluid catalytic cracker and gas plant. *Corrosion,* **16,** No. 5, 246t–52t, May 1960.

35. Sherwood, P. W. Flocculation and flotation of aqueous refinery wastes. *Werkstoffe u. Korr.,* **10,** No. 9, 541–4, 1959.

36. Freedman, A. J., and Dravnieks, A. Evaluation of refinery corrosion inhibitors. *Corrosion,* **14,** No. 12, 567t–70t, Dec. 1958.

37. Report of Panel on Cost of Corrosion in Refinery Equipment, *A.P.I. Subcommittee on Corrosion,* 1953–1954.

38. Bregman, J. I. Comptes Rendus du Symposium European sur les Inhibiteurs de Corrosion. *Annali dell' Universita di Ferrara,* N.S., Sez. V., 549–72, 1961.

39. Hulbert, C. C., and Rippetoe, J. A. Organic inhibitor controls refinery corrosion. *Oil Gas J.,* **52,** No. 15, 120–7, Aug. 17, 1953.

40. Landis, U. J. Estimating the cost of corrosion in refinery crude units. *Corrosion,* **16,** No. 10, 479t–86t, Oct. 1960.

41. Eiselstein, H. L., and Skinner, E. N. Effect of composition on the scaling of Fe-Cr-Ni alloys subjected to cyclic temperature conditions. A.S.T.M. S.T.P., 165, 1954.

42. Derungs, W. A. Naphthenic acid corrosion—an old enemy of the petroleum industry. *Corrosion,* **12,** 617t–22t, Dec. 1956.

43. Tandy, E. H. Inspection of petroleum refinery equipment. *Corrosion,* **10,** No. 5, 160–4, May 1954.

44. Piehl, R. L. Correlation of corrosion in a crude distillation unit with chemistry of the crudes. *Corrosion,* **16,** No. 6, 305t–7t, June 1960.

45. Sorell, G., and Hoyt, W. B. Collection and correlation of high-temperature hydrogen sulfide corrosion data. *Corrosion,* **12,** No. 5, 213t–34t, May 1956.

46. Bruns, F. J. Effect of hot hydrogen sulfide environments on various metals. *Corrosion,* **13,** No. 1, 27t–36t, Jan. 1957.

47. Marsh, G. A. Some notes on hydrogen blistering—a technical note. *Corrosion,* **10,** No. 3, 101–2, Mar. 1954.

48. Skei, T., Wachter, A., Bonner, W. A., and Burnham, H. D. Hydrogen blistering of steel in hydrogen sulfide solutions. *Corrosion,* **9,** No. 5, 163–72, May 1953.

49. Effinger, R. T. Hydrogen blistering in cat cracker gas plants. *Oil Gas J.,* **55,** No. 41, 222, 224–5, Oct. 14, 1957.

50. Ciuffreda, A. R., and Rowland, W. D. Hydrogen attack of steel in reformer service. *Proc. Am. Petrol. Inst.,* **37,** 116–28, 1957.

51. Bradley, B. W., and Dunne, N. R. Corrosion measurements in a hydrogen sulfide-water absorption pilot plant. *Corrosion,* **13,** No. 4, 238t–42t, Apr. 1957.

52. Smith, A. G. *Proc. A.P.I.,* 36 M (111), 313–9, 1956.

53. McCabe, J., and Eckenfelder, W. W., Jr. *Biological Treatment of Sewage and Industrial Wastes.* Vol. I: *Aerobic Oxidation* (New York: Reinhold Publishing Corporation, 1957).

54. Dravnieks, A., and Samans, C. H. Corrosion control in ultraforming. *Proc. Am. Petrol. Inst.,* **37,** Sect. 111, 100–15, 1957.

55. Hafsten, R. J., and Walston, K. R. Neutralizers and inhibitors today. *Petroleum Refiner,* **34,** No. 5, 163–9, May 1955.

56. Leboucher, B., and Larbre, J. B. Corrosion inhibitor for crude oil stills. Fr. 1,054,768, Feb. 12, 1954.

57. Hoover, C. O. Control of the corrosion of petroleum refining equipment. Brit. 822,841, Nov. 4, 1959.

58. Hoover, C. O. Preventing corrosion of petroleum refining equipment. U.S. 2,913,406, Nov. 17, 1959.

59. Parker, M. E. Ammonia for acid corrosion in refineries. *Oil Gas J.,* **50,** No. 37, 114, Jan. 21, 1952.

60. Faerman, L. I., and Alekseev, V. M. Corrosion of petroleum refining equipment. *Sbornik, Stud. Rabot Azerbaidzhan. Ind. Inst.,* No. 2, 79–86, 1956.

61. Anon. Maintenance is a major challenge at this Indonesian refinery. *Oil Gas J.,* **51,** No. 33, 274–6, Dec. 22, 1952.

62. Arunov, R. I., and Barannik, V. P. Corrosion inhibitor. U.S.S.R. 120,277, May 4, 1959.

63. Biehl, J. A., and Schnake, E. A. What Ohio Oil learned in 5 years of processing crude oil at low *p*H. *Oil Gas J.,* **57,** No. 23, 125–8, 1959.

64. Hur, J. J. Organic inhibitors improve ammonia control, reduce sulfide in refinery waste waters. *Corrosion* (New Sec.), **10,** No. 2, 1, Feb. 1954.

65. Pollard, W. R., and Lawson, J. V. Corrosion rates. *Ind. Eng. Chem.,* **47,** 2282–3, 1955.

66. Fierce, W. L., and Sandner, W. J. Preventing corrosion during distillation of sulfur-containing naphtha. U.S. 2,899,387, Aug. 11, 1959.

67. Banta, N. S., and Murray, C. A. How corrosion inhibitor solved refinery problems. *Oil Gas J.,* **53,** No. 45, 126–7, 1955.

68. Wilcox, M. J., and Watkins, F. M. How to control internal corrosion of crude still condensers. *Oil Gas J.,* **50,** No. 45, 290–3, Mar. 17, 1952.

69. Sudbury, J. D., Riggs, O. L., and Leterle, J. F. Lab inhibitor stops DEA corrosion. *Petroleum Refiner,* **37,** 183–4, May 1958.

70. Leboucher, B. Corrosion inhibitors. *Corrosion et Anti-Corrosion,* **3,** 147–63, 1955.

71. Fiske, C., and Mernitz, P. Use of organic corrosion inhibitor in refining processes. *Corrosion,* **12,** No. 7, 350t–4t, July 1956.

72. Dougherty, P. F. Corrosion inhibition in petroleum-distillation. U.S. 2,908,640, Oct. 13, 1959.

73. Bonner, W. A. To stop hydrogen attack. *Petroleum Refiner,* **37,** No. 7, 111–4, 1958.

74. Bonner, W. A., Burnham, H. D., Conradi, J. J., and Skei, T. Industry probes means of combating hydrogen attack on steel in refinery equipment. *Oil Gas J.,* **51,** 100, June 8, 1953.

75. Luvisi, G. W. Corrosion inhibitor for liquid hydrocarbons. U.S. 2,668,100, Feb. 2, 1954.

76. Sterlin, A. Glyoxalidine salts of dicarboxylic acids as corrosion inhibitors for liquid hydrocarbons. U.S. 2,773,879, Dec. 11, 1956.

77. Thompson, R. B. Distillation and storage equipment in refineries. U.S. 2,920,030, Jan. 5, 1960.

78. Rudel, H. W., and Seitz, W. Corrosion inhibitors containing water-displacing agents. U.S. 2,911,309, Nov. 3, 1959.

79. Saukaitis, A. J., and Gardner, G. S. Derivatives of rosin amines for corrosion prevention. U.S. 2,758,970, Aug. 14, 1956.

80. Oxford, W. F., Jr. Corrosion protection of ferrous metals. U.S. 2,914,475, Nov. 24, 1959.

81. Chenicek, J. A. Corrosion inhibitor for petroleum products. U.S. 2,848,414, Aug. 19, 1958.

82. Ogasawara, K. Use of high-molecular fatty amines as corrosion inhibitors. *Shoseki Giho,* **2,** 138–42, 1958; *Chem. Absts.,* **53,** No. 7, 6587, Apr. 10, 1959.

83. Fujii, S. Corrosion inhibitor for metals. Japan 860, Feb. 11, 1956.

84. Societe de produits chimiques industriels et organiques, Prochinor. Corrosion inhibitors. Fr. 1,112,514, Mar. 15, 1956.

85. Sudbury, J. D., Riggs, O. L., and Leterle, J. F. Corrosion studies in alkanolamine systems. *Proc. Am. Petrol. Inst.,* Sect. 111, **38,** 51–8, 1958.

86. Esso Research and Engineering Co. Petroleum-base corrosion-preventing compositions. Brit. 812,149, Apr. 22, 1959.

87. Wada, N., Shimada, M., and Nakagawa, S. Anticorrosive agent for metals. Japan 262, Jan. 23, 1958.

88. Toekelt, W. G. Water-soluble corrosion inhibitors. U.S. 2,923,599, Feb. 2, 1960.

89. Schiermeier, K. F., and Poitz, H. A. Rust-inhibiting composition. U.S. 2,661,296, Dec. 1, 1953.

90. Fischer, P. W. Corrosion prevention in gas recovery systems. U.S. 2,776,870, Jan. 8, 1957.

91. Esso Standard Societe anon. francaise. Corrosion inhibitors for petroleum fractions. Brit. 798,620, July 23, 1958.

92. Millidge, A. F. Prevention of corrosion of stainless steel in distillation of organic acid mixtures. Brit. 800,214, Aug. 20, 1958.

93. Sato, S. J. Effect of peroxide compounds on the anti-corrosive character of oils. *Chem. Soc. (Japan) Ind. Chem. Section,* **58,** No. 1, 26–7, Jan. 1955.

94. Spivack, J. D., and Kroll, H. Rust-preventive lubricating compositions containing amidocarboxylic acids. U.S. 2,790,778, April 30, 1957.

95. Johnson, C. E., and Thompson, W. H. Control of the formation of deposits from hydrocarbon oils in heat exchangers. U.S. 2,908,624, Oct. 13, 1959.

96. DeChellis, I. V. Increasing the on-stream time of heat-transfer units in petroleum refining. U.S. 2,941,937, June 21, 1960.

8

Petroleum—
Storage and
Transportation

Another major area of corrosion problems that are solved by the use of inhibitors is that of the storage or movement of both crude and refined products. Even though these materials already were treated with corrosion inhibitors at least once and frequently more often during production or refining, they become corrosive and require treatment. The reasons for this apparent anomaly will become apparent during the technical discussion of the problem later in this chapter.

The major areas covered in this chapter are discussed in terms of the two major classes as indicated by the title of this chapter. In addition, transportation is subdivided into pipelines and tankers.

LITERATURE

Perhaps the best sources of information on the problems discussed in this chapter are the periodic reports that are compiled and published by the following committees of N.A.C.E.:

1. *T-2 Pipeline Corrosion.*
2. *T-2-E Internal Corrosion of Product Pipelines and Tanks.*
3. *T-2-F Internal Corrosion of Crude Oil Pipelines and Tanks.*
4. *T-3-H Tanker Corrosion.*

The minutes of the meetings of these committees are usually extremely informative as they contain informal discussions by engineers who are working with these problems. These committees also conduct surveys which result in worthwhile information.

The corrosion of oil-industry storage tanks is discussed by Hume.[1] He presents the results of a survey on this subject, reviews the corrosive factors and solutions, and gives a selected bibliography of tank-corrosion articles with abstracts. Newberg and Barrett[2] review the problem of vapor-zone corrosion in sour-crude tanks; a problem that cannot be separated from that of the liquid phase. Tandy[3] presents an analysis of the important factors governing corrosion in light-oil storage tanks, the corrosion mechanism, and control measures.

Pipeline corrosion is the subject of a number of papers. The general topic is discussed by Deering,[4] while Smith, Curry, and Rush[5] review corrosion experience in Shell's product pipelines. Parker[6] describes the use of corrosion inhibitors in a pipeline. Murdison[7] presents his experiences in corrosion control on a products pipeline in Canada. Vincent-Genod[8] presents a similar discussion of corrosion control techniques used in the Paris-LeHavre pipeline. Meyer and Sheldahl[9] discuss the types of inhibitors that are used to solve the corrosion problem. Geoffray and Giampaoli[10] detail the use of inhibitors in the internal protection of gas pipelines.

Probably the best documented of the three phases of corrosion is the problem of tanker corrosion. Although the papers in this field are not too numerous, they are very complete in their evaluation of the problem, its causes, and possible solutions. Perhaps the best of these papers consist of a publication of a symposium on control of internal corrosion of tankers.[11] The symposium consisted of three parts, as follows:

1. *The Nature of Corrosion and Its Control.*
2. *Inhibitors in Cargo.*
3. *Corrosion Control in Practice.*

The first part, prepared by Jupp, is broken into a detailed discussion of the extent of the problem, corrosion rates and costs, methods of control, types of control, and a selected bibliography. The second part of the symposium, presented by Malcolmson, Quimby, Pingrey, and Oosterhout, is a detailed discussion of inhibitors. The third section by Kurz describes the application of a full corrosion control program to a fleet of tankers. Several other symposia on this subject have been held. Two very good ones were sponsored by the American Petroleum Institute. One was held at Absecon, New Jersey,[12] and the other in San Francisco, California.[13]

Hurlen[14] discusses the nature and the causes of corrosion in tankers carrying crude oil. Coy[15] goes into the general problem, while Dillon[16] emphasizes countermeasures. A number of other papers are devoted to the control problem. Karepina and Sushkov[17] as well as Oosterhout, Stanley, and Quimby[18] discuss corrosion inhibitor techniques. Koehler[19] and Maass and Merrick[20] review other approaches to controlling corrosion in addition to inhibitors, while Hodgson[21] restricts his article to a study of ballast tank protection.

ECONOMICS

No meaningful figures are available to establish corrosion costs for storage tanks. The reason for this lack is readily apparent. Tanks can come in almost any size and be used for many different purposes. The cost of corrosion must be considered to be a function of many different factors. Obviously the catastrophic destruction of the tank itself presents a measurable sum of money. In addition, however, such factors as the cost of downtime repairs, the loss of product or its undesirable contamination, the need for periodic inspection and cleaning procedures must all come into the total economic picture. A measure of these against the cost of inhibitors or other protective methods is extremely difficult, but it would make sense that protection at reasonable inhibitor levels might be very economical.

The life of storage tanks is variable. An interesting report by Parker[22] states that on the Gulf Coast two tanks in identical service, one for 26 years and one for seven years, both collapsed within two weeks of each other. On examination they showed practically identical conditions and corroded areas. The large economic loss attendant with the collapse of an oil tank would appear to favor adequate treatment costs.

The ability to estimate the damage caused by corrosion in pipelines or the possible limit on corrosion inhibition costs is also limited. The loss of pipe may be minor compared to the loss of product, the cost of the downtime, and the repair work necessary. Quimby[23] states that a major United States pipeline reported several years ago that $800,000 per year was involved in reconditioning badly corroded lines. Another calculated a saving of almost $400,000 for a 250-mile products pipeline if corrosion could be controlled and a thinner wall pipe used with safety. In discussing inhibitor costs, he points out that in most cases, this technique is the most economical protective measure. However, in isolated instances, such as short movements by pipelines, the unit cost per barrel-mile can become excessive and other means such as coatings must be substituted.

There are a wide variety of figures presented in literature for the cost of corrosion in tankers. All the authors are in agreement on one thing however: the corrosion suffered by oil tankers actively engaged in the transportation of crude and refined products is extremely high since these tankers are subject to very severe corrosion. Sudbury, Shock, and Mann[24] in 1954 estimated the cost of corrosion of the existing United States tanker fleet at $360 million during the next 20 years. This figure was reached on the premise that the normal useful life of a ship is 20 years and the corrosive condition is the transportation of clean rather than crude products. Estimated to be in service were 1,700 tankers, of which 700 were on clean service. Assuming a minimum cost of $400,000 to maintain each ship in clean service for 20 years, the $360 million figure was reached.

Other authors feel that those figures are too low. Thus, Watkins[25] and Koehler[19] both state that the cost of corrosion for a tanker in clean service can be as high as $150,000 per year. (It will be pointed out later that a ship cannot operate for 20 years in clean service. Rather, the estimated 20-year life is based on a combination of both clean and dirty service.) In arriving at his figures, Koehler states that it cost Esso $73,000 per year for reconditioning and repairs for each of its 16 T-2 vessels per year of clean service. Replacement of bottom shell plating due to pitting-type corrosion has cost an average of $29,000 per year for each year of dirty service. When other items such as interim repairs, cleaning and rust removal, pipeline, valve, and pump repairs, and initial cost and revenue loss, all of which are directly attributable to corrosion in cargo compartments, are added to the clean cost figure, Koehler arrives at the $150,000 annual figure. Jupp[26] presents figures for costs to Gulf-East Coast tankers that are in alternate clean and dirty service for their 20-year life period. For a fleet of 20 ships in service, half of which are in each type of service, his estimated total corrosion costs are $1 million per year, three fourths of which is for those in clean service.

Interesting cost figures on British ships are also presented. One 12,000-ton Shell tanker was so badly corroded after seven years of service that the cost of renewing bulkheads amounted to about $468,000.[27] Another report[28] states that the cost (for a working life of 20 years) of tank corrosion in 18,000-d.w. vessels in the white oil trade may amount to $1,560,000; i.e., $78,000 per year. There have been cases where a 12,000-d.w. ship had to be repaired after eight years of service. The total cost of repairs and demurrage came to $65,000. It thus becomes apparent that price is no object as far as inhibitors are concerned. Thus far they have been relatively unsuccessful, but a considerable research effort is still under way to find effective materials in view of the favorable economics. In the meantime, other protective techniques have gained more favor.

THE PROBLEM

Storage Tanks

The problem is very simple to picture. A product, either crude or finished to various degrees, is stored in a tank. The tank can be of almost any size. Corrosion occurs at the bottom, along the sides, at the waterline, and in the vapor zone, both on the sides and the top. For purposes of discussion here, the crude problem is considered first and then the problem of finished products is considered.

The crude oil tanks include those that are erected at the production sites in order to store the produced oil before it is shipped to the refinery, as well as those which store the crude at refineries. The former tanks are usually field-erected and may not be required to have as long a life as the larger and more expensive ones that are used at refineries to receive the crude. The material of construction is invariably structural steel, although on occasion galvanizing may be employed. The galvanizing is generally limited, however, to those small tanks of bolted construction that have a capacity of less than 10,000 barrels, such as those commonly used on producer's leases and at small pipeline pump stations where the oil is gathered.[29] The refinery storage tanks are almost always made of steel.

The liquid handled in the tanks is the crude as it is produced, with contaminants such as appreciable quantities of brine, sand, and dissolved gases. The corrosivity of the system is similar to that in the producing well. The liquid at the refineries can be further contaminated by iron corrosion product picked up during the transportation process from the well site.

Corrosion at the bottom of the tank is associated with the presence of brine, which settles out, and hydrogen sulfide or other acids that may be present. It is quite severe and general in nature. Attack on the sides of the tank is less severe since they are primarily in contact with oil. Water line attack will be severe. The ring showing the highest corrosion rate values is determined by the most frequent tank level. Another form of corrosion that must be reckoned with is the attack on the vapor space above the liquid. This attack is commonly caused by hydrogen sulfide vapor, water vapor, or oxygen, or combinations of the three. It can lead to intensive pitting, since localized strongly acidic areas can be created. This will apply to the sides of the tank and also the roof. While the problem of vapor-phase corrosion is generally not treated in this book, it must be considered in this particular section because of the intimate relation to the liquid makeup.

Hume[1] reports that results of a survey of tank corrosion show that severe corrosion in the vapor zones is not necessarily a function of the sulfur content, since examples are reported wherein severe corrosion occurred over a sulfur range of 0.02 to 3.0 per cent. It is more closely related to the hydrogen sulfide, oxygen, and water contents as indicated above. Factors that increase the concentrations of those corrodents tend to increase corrosion severity.

Corrosion of refined products storage tanks represents a more complicated situation. Tandy[3] states that it varies directly with the API gravity of the oil. Tanks handling black oil (10° API and heavier) have shell corrosion rates of less than 1 mpy, while gasoline tanks of 55° API and lighter have rates as high as 20 mpy. There is also considerable discussion concerning the relative corrosivity of kerosene and gasoline. While it is generally agreed that gasoline (50° API and lighter) is very corrosive, some authors say that kerosene (50° API and heavier) is not very corrosive, while others say it is and that, depending upon the conditions, its corrosivity is anywhere from one third that of gasoline to equal to it. A substantial amount of research on relative corrosivities of kerosene and gasoline was conducted by Putilova and his associates.[30-32] They suggest that an autocatalytic oxidation of kerosene occurs when it is in contact with steel. Tandy[3] states that in actual practice the corrosivity is generally low, but that maximum corrosion takes place on the top course and on the roof and supports of cone roof tanks. In floating roof kerosene tanks, the corrosion rate approaches that of gasoline in the lower third of the tank and then drops rapidly to the atmospheric rate near the top.

The corrosive composition of the liquid is quite different in the case of refined or partially refined products. There is no large amount of brine that covers the bottom. Instead, entrained or emulsified water settles out. These small droplets of water become highly corrosive as they extract salts and acids from the refined products. Severe localized pitting then follows. In many systems, a blanket of water is deliberately introduced into the bottom of the tank to prevent the localized corrosion. The dilution of the water that comes out of the oil is sufficient so that the water blanket is only mildly corrosive and can be readily removed and replaced before the concentration of corrosive agents becomes too heavy.

Other corrosive factors include dissolved oxygen, the frequency with which the tank is filled and emptied, the temperature, the vapor pressure of the oil, and the type of roof. Tandy[3] points out that the solubility of the water is a function of the temperature and not of the nature of the oil, whereas the solubility of the oxygen varies inversely with the temperature and directly with the API gravity of the oil. He also studied the scales that accumulate on the shells of cone roof gasoline and solvent tanks. He found that in the lower part of the tank, tubercules are present that contain ferrous hydroxide adjacent to the metal under a hard cover of hydrated ferrous and ferric oxides. Elsewhere the scale is a thin, hard adhering layer of magnetite ($Fe_3O_4 \cdot nH_2O$). Over this scale is a layer of red-brown hematite (Fe_2O_3).

An extremely interesting observation has been made by Parker.[22] She points out that the corrosivity of refined products has been increasing during the past several years and attributes it to the fact that finished products have been improved greatly by refineries. Consequently, practically no gums are left after evaporation. These residuals would have tended to act as protective coverings, preventing access to the bare metal surface by oxygen and water. Tandy, however, attributes the increased corrosion to the use of more light components in present-day gasoline and the greater capacity of these light ends for oxygen.

Pipelines

Pipelines can also be examined in terms of their corrosion problems in both crude service and when carrying refined products. The former situation prevails when the crude is being transported from the producing area to the refineries, and the latter exists from the refinery to the seller. An example of severe corrosion in a pipeline ell fitting is seen in Figure 8-1.

Even after water separation prior to entering the pipeline, crudes can still be very corrosive. A certain amount of the water which has not been removed comes out at the low points in the line. This fact is especially true when the water in the pipeline drops to a temperature that is cooler than that at which the original separation took place. This water is quite corrosive for the same reasons as indicated previously for crude storage tanks. The crude can also become saturated with air, with the result that oxygen is available in considerable quantities for severe attack.

The accumulation of rust in the pipeline has undesirable consequences in addition to the danger of perforation and consequent loss of product. The rust is rough and increases the friction factor, thus reducing the pumping efficiency.[23] It must be removed by the use of a scraper that is forced through the line under hydraulic pressure. This removal can become almost a weekly operation. It is expensive, time consuming, and interferes with operations. Quimby[23] describes how on occasion rust built up to the extent that the scraper could not function and became stuck. An extremely costly procedure then took

FIGURE 8-1. Corrosion in a Pipeline Ell Fitting

Photograph Courtesy of Petrolite Corporation

place when the scraper had to be located accurately, the line excavated and cut, the scraper and rust accumulation removed, and a new piece of pipe installed. The operation took about four days, during which time the line was out of service. This plugging occurred several times each year for some lines. It should be pointed out that this particular problem could develop for either crude or refined products.

Refined products are more corrosive to pipelines than are the crudes. This fact is evident by analogy with the earlier discussion regarding their relative effects on storage tanks. The problem of contamination of the finished product by corrosion product also becomes a serious one, especially in the case of fuels for military use. The attack tends to become more localized in nature than was the case with crudes and is therefore more dangerous. In addition, when large quantities of water are present, as with crudes, provisions can be made for periodic draining of the water from places in the pipelines where it is evident that it will accumulate because of low points. On the other hand, when the water is present only in droplets at a variety of locations, no protective measures can be taken.

Tankers

The corrosion problems in tanker transportation are thoroughly documented in a number of articles because of the magnitude of the economics involved. The term problems is used because there is really a series of separate problems involved, and control measures for only a single one may be of little value insofar as the entire picture is concerned. For that reason, this discussion begins with a look at the life cycle of a typical tanker and the corrosive conditions encountered during that cycle.

A tank in a typical ship is first loaded with cargo: either crude or refined products. The cargo, which also contains considerable water is transported (under a humid salt environment) to a point at which it is unloaded. The tank then sits empty for a brief period except for the remains of the cargo which may be on the bottom and clinging to the sides. During this period it is also exposed to the humid, salty atmosphere. It is then cleaned by a process known as *Butterworthing*. This process involves washing down the sides with hot salt water under pressure to remove the remnants of the adhering cargo. Then the tank once again sits empty for a period of time; this time with sea water coating its sides. It then is reloaded. Let us assume that on this trip it is used as one of the ballast tanks. In that case, the cargo has become sea water. After arrival at destination, the water is drained, the tank sits empty for a while, cargo is reloaded, and the entire cycle begins again. It thus becomes apparent that a number of very corrosive situations occur during the operational cycle and that they are so different from each other insofar as the causes of corrosion are concerned that any solution to the problem must take them all into account rather than just one part. For example, use of an inhibitor in the cargo only protects that part of the cycle and may not have much effect on the life of the tank.

Consider first the nature of the storage tanks. These tanks are made of steel because of the economic impossibility of using more expensive materials of construction for so much surface area. The steel is sometimes coated with various organic or metallic coatings to combat corrosion. A good deal of research is going on in that area, and the chances of success are at least as good as by means of inhibitors.

While corrosion is general all over the metallic surface, there also is severe local corrosion that occurs at hard points or at points of maximum flexure or strain. Specifically, this corrosion occurs at the points of working of the structure or the points of high cyclic stress, not necessarily at the parts of the structure under the heaviest loads or stress. A distinction must be drawn between uniformly distributed stresses and local hard points where cyclic stress or fatigue play an important part.[26] Examples of these points that are especially subject to severe local corrosion are presented by Jupp.[26] Some of these are the following:

1. The limber hole in the horizontal web below a bulkhead plate.

2. The web and bulkhead plates themselves.

3. The middle of the panel in a fluted bulkhead where the shape of the sides of the flute allow the flexuring to take place.

4. The bracket through bulkheads for shell longitudinals. This condition does not occur at brackets adjacent to a cargo pipe through the bulkhead which helps stiffen the plate at the nearby brackets and thereby restricts the working of the plate.

Jupp points out that cyclic stresses or fatigue have accounted for rapid failures at those points. In each case the scale was broken, presumably because of flexure or working of the plate. In each case the condition was more marked on the upper surface of a horizontal stiffener than on the underside, and for brackets with their points up rather than on deck longitudinal brackets with their points down. It was noted that a considerable amount of moisture was draining down on these points from the scale above them. This moisture probably contained brine and resulted in intense local electrolyte concentrations.

The cargo being carried is divided into two categories: clean and dirty. The term *clean* refers to refined products such as gasoline, while the term *dirty* denotes crudes. Their relative corrosion rates vary, but it is generally accepted that clean cargoes are two to three times as corrosive as dirty cargoes. When possible, tankers are therefore assigned to one type of service for a certain number of years and then switched to the other type. Sudbury, Shock, and Mann[24] state that after seven to ten years of clean service, corrosion is usually sufficiently advanced so that the ships must be put into the less corrosive dirty service or the ship owners must prepare to spend large sums in repairs of failures due to corrosion.

In all likelihood the lesser degree of corrosivity of the crudes is due to a number of reasons. For one thing, the crudes tend to emulsify water much more readily than do the refined products. This emulsification prevents their settling out and causing local attack. The crudes also appear to contain corrosion-inhibiting substances as part of their composition. These materials cover the metal surface with an adherent protective film and prevent contact by the corrosive substances. Refining generally removes these protective ingredients. The crudes also contain natural detergents which keep the metallic surfaces clean of corrosion products and minimize the formation of local cells. Under certain circumstances, the crudes can also become quite corrosive. This corrosivity is generally the case when they are high in sulfur content and especially when sulfate-reducing bacteria are present. The result is intense local corrosion similar to that produced by these bacteria in secondary production.

During transportation of the cargo, corrosion can occur in a number of places. The bottom of the tank can be corroded by the water that settles out. Weak points along the sides are attacked in a manner similar to that already discussed. Attack is especially severe at the level of the liquid being transported. Here the alternate exposure to the oxygen from the air during the sloshing around replenishes this corrosive ingredient. Severe attack also takes place in the tank above the liquid phase because of vapor phase attack by oxygen and splattered or condensed electrolyte.

After unloading, the tanks sit empty except for adhering product for a period of time. During that time a more corrosive situation exists than was the case during the time the tank contained cargo. Now the corrosive conditions that prevailed at the cargo line and in the vapor phase during the transportation are present throughout the entire tank. The accessibility of the entire tank to oxygen speeds corrosion throughout.

The next step, the process of Butterworthing, is an especially corrosive one. All the ingredients needed for severe attack are present. The remaining protective film of organic material is removed from the metal surfaces, sea water makes contact throughout, and a high temperature exists. The pressure at which sea water is applied makes an erosive condition which accelerates attack at points that were already weakened. Oxygen is present throughout the system. After the process of Butterworthing is completed, the tank sits empty awaiting the next cargo. The corrosive situation is now similar to that which existed before the Butterworthing, except that all the protective organic films and inorganic scales have been removed and the last barriers to severe atmospheric corrosion under humid salt conditions have disappeared.

When the ship is loaded with ballast, still another corrosive condition appears. Here is a steel tank that has sea water in part of it and a corrosive vapor phase above it. This part of the cycle can lead to fairly serious damage if proper control measures are not taken. After the ballast is unloaded, the same corrosive situation that occurred before loading prevails. Reloading with a new shipment of cargo then completes the cycle. It therefore becomes apparent that protective measures must be devised to guard against each phase of the cycle. Either one control technique that will serve throughout all the phases is necessary or else separate control techniques must be used for each phase. In the case of the use of corrosion inhibitors, the latter course appears to be the more realistic and the disadvantages of such a course of action have weighed heavily against inhibitor use. It is more likely that a combination of inhibitor application together with a universal technique such as cathodic protection or protective coatings may be the final solution.

LaQue and May[11] present a number of interesting comments with regards to the corrosion problem. In considering the relative corrosivities of the various phases of the cycle, they conclude that corrosion by a salt atmosphere averages about twice that of steel immersed in sea water. Corrosion by a clean cargo (gasoline) is about the same as that by a salt atmosphere. It is about the same in the vapor phase in clean service whether or not ballast is used on return trips. The use of ballast, however, reduces corrosion of submerged surfaces by as much as 50 per cent. Corrosion by dirty cargo is about one-third that of clean cargo in both submerged and vapor phases. Corrosion in vapor phases is from 50 to 75 per cent greater than that of submerged phases in clean service and four times greater than in dirty service.

Other observations made by LaQue and May include the following:

1. Roughening of a surface by corrosion increases the rate but not the local intensity.

2. The empty side of a plate separating the ballast from an empty tank accounts for about two-thirds to three-fourths of the total corrosion due to sweating from differences in temperature of the two sides.

3. Removal of the scale accelerates corrosion.

4. Replacing salt water spray by fresh water reduces the corrosion rate somewhat but not as much as would be expected. This fact is true because of the increased oxygen solubility. The greatest value would be attained by the removal of hydroscopic salt particles.

Another interesting observation was made by Rear Admiral Wheelock.[11] He states that the Navy uses sea water displacement gasoline storage systems. The tanks are always kept full, and as gasoline is removed from the top, sea water is allowed to enter at the bottom. Air which enters with the sea water is either dissolved or is removed with the gasoline. Use of this method for many years in several ships revealed little or no attack. At the same symposium, Kurz revealed that the use of cold sea water for Butterworthing instead of hot sea water at low pressures rather than at high pressures reduced corrosion very markedly.

INHIBITION

Storage Tanks

Corrosion inhibitors used for storage tanks can be of three types: (1) Conventional *water-soluble inorganic* inhibitors such as nitrites or polyphosphates can be added to the water phase. This addition is frequently done when a water layer is deliberately maintained in the bottom of the tank. (2) *Oil-soluble organic* inhibitors such as those described earlier can be added to the oil phase. These inhibitors are generally quite effective. Their composition may be severely limited by military specifications in the cases of aviation gasoline or jet fuel. (3) *Volatile amines* can be added with other inhibitors. Their purpose is to protect the roof and the parts of the wall which are above the oil-air interface.

Let us examine each of these three types of protection separately. In considering the inhibition of the water layer first, it is obvious that conventional water inhibitors should have merit when a layer of water is maintained on the bottom of the tank either by design or because there is no choice. The economics are such that continual replenishment of the inhibitor because of frequent withdrawal of the water layer leaves no choice but to use the cheaper inorganic inhibitors. *Nitrites* are commonly used for this purpose. Krotov and Klubova[33] made a detailed study of the effectiveness of nitrite for prevention of attack by either distilled water or sodium chloride which comes out of aviation gasoline, normal gasoline, or kerosene. *Polyphosphates* are occasionally used for this purpose. A different approach was taken by Arunov and Barannik.[34] They recommend the use of a solution containing a mixture of *ammonium hydroxide and ammonium benzoate* for this purpose, especially when the corrosion is due to the presence of sulfur compounds. Another category of inhibitors that is being added to the water phase is that of *borax-nitrite*. Here one obtains a buffering action that keeps the *p*H of the water at an alkaline point where corrosion is much less, together with the straight corrosion inhibitor properties of the nitrite. Wisherd[35] proposed the addition of a small amount of an oil-soluble ammonia neutralized *sulfonated mixture of polyalkylated benzene*. He adds it in the ratio of 3 to 10 lb per 1,000 barrels of gasoline or fuel oil. The inhibitor presumably distributes itself between both phases and protects by a three-layer mechanism similar to that described earlier.

A wide variety of inhibitors are being used for addition to the oil phase. These same inhibitors are being used for most gasoline-water applications rather than for storage tanks alone. There are certain requirements for an inhibitor of this type, many of which requirements are derived from the fact that the inhibitor, or at least a substantial portion of it, remains with the fuel until its final use for gasoline, heating purposes, or in aviation. Quimby[23] summed up the requirements by saying that each of these inhibitors must:

1. Be an effective inhibitor under varying field conditions.
2. Be readily soluble in the product.
3. Have no adverse effect on other chemical or physical properties of the product.
4. Be free of deposit-forming ash.
5. Be permanent in its effectiveness and not removed or made ineffectual by handling or storage.
6. Not promote emulsification of water.
7. Be compatible with other inhibitors or additives, such as for corrosion, gum, dyes, or tetraethyl lead.
8. Be nontoxic.
9. Be easily handled.
10. Be odorless.
11. Not be seriously affected by traces of contamination resulting from normal refining or transportation handling.
12. Be insoluble in water.
13. Be low in cost.[23]

In addition to all these, another very important requirement is that the inhibitor be capable of passing all the requirements that are laid down for use of additives in military fuels. Probably the most difficult of these is the requirement that the inhibitor shall in no manner promote water retention by the fuels. The nature of the inhibitors is such that they are good surface-active agents and therefore promote emulsification. In addition, this ability to prevent the entrained or dissolved water from settling out is one of the desirable attributes of a good corrosion inhibitor.

Probably the most successful and commonly used inhibitor for this purpose is a commercial material known by the trade name of *Santolene C* and manufactured by the Monsanto Chemical Company. It is speculated that this inhibitor is related to a series of patents such as the one by Faust.[36] In that patent he used a combination of *dicarboxylic acid dimer* and an oil-soluble *ester of orthophosphoric acid* having the general formula $RPO(OH)(:O)OR'$. The dicarboxylic acid dimer is produced by the condensation of two like or unlike moles of polyolefinic monocarboxylic acids having 16 to 18 carbon atoms, such as by polymerization of linoleic acid or else as the residue of the dry distillation of castor oil in the presence of caustic. An example of the phosphate is bis-(diamylphenyl)orthophosphate.

The dimer acid by itself is an excellent corrosion inhibitor. Another example of a formulation containing it as the major ingredient is the inhibitor of Boies and Nordsell.[37] In this one, the dimer acid is used together with an equal amount of a wetting agent, such as the alkylarene sulfonates or polyoxyethylene glycol ethers. Still other inhibitor combinations based on the dimer acid use salts of it with various amines such as glyoxalidines or fatty amines. Beiswanger and Burnard[38] patented a combination of the dimer acid with a reaction product such as that of soybean oil and diethylenetriamine which was ethoxylated. O'Kelley and Weltman[39] patented a mixture of the dimeric acid with the oil-soluble quaternary dimethyldialkylammonium chloride. Monoamides of the dimer acid are reported to be good corrosion inhibitors by Rocchini.[40] He uses C_{18} primary alkenyl amines.

Acylsarcosines which have the formula $RCON(CH_3)CH_2COOH$ are effective either by themselves or as amine salts. When combined with imidazolines they are especially effective. Martin and Titsworth[41] patented that combination, as well as the addition of tall oil to it. Similar materials such as iminodiacetic acid and especially its long-chain derivatives and various glycines are also effective. A number of these are enumerated by Spivack *et al.*[42, 43] They are claimed to be even more effective than the dimer acids.

Itaconic acid salts such as the reaction product with soya-aminopropylamine[44] are effective inhibitors, as are tall oil salts. Combinations of the latter with various imidazolines are described by O'Kelley, Titsworth, and Martin.[45] *Oleic acid* salts of various amines are frequently used. Thus their salts with such amines as the C_{18} trimethylene diamines[46] are used as gasoline inhibitors. Maleic anhydride adducts of oleic acid and its derivatives are described by Sato[47] as being effective for a large number of different metals.

Many *phosphate* salts are reported in patent literature. Chenicek[48] finds that the ortho- or pyrophosphate salts of N-alkyldiamino-alkanes work. A British patent[49] teaches the use of salts of *n*-alkylamines containing 8 to 18 carbon atoms with di-"oxo-octyl" hydrogen phosphate.

Thompson[50] uses an alkyl acid phosphate salt of an N-alkyldiaminoalkane. Cantrell and Peters[51] report the use of the neutral addition product of a C_2 to C_4 olefin oxide and a dialkylorthophosphoric acid with an oil-soluble aliphatic amine containing 8 to 18 carbon atoms for gasoline. Rudel and Gargissa[52] in a novel approach make an inhibitor by mixing the ammonium salt of a petroleum sulfonic acid with the ammonium salt of isooctyl phosphoric acid. This inhibitor is used primarily for heating oils.

The use of *sulfonic acids* and their salts is also a common one. Thus,

King and Thielcke[53] report that the sodium, calcium, magnesium, barium, zinc, ammonia, or amine salts of dinonylnaphthalenesulfonic acid are effective inhibitors in motor fuels. Varvel[54] uses hexadecyldimethylamine petroleum sulfonate for a variety of applications. Noel[55] prepared formulations of (1) metallic petroleum sulfonates, (2) other inhibitors such as lanolin, amines, or amido amines, and (3) an oil-soluble polyisobutylene. A mixture of a lead alkylbenzenesulfonate and a polyglycol was used by Fontana.[56]

Examples of *other reported inhibitors* are as follows:

1. Rudel and Gargisa[57] report the use of two synergistic inhibitors such as (dodecylthio) acetic acid and dioctylphosphoric acid.

2. Mayhew, Copes, and Williams[58] use the reaction products of certain organic amines with γ-butyrolacetone or γ-valerolacetone.

3. Thompson[59] makes long-chain carboxylic salts of imidazolines, alkyl amines, or alkylene polyamines and uses them with an alkaline agent.

4. Kelley[60] found the reaction product of naphthenic acid and nitric acid, using ammonium metavanadate as a catalyst, to be effective.

5. Mayhew and Jelinek[61] trimerize propargyl alcohol to form mixtures of tri-tris(hydroxymethyl)-benzene and treat it with various acid chlorides in the presence of pyridine to form esters. These compounds are good inhibitors.

6. Schiermeier and Poitz[62] dissolve a paraffin wax, petrolatum, or oxidized petrolatum with lead naphthenate in an aromatic solvent to form their inhibitor.

7. Barauch and Fontana[63] report that polyalkylene glycol esters of oleic acid are effective for storage of motor fuel.

8. Kleinholz[64] shows the value of oxidized monocrystaline wax.

9. Preston[65] and Pines and Spivack[66] describe the rust preventive properties of nonylphenoxyacetic acid. The lead salt or amine salts of this material are also effective.

10. Amine inhibitors effective by themselves include N-coco-1,3-propylene diamine, and the tallow analogue.

The third and final type of inhibitor that is used in storage tanks is the vapor phase inhibitor. There are a wide variety of materials used for this purpose. They all have in common the fact that they are very volatile and after being added to the liquid in the tank they volatilize very rapidly and coat the roof and the portions of the sides that are exposed to the vapor only. The chemicals involved are usually *low-molecular-weight amines* and *organic nitrites,* such as *cyclohexylammonium nitrite.* These chemicals are usually added directly with the oil-soluble inhibitors that are used for the liquid wetted portion. Jones and Barrett described the development of volatile inhibitors for this purpose and especially for control of attack by hydrogen sulfide. They find that the most widely used inhibitor for this purpose is *diethylamine*. It gives good inhibition at dosages as low as 5 ppm, is completely miscible with oil and water, volatilizes easily, and can be handled conveniently.

Other techniques that are used include pressure storage, gas blanketing, floating roof tanks, or special breathing systems. The objective of these approaches is to keep the amount of oxygen that is drawn into the system to a minimum.

Pipelines

The earlier solutions to the problem of pipeline corrosion involved the use of *inorganic* inhibitors (primarily nitrite or chromate) and gave spotty results. The inorganic inhibitors were supposed to dissolve in water and provide protection at the points where water dropout occurred. The length of the pipelines, however, defeated the practicality of this approach. An interesting variation of it was patented by Brown.[67] He adds an anodic corrosion inhibitor such as *sodium phosphate* to a soluble plug which is inserted to clean out the pipeline. The plug also has an abrasive and a wetting agent and is quite effective. By and large, however, pipeline users have abandoned the use of inorganic inhibitors and have gone over to oil-soluble organics.

Many of the *oil-soluble organics* that are described above for use in storage tanks are also used in pipeline applications, since the products can be identical and the corrosion problems are similar. For that reason, identification of many inhibitors is not repeated here. In a similar manner, inhibitors that are effective in primary or secondary production of petroleum are also effective for the transportation of these crudes by pipelines to the refinery. Thus, for example, a case of 95 per cent protection was reported by the use of 8 lb of an *aliphatic quaternary* per 1,000 barrels of oil. *Acetate salts* are also valuable because they are cheaper and also display paraffin dispersing properties. The acids by themselves can be used successfully for pipeline applications. The *sulfonates* and the *dimeric acids* are both presumably anodic inhibitors and also form the multilayer protective films that already were discussed.

An inhibitor that was not already mentioned is that of Oosterhout[68] who used an oxidized, deoiled *microcrystalline wax*. Potassium permanganate and atmospheric oxygen are used for the oxidation at high temperatures and pressures.

Corrosion inhibitors for natural gas lines are suggested by Hughes and Lembcke[69] and Geoffray and Giampaoli.[70] The former author utilizes a *quinoline-acetone* water-soluble inhibitor to combat the corrosion caused by the formation of carbonic and other organic acids as a result of water condensation. The latter authors use *volatile inhibitors,* such as cyclohexylamine, morpholine, and diethylamine, and add them to the gas.

Examples of the value of inhibitors for pipeline corrosion are presented by Quimby.[23] He cites one case where use of a high-molecular weight dibasic acid inhibitor at 10 ppm resulted in restoration of throughput and efficiency to as-new conditions. Scrapers were run until most of the rust was swept from the lines and then their use was discontinued. Essentially 100 per cent protection was obtained on 900 miles of pipeline for six years. He cites another case where five different inhibitors are being added at the same time, one by each company using the pipeline, with no adverse compatibility effects.

The inhibitor dosage level depends upon the condition of the pipeline. In the case of a new line or a relatively uncorroded one, only minimal dosages are required. The inhibitor appears to lay down a monomolecular film over the whole length of the pipeline and further inhibitor is needed only to keep this very thin film in good repair. If the inhibitor is added to a corroded pipeline, however, large quantities are consumed because of the absorption of the inhibitor by the corrosion product. It is much cheaper and more effective to remove the corrosion product from the lines before beginning inhibitor addition.

In general, when oil-soluble inhibitors are being used for pipelines, there is very little corrosion difficulty. Inhibitors at a low cost present an ideal solution to this problem, regardless of the type of product being transported.

Tankers

A number of protective systems were devised, none of which is completely satisfactory. In addition to inhibitors for the cargo and ballast, these methods include tank coatings (both plastic and metallic), spray systems for protection of the empty tanks against atmospheric corrosion, sacrificial anodes in ballast tanks, and gas blanketing of the loaded cargo as well as maintaining an atmosphere of dry air in empty compartments. The purpose of the gas blanket is to keep the oxygen that is in contact with the metal at a minimum. Since we are concerned with inhibitors here, we restrict our discussion of these other approaches only to the cases when they supplement inhibitor use.

A wide variety of inhibitors were tested and fairly well encompass the range of both inorganic and organic materials. *Water-soluble* inhibitors in the ballast are not very successful and are costly. Malcolmson *et al.*[11] make the flat statement that application of water-soluble inhibitors to the ballast would cost more than replacing the steel. On the other hand, Dillon[16] found that in laboratory testing, orthophosphoric acid is effective at dosages of 50 to 100 ppm. Rogers[71] also found that aniline phosphate, pyridine phosphate, phosphoric acid, and alkylated pyridine *phosphates* all are effective at dosages of 20 to 150 ppm for ballast tanks, provided that the pH is maintained at 4.5 or greater. Another means of inorganic inhibition is the simple one of keeping the pH of the corrosive water film *above 10,* where attack is greatly retarded.

A number of *organic* materials are suggested for addition to the salt water ballast. Pier[72] recommends the use of an inhibitor which is made by oxidizing de-oiled macrocrystalline paraffin waxes and then by reacting them with quaternary ammonium hydroxides, such as phenyl trimethyl ammonium hydroxide. Other inhibitors were tested that are similar to those used in secondary recovery of petroleum. In general, however, this approach has suffered from economics and a poor degree of protection.

A unique approach was devised, however, by means of which it is possible to achieve satisfactory inhibition of the ballast tanks by organic inhibitors at reasonable cost. This technique is known as *flotation* and is similar to that described earlier for storage tanks. The procedure involves placing a small layer of inhibitor (10 to 20 gal) on top of the ballast water. The inhibitor rises and falls with the level of the water and thus is present in concentrated form at the interface where the attack would normally be the most severe. In addition, the areas that were covered by water and then were left dry as the level receded are now covered with inhibitor and another very corrosive situation is under control. By lowering the level of the tank down to the bottom, the entire area of the walls can also be covered by inhibitor, although the problem of continual replenishment of the coated film is not solved.

A number of inhibitors are used successfully in this flotation technique. Westlund and Rudel[73] patented a combination of a heavy distillate petroleum oil, a substituted imidazoline, a metal sulfonate, and an unsaturated fatty acid. Lanteri[74] covered a film of a naphthene-base residual oil thinned with light lubricating distillate and containing tall oil. He states that several passes of the coating film (by raising and lowering the water level) may be necessary to form an adequate film on the walls. Keating and Heisig[75] used the same combination as Lanteri, but they also added a diamine to give added inhibition.

A detailed study of the effectiveness of the flotation procedure was conducted by Oosterhout *et al.*[18] They used a dosage of 16 gal of inhibitor in a 9,000 gal tank during ballasting operations. Half of the inhibitor was added at the start of the operation and the other half when the tank was nearly full. The tank was then completely filled with water and the inhibitor was pressed against the underdeck. Test results indicated that the inhibitor reduced corrosion on the underdeck (i.e., above the liquid level) from 75 to 90 per cent, but that it did not materially affect corrosion below the top of the liquid.

A common technique for protecting empty tanks that is being used with considerable success is that of *spraying* or *fogging* inhibitors. The inhibitors are sprayed after each unloading of cargo through a system of nozzles. Fresh water is used as the dilution medium. In the case of fogging, a mixture of inhibitor solution and inert gas or steam is injected into the tanks as a fine mist which condenses on all of the exposed surfaces in the tank. In either event, the purpose is to protect against corrosion during the period that the tank stands empty by covering the surface with an inhibitor and thus blocking off the corrosive oxygen.

Sudbury, Shock, and Mann[24] reported that sodium dichromate and alkaline sodium nitrite sprays are effective in preventing the atmospheric corrosion. The dichromate is limited in its use because it reacts with residual leaded gasoline and precipitates out lead chromate. The sodium nitrite does not appear to have a long protective film life. A number of additional inhibitors are evaluated by those authors who found that soluble oils and sulfonates are also very effective. Their best results were obtained from a formula containing calcium sulfonate, sodium sulfonate, and resin amine stearate as a tackifying agent. Kurz[11] found sodium silicate to be ineffective, but that a mixture of sodium nitrite and hydroxide with a wetting agent added gave about 90 to 95 per cent protection in test runs of empty tanks. Treseder[76] found that spraying the walls that contain petroleum residues with an alkaline solution of pH greater than 7.8 will both clean and inhibit them.

The fogging procedure was studied by Oosterhout *et al.* for various inhibitors. Using a field test dosage of 15 gal per 9,000 barrel-tank, they found that an oil-soluble compound was more effective than a water-dispersible one, and both were superior to water-soluble and water- and oil-insoluble compounds. The use of steam for fogging and the use of air for fogging gave comparable results. Fleishhacker[77] found that fogging gave better results than spraying with the same inhibitor. Wool grease and its derivatives or fatty acid reaction products with long-chain aliphatic amines or diamines gave satisfactory results.

The addition of *oil-soluble inhibitors to the cargo* is an obvious method for protecting that part of the cycle. This addition has been an effective technique. Inhibitors that have shown merit in other gasoline and kerosene applications are also effective here. Dimerized acids are used frequently for this purpose.[11] They remain effective, at least in part, during ballast or empty return voyage. The Butterworthing procedure, however, removes the residual film from the wall.

A number of attempts have been made to incorporate inhibitors into the Butterworthing procedure. Thus far they have met with little success, although the use of *inhibitors with fresh water* in the Butterworthing process has shown a reduction in corrosion rates. In all likelihood, the lesser corrosivity of fresh water is the major factor.

An interesting approach that is being taken in the tanker problem with increasing frequency is that of a *combination of cathodic protection and use of organic inhibitors.* Antropov[78] presents a detailed discussion of the reinforcement of the electrical protection by the change in the degree of cathodic protection due to the inhibitor. Koehler[19] cites test results showing that a combination inhibitor-magnesium anode protection is more effective than a full-scale anode use.

REFERENCES

1. Hume, J. S. Corrosion of oil-industry storage tanks. *Oil Gas J.*, **55,** No. 45, 153–4, 156, 158, 160, Nov. 11, 1957.

2. Newberg, A. H., and Barrett, J. P. How to control vapor-zone corrosion in sour-crude tanks. *Oil Gas J.*, **53,** No. 28, 189–90, 192; *Petroleum Engr.* **26,** No. 12, D22–6, 1954.

3. Tandy, E. H. Corrosion in light oil storage tanks. *Corrosion,* **13,** No. 7, 427t–32t, July 1957.

4. Deering, R. G. Here's how to control corrosion in pipelines. *Oil Gas J.,* **53,** 80, Oct. 18, 1954.

5. Smith, S. S., Curry, W. J., and Rush, E. H. Corrosion experience in Shell's products pipelines. *Corrosion,* **7,** 20, Jan. 1951.

6. Parker, I. M. Use of corrosion inhibitors in products pipelines. *Corrosion,* **3,** 157, Apr. 1947.

7. Murdison, A. R. Experiences in corrosion control on a petroleum products pipeline. *Can. Chem. Processing,* **38,** No. 8, 38–40, 1954.

8. Vincent-Genod, J. Use of internal corrosion inhibitors in the Paris–Le Havre pipeline. *Bull. Assoc. Francaise Techniciens Petrole,* No. 112, 405–18, July 31, 1955.

9. Meyer, R. H., and Sheldahl, D. B. Is your inhibitor doing its job? *Oil Gas J.,* **54,** No. 72, 224–8, 231–2, Sept. 16, 1956.

10. Geoffray, C., and Giampaoli, A. Use of corrosion inhibitors in the gas industry. Case of pipeline production. *Rev. Inst. Franc. Petrole et Ann. Combustibles Liquides,* **15,** No. 1, 186–216, Jan. 1960.

11. Society of Naval Architects and Marine Engineers. Symposium on control of internal corrosion of tankers. *Trans. Soc. Naval Architects and Marine Engrs.,* **60,** 382–441, 1952.

12. American Petroleum Institute. Report of meeting, Absecon, N.J., June 13, 1956. *A.P.I. Central Committee on Transportation by Water,* 1956.

13. American Petroleum Institute. Tanker corrosion symposium, San Francisco, May 20, 1957. *A.P.I. Central Committee on Transportation by Water,* 1957.

14. Hurlen, T. Central Inst. for Industry Research, Oslo, Norway, Mar. 1956.

15. Coy, A. J. *British Pet. Magazine,* **10,** June–July, 1958.

16. Dillon, C. P. Countermeasures for control of internal corrosion of a tanker ship. *Corrosion,* **11,** No. 9, 393t–405t, Sept. 1955.

17. Karepina, M., and Sushkov, B. Use of corrosion inhibitors for the protection of tank surfaces of tankers. *Morskoi Flot,* **18,** No. 12, 15–6, 1958.

18. Oosterhout, J. C. D., Stanley, M. E., and Quimby, W. S. Corrosion prevention in tankers and storage tanks by fogging or flotation with an inhibitor solution. *Corrosion,* **15,** No. 5, 241t–4t, May 1959.

19. Koehler, J. F. Controlling internal corrosion of tank ships. *Corrosion,* **15,** No. 11, 557t–60t, Nov. 11, 1959.

20. Maass, R. H., and Merrick, R. D. Protection against corrosion in light-oil tank ships. *Werkstoffe u. Korr.,* **10,** No. 5, 305–11, May 1959.

21. Hodgson, K. V. Ballast tank protection. *Corrosion Prevent. and Control,* **4,** No. 12, 45–6, Dec. 1957.

22. Parker, I. M. Corrosion in light oil storage tanks. *Corrosion,* **13,** No. 12, 838t, Dec. 1957.

23. Quimby, W. S. Oil-soluble inhibitors for controlling corrosion in tankers and pipelines. *Corrosion,* **16,** No. 3, 9–18, Mar. 1960. List reprinted by courtesy of W. S. Quimby and CORROSION.

24. Sudbury, J. D., Shock, D. A., and Mann, F. W. A promising spray-applied inhibitor of internal corrosion of oil tank ships. *Corrosion,* **10,** No. 8, 253–8, Aug. 1954.

25. Watkins, F. M. Report, Absecon, N.J., June 13, 1956. *A.P.I. Central Committee on Transportation by Sea Water,* 1956.

26. Jupp, W. B. The nature of corrosion and its control. *Corrosion,* **9,** No. 11, 388–94, Nov. 1953.

27. Anon. Corrosion of oil tanks. *The Motor Ship,* **32,** 46, May 1951.

28. Anon. Refinery problems in Russia. *Corrosion Technol.,* **6,** 325, Nov. 1959.

29. Carter, R. M. Coatings for crude oil tank bottoms. *Corrosion,* **13,** No. 4, 270t–6t, Apr. 1957.

30. Putilova, I. N., Gindin, L. G., Artamonova, E. V., and Kazakova, V. A. Corrosion of steels by kerosine and methods of its inhibition. *J. Appl. Chem. U.S.S.R.,* **26,** 127–32, 1953.

31. Putilova, I. N., Gindin, L. G., Artamonova, E. V., and Kazakova, V. A. Corrosion of steels by kerosine and methods of its inhibition. *J. Appl. Chem. U.S.S.R.,* **26,** 148–54, 1953.

32. Putilova, I. N., Gindin, L. G., and Artamonova, E. V. Corrosion of metals by saturated (hydrocarbon) fuel. *Doklady Akad. Nauk. S.S.S.R.,* **94,** No. 3, 489–92, Jan. 21, 1954.

33. Krotov, I. V., and Klubova, V. V. Corrosion of iron in contact with aqueous solutions containing sodium nitrate and a liquid fuel. *J. Appl. Chem. U.S.S.R.,* **27,** 201–6, 1954.

34. Arunov, R. I., and Barannik, V. P. Corrosion inhibitor. U.S.S.R. 120, 277, May 4, 1959.

35. Wisherd, G. T. Prevention of corrosion by wet gasoline. U.S. 2,739,050, Mar. 20, 1956.

36. Faust, H. W. Corrosion inhibition of petroleum compositions. Brit. 790,231, Feb. 5, 1958.

37. Boies, D. B., and Nordsell, T. A. Noncorrosive petroleum distillates. U.S. 2,904,415, Sept. 15, 1959.

38. Beiswanger, J. P. G., and Burnard, J. W. Synergistic corrosion-inhibiting compositions for gasoline. U.S. 2,883,277, Apr. 21, 1959.

39. O'Kelley, A. A., and Weltman, C. A. Corrosion inhibitors for petroleum solvents and fuels. U.S. 2,861,874, Nov. 25, 1958.

40. Rocchini, A. G. Corrosion inhibitors from monoamides of dimerized fatty acids. U.S. 2,718,503, Sept. 20, 1955.

41. Martin, E. C., and Titsworth, A. R. Rust inhibitor for gasoline. U.S. 2,919,979, Jan. 5, 1960.

42. Spivack, J. D., and Gardner, W. M. Rust-preventive properties of N-acyl amino acids in petroleum oil. *Am. Chem. Soc., Div. Petroleum Chem., General Papers No. 33,* 365–70, 1955.

43. Spivack, J. D., and Kroll, H. Rust-preventive lubricating compositions containing amidocarboxylic acids. U.S. 2,790,778, Apr. 30, 1957.

44. Halter, R. E., and McGrath, J. J. Corrosion inhibitor for gasoline. U.S. 2,908,711, Oct. 13, 1959.

45. O'Kelley, A. A., Titsworth, H. R., and Martin, E. C. Corrosion inhibitors for hydrocarbon fuels. U.S. 2,907,646, Oct. 6, 1959.

46. Pfohl, F. W., and Gregory, V. P. Corrosion inhibitors. U.S. 2,736,658, Feb. 28, 1956.

47. Sato, S. J. Rust inhibitors. I. *Oil Chemists' Soc. Japan,* **3,** 149–54, 1954.

48. Chenicek, J. A. Corrosion inhibitor for petroleum products. U.S. 2,848,414, Aug. 19, 1958.

49. Gulf Oil Corp. Alkylammonium dialkyl phosphates as corrosion inhibitors. Brit. 791,187, Feb. 26, 1958.

50. Thompson, R. B. Corrosion inhibitors. U.S. 2,857,333, Oct. 21, 1958.

51. Cantrell, T. L., and Peters, J. G. Anticorrosion compositions, and mineral oil compositions containing the same. U.S. 2,934,500, Apr. 26, 1960.

52. Rudel, H. W., and Gargisa, M. Rust-inhibited petroleum products. U.S. 2,791,495, May 7, 1957.

53. King, R. G., and Thielcke, G. W. Dinonylnaphthalenesulfonates. Brit. 812,131, Apr. 22, 1959.

54. Varvel, C. W. Corrosion inhibitor for petroleum products. U.S. 2,845,393, July 29, 1958.

55. Noel, B. Corrosion inhibitors for ferrous metals. Fr. 1,157,555, May 30, 1958.

56. Fontana, B. J. Corrosion-inhibited gasoline. U.S. 2,936,224, May 10, 1960.

57. Rudel, H. W., and Gargisa, M. Rust inhibitors for hydrocarbon oils. U.S. 2,718,500, Sept. 29, 1955.

58. Mayhew, R. L., Copes, J. P., and Williams, E. P. Prevention of rust. U.S. 2,898,301, Aug. 4, 1959.

59. Thompson, R. B. Distillation and storage equipment in refineries. U.S. 2,920,030, Jan. 5, 1960.

60. Kelly, P. B. Corrosion inhibitors for hydrocarbons. U.S. 2,894,828, July 14, 1959.

61. Mayhew, R. L., and Jelinek, C. F. Oil-soluble corrosion inhibitors and surface-active agents. U.S. 2,835,635, May 20, 1958.

62. Schiermeier, K. F., and Poitz, H. A. Rust-inhibiting composition. U.S. 2,661,296, Dec. 1, 1953.

63. Barauch, M. R., and Fontana, B. J. Rust inhibitors for motor fuels. U.S. 2,929,696, Mar. 22, 1960.

64. Kleinholz, M. P. Rust preventive. U.S. 2,667,408, Jan. 26, 1954.

65. Preston, R. G. Gasoline additives. Brit. 812,938, May 6, 1959.

66. Pines, R. M., and Spivack, J. D. Nonyl phenoxyacetic acid effective inhibitor for both aqueous and nonaqueous systems. *Corrosion,* **16,** No. 1, 16, 18–9, 1960.

67. Brown, J. R. Corrosion-inhibiting soluble plug for pipelines. U.S. 2,744,880, May 8, 1956.

68. Oosterhout, J. C. D. Prevention of rust in pipelines and tankers with ester-type wax oxidates. U.S. 2,862,802, Dec. 2, 1958.

69. Hughes, W. B., and Lembcke, R. E. Corrosion inhibitor for natural-gas lines. U.S. 2,706,714, Apr. 19, 1955.

70. Geoffray, C., and Giampaoli, A. Corrosion inhibitors in the natural gas and pipeline industry. *Metano (Padual),* **14,** 327–47, 1960.

71. Rogers, L. M. Corrosion inhibitors for ferrous metals in sea water. U.S. 2,910,438, Aug. 25, 1959.

72. Pier, S. M. Oil-tanker water ballast. U.S. 2,892,860, June 30, 1959.

73. Westlund, R. A., Jr., and Rudel, H. W. Rust preventive suitable for floating on water. U.S. 2,892,724, June 30, 1959.

74. Lanteri, A. C. Corrosion prevention. U.S. 2,785,089, Mar. 12, 1957.

75. Keating, P. J., Jr., and Heisig, T. C. Composition for preventing the corrosion of metals. U.S. 2,785,078, Mar. 12, 1957.

76. Treseder, R. S. Cleaning and inhibiting corrosion of metal tanks of ships. U.S. 2,653,882, Sept. 29, 1953.

77. Fleishhacker, A. H. Inhibiting corrosion in tankers. U.S. 2,845,328, July 29, 1958.

78. Antropov, L. I. Simultaneous action of organic inhibitors and cathodic polarization on the corrosion of iron. *J. Sci. Ind. Research (India)* **18B,** 314–9, 1959.

INDEX OF AUTHORS

A

Abd El Wahed, A. M., 102
Abramo, F., 150
Adams, M. E., 232
Agnew, R. J., 128, 136
Akahane, M., 47
Akers, J. R., 84, 85, 117, 118, 119
Akimov, G. V., 29, 52
Akolzin, P. A., 28, 50, 52, 53, 60
Alderman, E. N., Jr., 243
Alekperova, R. Y., 189
Alekseev, V. M., 270
Amstutz, R. W., 224, 225, 238, 242, 243, 246
Anchev, K., 46
Andersen, D. L., 200
Andres, R. F., 26, 37, 53
Andrews, H. W., 179
Andrews, W. L., 22
Antinori, E., 140
Antropov, L. I., 204, 207
Apel'tsin, I. E., 101
Aramaki, K., 206, 207
Archibald, F. L., 37
Artamonova, E. V., 291
Arthurs, J., 19, 38
Arunov, R. I., 270, 299
Ashcroft, W. K., 56
Atkins, G. R., 94

B

Babakov, A. A., 28
Babitskaya, S. M., 28
Backensto, E. B., 253, 261
Bacon, H. E., 94
Bailey, K. C., 196
Baker, H. R., 209, 211
Balayan, A., 189, 191
Balezin, S. A., 56, 145, 149, 190, 192
Banfi, G., 150
Banta, N. S., 273
Barannik, V. P., 145, 149, 299
Barauch, M. R., 302
Bardwell, R. C., 140
Barker, R. C., 151
Barrett, J. P., 176, 212, 286
Barton, J. K., 239
Barton, K., 245
Bartonicek, R., 208
Bass, D., 177, 240
Beck, A. F., 97
Beck, J. U., 239
Beecher, J. S., 105, 161, 162
Beerstecher, E., Jr., 224, 233
Beiswanger, J. P. G., 301
Bell, W. E., 238
Bennett, H., 252, 259
Benton, M., 127
Berk, A. A., 50

Bernard, G. G., 224, 228, 229, 237
Bertness, T. A., 176, 213
Best, G. A., 148, 151, 166, 167
Betz, L. D., 76, 77, 78, 89, 90, 91
Betz, W. H., 76, 77, 78, 89, 90, 91
Biehl, J. A., 176, 271
Bigelow, W. C., 59, 207
Bilhartz, H. L., 176
Binger, W. W., 85
Bird, P. G., 48, 110, 111
Bishop, C. A., 112
Blackwood, A. K., 127, 131
Blair, C. M., Jr., 176, 179, 205
Blaisdell, F. W., 144
Blohm, C. L., 253
Boelke, M., 47
Bogachev, I. N., 133
Bogatyreva, E. V., 149
Boies, D. B., 113, 131, 136, 137, 142, 143, 146, 153, 188, 300
Bombara, G., 154
Bonner, W. A., 263, 275
Bootzin, D., 211
Bradley, B. W., 176, 179, 265, 274
Brandel, A. J., 109
Brasher, D. M., 97, 148, 151
Bregman, J. I., 74, 82, 111, 113, 131, 136, 137, 142, 143, 147, 153, 176, 206, 255
Breston, J. N., 59, 106, 107, 205, 240, 245
Bret, Z., 32
Brindisi, P., 19
Brinker, W. N., 154
Brinkmann, G., 39
Brock, P. C., 215
Brooke, J. M., 111
Brooke, M., 19, 46, 50, 53, 71, 77, 92, 94, 253
Brooks, D. B., 128
Brown, C. F., 239
Brown, F., 102
Brown, J. K., 55, 60
Brown, J. R., 303
Bruns, F. J., 261, 262
Bryant, A. R., 92
Buehrer, T. F., 44
Bukowiecki, A., 150
Bulow, C. L., 142
Burghart, L. M., 152
Burmeister, H., 210
Burnard, J. W., 301

Burnham, H. D., 263, 275
Burns, L., 204
Butter, G. N., 202

C

Caldwell, J. A., 176, 177, 178, 212, 214, 232
Calise, V. J., 19
Campbell, H. S., 163
Cannon, D. R., 58
Cantrell, T. L., 301
Carbonnel, 160
Carter, R. M., 290
Cartledge, G. H., 107, 108
Case, E. N., 199
Case, L. C., 183, 229
Cavallaro, L., 115, 176, 252
Cessna, J. C., 142
Chambers, C. W., 92
Chambers, L. A., 92
Chandler, W. B., 150
Channabasappa, K., 86
Chapel, E. L., 196
Chen, N. G., 167
Chenicek, J. A., 203, 277, 301
Chesnel, J., 202
Chiddix, M. E., 203
Chittum, J. F., 88
Ciuffreda, A. R., 264
Clarke, F. E., 22, 23, 24, 30, 50
Clements, F. H., 176
Cogbill, A. F., 229
Cohen, M., 97, 102, 105, 107, 145, 161
Colbeck, E. W., 142, 147
Collins, H. H., 128, 136
Collins, L. F., 33, 34
Comeaux, R. F., 92, 93
Connors, J. S., 252, 274
Conradi, J. J., 275
Cook, C. H., 71
Cook, E. I., 205
Copes, J. P., 302
Copson, H. R., 131, 134
Core, C. D., 195
Coy, A. J., 287
Crane, L. S., 139
Crewdsen, E., 133
Cropper, W. V., 168
Cross, J. M., 92, 242

Crossett, J. W., 127
Curry, W. J., 286
Cutlip, E. R., 150

D

Daino, P., 252
Dalbke, R. G., 71
Daniel, S. G., 206
Darrin, M., 98, 99, 138, 140, 166, 167
Daugherty, M. W., 147
Davenport, W. H., 157
Davie, F. E., 196
Davy, P. S., 154, 157, 163
De, C. P., 97
DeChellis, I. V., 279
Decker, J. M., 37
Deering, R. G., 286
Deev, I. T., 23, 38
DeHalas, D. R., 83, 163
Dempster, A. T., 154, 156
Denman, W. L., 47, 48, 59, 60, 61
Derungs, W. A., 259, 260, 269
Deuber, C. G., 232
Devereux, T. L., 109
Dickenson, N. L., 39, 40
Dillon, C. P., 287, 305
Dix, E. H., 29
Dixon, T. W., 152
Dodson, R. E., 154, 160, 164
Dolph, A. A. H., 212
Dornbush, A. C., 241
Doscher, T. M., 224, 242
Dougherty, P. F., 274
Drane, C. W., 71, 88
Dravnieks, A., 254, 258, 266, 273
Drew, R. D., 253, 261, 262
Duff, J. H., 19
Duffer, E. F., 106
Dunne, N. R., 265, 274
Dunning, H. N., 216
Dwyer, J. J., 140

E

Eakin, J. L., 216
Earlougher, R. C., 195, 224, 238
Easton, C. L., 252, 254, 255, 273
Eberman, J. W., 107

Eckenfelder, W. W., Jr., 265
Edeleanu, C., 30
Edwards, J. D., 118
Effinger, R. T., 264, 275
Ehmke, E. F., 253, 264, 275
Eisenstein, H. L., 259
Eisenstecken, F., 19
Eisler, S. L., 208, 211
Eldredge, G. G., 140, 142, 147
Eliassen, R., 103, 104, 153, 162
Elliott, D. J., 213
Elliott, E., 61
Engell, H. J., 24
Erwall, L. G., 97, 108
Evans, U. R., 19, 37, 49, 50, 52, 71, 94,
  97, 102, 105, 140, 141, 142, 147, 149,
  150, 161, 163, 235

F

Faerman, L. I., 270
Fairweather, H. G. C., 244
Fariss, R. E., 192, 243
Farrer, T. W., 232
Faust, H. W., 300
Felgar, D. N., 39, 40
Felsenthal, M., 224, 237, 240
Ferri, A., 142
Fierce, W. L., 272
Fincher, D. R., 214
Fisch, K. R., 210
Fischer, H. C., 159
Fiser, W. O., 152
Fisher, P. W., 203, 209
Fiske, C., 274
Fiss, E. C., 39, 41
Fittinger, H., 132
Fitzpatrick, L. W., 19, 24, 44, 45, 46, 71,
  90
Flamand, R. J., 87
Fleishhacker, A. H., 307
Fontana, B. J., 302
Forbes, M. C., 71, 110
Francis, H., 27, 31
Freedman, A. J., 254, 258, 273
Frisius, E. N., 196
Fritts, H. W., 85
Fry, D. J., 151
Fujii, S., 200, 206, 207, 208, 277
Furth, M. A., 253

G

Gambill, M., 88
Gant, P. L., 211
Gardner, G. S., 276
Gardner, W. M., 301
Gargisa, M., 301, 302
Garner, B. L., 202
Garner, F. H., 252
Gaucher, E., 152
Gaughan, P. J., 61, 108
Geiman, M. A., 224
Geoffray, C., 286, 304
George, C., 108, 110, 111
Gerard, W. F., 46
Gerischer, H., 97
Gerke, F. K., 24
Giampaoli, A., 286, 304
Gianni, F., 154
Gibson, J. W., 71
Gilbert, P. T., 163
Gindin, L. G., 291
Glikman, L. A., 133
Glushenko, V. V., 36
Godfrey, D. J., 127
Gossom, J., 71
Grabowski, H. A., 37, 38
Gray, J. A., 46
Green, J., 22, 44, 146, 203
Greenwell, H. E., 176, 181, 182, 183, 214
Gregory, V. P., 199, 240, 301
Grobner, P., 32
Groninger, C. R., 240
Gross, W. F., 179
Grubitsch, H., 154, 159
Guest, R. M., 154, 159
Gunderson, L. O., 199
Guttenplan, J. D., 147

H

Haase, L. W., 94, 154
Hackerman, N., 58, 193, 204, 205
Haddon, S. E., 163
Haering, D. W., 106
Hafsten, R. J., 268, 269, 270
Haines, G. A., 176
Hale, A. R., 252
Hall, R. E., 27, 28, 47, 52
Halter, R. E., 301

Hamer, P., 19, 50, 52, 142, 147
Hancock, I. P., 144
Hancock, J. S., 141
Hanlon, R. T., 24, 56, 57
Hanson, M. A., 127, 129, 131, 138, 142
Harbert, L. C., 130
Harper, G. M., 179
Harrison, A., 211
Harshman, R. S., 39
Hartmann, H., 39, 40
Hass, E., 32
Hatch, G. B., 42, 43, 44, 75, 87, 101, 102, 103, 115, 118, 139
Haygood, A. J., 84, 117
Hecht, F., 29, 52, 53, 228
Heck, E. T., 239
Heisig, T. C., 306
Helwig, J. D., 71
Henderson, E. L., 33
Heron, P. N., 56
Hertel, O., 203
Hess, W. A., 99, 109
Higgins, R. I., 128, 136
Hijikata, H., 252
Hill, G. R., 158
Hill, P. W., 196
Hinst, H. F., 19
Hitzman, D. O., 242
Hoar, T. P., 97, 144
Hodgson, K. V., 287
Hold, P. Z., 131
Holmes, J. A., 47
Homig, H. E., 37, 38
Hong, V., 211
Hoover, C. O., 269
Hopkins, R. D., 22, 23, 24
Howard, F. L., 128
Howell, R. H., 150
Howells, E., 23
Hoyt, W. B., 261, 262
Huckleberry, S. A., 215
Hughes, W. B., 199, 200, 201, 202, 203, 204
Hulbert, C. C., 255
Hume, J. S., 286, 290
Hur, J. J., 271
Hurd, R. M., 192
Hurlen, T., 287
Hurst, E. H., 83, 92, 93, 95
Hutchison, C. B., 241
Hutchison, M., 166

Hutlin, C., 58, 59
Hwa, C. M., 60, 61

I

Illi, O., 154, 159
Indelli, A., 115
Iofa, Z. A., 58
Ishida, H., 208
Ismailov, A. G., 167
Ison, H. S. K., 148, 151
Ivancic, R. E., 152

J

Jacklin, C., 46, 55, 56
Jacoby, A. L., 48, 139
Jelinek, C. F., 302
Johnson, C. E., 47, 48, 279
Johnson, J. O., 71
Jolly, S. E., 199
Jones, A. W., 140, 142
Jones, C. H., 224, 226, 243
Jones, D. T., 245
Jones, E. H., 195
Jones, L. W., 199, 212, 213
Jorss, R., 47
Joyner, J. A., 128
Jupp, W. B., 287, 289, 295
Jursich, M. J., 47

K

Kabler, P. W., 92
Kadner, R., 47
Kagan, D., 19, 50, 52, 53
Kahler, H. L., 47, 55, 60, 89, 108, 109, 110, 111, 112
Kalish, P. J., 210
Kaputskaysa, V. A., 152
Karagounis, G., 211
Karasik, N. Y., 23
Karepina, M., 287
Kato, Y., 60
Kaufman, C. E., 27
Kazakova, V. A., 291
Keating, P. J., Jr., 306
Keller, F., 118
Keller, H. F., Jr., 203, 238
Kelly, P. B., 302
Kemkbadze, V. S., 192

Kempf, L. W., 147
Kendall, J. D., 151
Kennedy, E. F., 71
Kerst, H., 199
King, R. G., 302
King, R. M., 156
Kingsbury, A. H., 97
Kipps, H. J., 195, 238
Kirkpatrick, W. H., 60, 61
Klas, H., 154, 156
Kleber, J. P., 87
Klein, H. A., 19, 38
Kleinholz, M. P., 302
Kleshcheva, G. V., 56
Klilapova, A. N., 23
Klubova, V. V., 299
Knoedler, E. L., 94
Knutson, C. F., 224, 237, 240
Kobayashi, T., 168
Koehler, J. F., 287, 288, 289, 307
Kofman, L. D., 152
Koger, W. C., 176
Kot, A. A., 25, 47, 50, 52, 53
Kovacs, K., 32
Kraemer, K., 196
Krejci-Graf, K., 228
Kroll, H., 277, 278, 301
Kronig, W., 210
Krotov, I. V., 299
Kuhr, C. A. H. v. W., 154, 232
Kurcheninova, N. K., 28
Kurosawa, A., 47
Kurz, 287, 298, 306
Kuznetsov, S. I., 232
Kuznetsov, V. A., 58
Kwaciszewska, A., 224, 237, 238

L

Laird, A., 19
Laird, R. W., 229
Lamb, J. C., 103, 104, 153
Landis, U. J., 255
Lang, F. S., 253, 266
Lanteri, A. C., 306
LaQue, F. L., 297
Larbre, J. B., 269, 277
Lariviere, F. J., 163
Larson, T. E., 155, 156, 160
LaSusa, C. D., 240
Lauer, B., 58, 59

Laurence, P. S., 105, 161, 162
Lawson, J. V., 272
Lazareva, L. I., 60
Lea, B. A., 151
Leboucher, B., 202, 269, 274, 277
LeClerc, E., 154
Lecornu, A. P., 47, 88
Lee, G. A., 176
Lehrman, L., 104, 105, 106, 161, 162
Leicester, J., 39, 40, 41
Leick, J., 55
Leith, W. C., 134, 146
Lembcke, R. E., 304
Leterle, J. F., 274, 277
Liepina, L., 234
Lindberg, R. I., 199
Lissant, R., 216
Little, A. D., 163
Longtin, B., 29
Lorking, K. F., 150
Love, W. W., 195, 224, 238
Lung, J. D., 224, 237, 240
Luvisi, G. W., 201, 275
Lytle, M. L., 201, 203, 212, 214, 232

M

Maase, R. H., 287
McCabe, J., 265
McCarthy, B. Y., 196
McCloud, D. M., 195, 196
McConomy, H. F., 71
McDonald, H. J., 29
McFaddin, D. E., 182, 253
McGovern, J. J., 34
McGrath, J. J., 301
McGrew, J. W., 166, 167
McKinney, D. S., 34, 106
McNary, T. A., 23
Maguire, J. J., 55, 58, 61, 76, 77, 78, 89, 90, 91, 92
Makrides, A. C., 204
Malcolmson, 287
Malicet, R., 19
Mal'tsera, A. E., 152
Manakhoua, T. K., 189
Manet, A. P., 36
Mann, C., 58, 59
Mann, F. W., 288, 296, 306
Mansa, J. L., 103
Manuel, R. W., 253, 261, 262

Maraboe, E. C., 134
Marsh, G. A., 212, 263
Marsh, J. C., 37
Marshakov, I. K., 110
Martin, A. E., 107
Martin, E. C., 200, 201
Mason, J. F., Jr., 252, 253, 259, 265, 266, 272
Massart, R., 41
Masterson, J. M., 71
Maxcy, W. J., 203
May, T. P., 297
Mayhew, R. L., 302
Mayne, J. E. O., 96, 102, 144
Mears, R. B., 103, 140, 142
Menaul, P. D., 194
Menter, J. W., 102, 144
Mercer, A. D., 97, 148, 151
Merkt, E. E., Jr., 230, 231
Mernitz, P., 274
Merrick, R. D., 287
Meyer, R. H., 286
Michel, J. M., 148
Miller, D., 71
Millidge, A. F., 277
Minford, J. D., 84, 117, 118
Mints, R. I., 133
Missa, L., 41
Mitami, Y., 98
Miyazawa, T., 208
Mondoux, R. G., 56
Moore, K. L., 253, 266
Moore, S. C., 176
Moran, J. J., 252, 259
Morton, B. B., 190
Murdison, A. R., 286
Murphy, F. B., 117
Murray, C. A., 253, 273
Murray, R. G., 83

N

Nagayama, N., 98, 168
Nagel, H., 88
Nakagawa, S., 277
Nathan, C. C., 59, 206, 207, 208, 209, 213
Negreev, V. F., 189, 191
Newberg, A. H., 286
Newell, I. L., 154, 159
Newlin, J., 144
Newman, T. R., 74, 111, 235, 236, 246

Niedenberger, R. B., 30
Nikitina, N. S., 233
Nikol'skii, I. V., 190
Nissen, W., 91
Noel, B., 302
Nole, V. F., 157
Nordsell, T. A., 300
Nowak, T. J., 238
Nowotny, H., 128, 131, 133
Nurse, T. J., 81

O

Oakes, B. D., 107
Obrecht, M. F., 59
Oertel, R., 39
Ogasawara, K., 277
Okamato, G. O., 98
O'Kelley, A. A., 301
Oosterhout, J. C. D., 287, 304, 306
Ondrejcin, J. J., 128, 136
Ongman, H. D., 37, 39
Osipowe, L. I., 59, 60, 61
Osmond, M. E., 34, 61
Oxford, W. F., 88, 107, 199, 276

P

Palen, T., 113
Parham, P. N., 104, 161
Parker, I. M., 286, 287, 292
Parker, M. E., 270
Parkins, R. N., 29, 53
Partridge, E. P., 27, 29, 42, 44, 50, 52, 53
Pasler, W., 228
Patterson, W. S., 140, 142
Patzelt, H., 55, 57, 61
Paulsen, G. C., 71
Pelcak, E. J., 241
Pereda, C., 153
Peters, F. K., 24
Peters, J. G., 301
Pfohl, F. W., 199, 301
Phillips, C., Jr., 253, 261, 262
Phillips, J. H., 30, 53
Picarazzi, J. J., 83
Pickett, S. C., 59, 207
Piehl, R. L., 261, 262
Pier, S. M., 305
Pincus, L. I., 19, 49
Pines, R. M., 245, 302

Pingrey, 287
Pirsh, E. A., 39, 40
Plitz, H. A., 127
Plummer, F. B., 230, 239
Podgornyi, I. G., 28, 53
Poetker, R. H., 215
Poitz, H. A., 277, 302
Pollard, W. R., 272
Potter, E. C., 19, 37
Pourbaix, M., 102
Powell, J. L., 83, 115
Powell, J. P., 224, 237
Powell, L., 142, 147
Powell, S. T., 94
Power, H. H., 230
Powers, R. A., 142
Prange, F. A., 224, 253
Preston, R. G., 302
Prilleux, M., 200, 202, 203
Pringsheims, E. G., 231
Prochinor, 277
Prusick, J. H., 240
Pryor, M. J., 96, 97, 102, 105, 107
Puckorius, P. R., 113, 114
Pullig, T. R., 209
Purcell, T. E., 37, 51
Purins, B., 234
Putilova, I. N., 145, 149, 291

Q

Quimby, W. S., 287, 288, 292, 299, 300, 304, 306

R

Raifsnider, P. J., 209, 236
Raistrick, B., 103
Rama Char, T. L., 111
Ramsay, W., 132
Rassonskaya, I. S., 23
Rath, R., 50
Ratner, A. V., 28, 52
Reif, K., 87, 93
Reitemeier, R. F., 44
Rels, H. Z., 211
Resch, G., 39, 40
Rice, J. K., 71
Rice, O., 42, 43, 44, 75, 87, 101, 102, 104
Richardson, E. G., 133

Richter, H., 37, 38
Ries, W. J., 241
Riesenfeld, F. C., 253
Riggin, D. M., 183, 229
Riggs, O. L., 166, 201, 211, 213, 274, 277
Rippetoe, J. A., 255
Ristaino, A. J., 30, 50
Robb, R. M., 252
Robertson, W. D., 107, 128, 136, 157
Robins, J. A., 19, 38
Robinson, J. B., 224, 226, 244, 247
Robinson, W. W., 91
Rocchini, A. G., 301
Roche, E. A., 148, 151
Roche, M., 88
Roebuck, A. H., 211
Roetheli, B. E., 196
Rogers, L. M., 167, 305
Rogers, W. F., 189, 210
Rohrback, G. H., 88, 195, 196
Romeo, A. J., 153
Rowe, J. A., Jr., 189, 210
Rowe, L. C., 134, 135, 149, 151, 152
Rowland, W. D., 264
Rozenfel'd, I. L., 35, 110, 145
Rudel, H. W., 202, 212, 276, 301, 302 306
Rush, E. H., 286
Rydell, R. G., 245
Ryznar, J. W., 48, 60, 61, 113

S

Samans, C. H., 266, 273
Samilov, Y. F., 24
Samuelson, G. J., 216
Sandner, W. J., 272
Sato, S., 60, 277, 301
Saukaitis, A. J., 276
Sawin, H. J., 230
Scheer, R. D., 150
Schiermeier, K. F., 277, 302
Schillmoller, C. M., 253, 265, 272
Schlapfer, P., 150
Schnake, E. A., 176, 271
Schnarrenberger, W. R., 27
Schoofs, J., 31
Schram, A. F., 204
Schroeder, W. C., 29, 50, 52, 53
Schudlich, H. M., 26, 131
Schwarz, L., 42

Scott, W. R., 195, 196, 202
Seeles, H., 210
Seelmeyer, G., 161
Seitz, W., 212, 276
Seyer, C. L., 252, 274
Shaw, T. J., 238
Sheldahl, D. B., 286
Sherwood, P. W., 254
Shields, H., 114
Shimada, M., 277
Shock, D. A., 176, 184, 186, 213, 214, 288, 296, 306
Shuldener, H. L., 104, 105, 106, 154, 156, 161, 162
Simkhovich, F. M., 152
Simnad, M., 97
Simonoff, R., 119
Singleterry, C. R., 209, 211
Singley, W. J., 30, 53
Sinigo, J., 154, 159
Sjoberg, J. W., 253, 261, 262
Skaperdas, G. T., 33, 34
Skei, T., 263, 275
Skinner, E. N., 252, 259
Skold, R. V., 155, 160
Skrinde, R. T., 153
Slough, J. M., 71, 107
Smart, A. H., 110
Smirnov, O. K., 24
Smith, A. G., 265
Smith, G. H., 237
Smith, R. L., 215
Smith, S. S., 145, 286
Snider, F. M., 210
Snowden, P. P., 30
Solomon, E. M., 209, 211
Sorell, G., 261, 262
Sorg, L. C., 114
Speery, S. M., 55, 56
Speller, F. N., 38, 106, 140
Spivak, J. D., 245, 277, 278, 301, 302
Splittgerber, A., 94, 95
Sproule, L. W., 152
Squires, A. T. P. B., 150
Standing, M. B., 185
Stanisavlievici, L., 52, 53
Stanley, M. E., 287, 306
Stanton, J. P., 176, 180, 183, 184, 187, 190, 191, 215
Stedt, T. P. G., 212
Sterlin, A., 201, 275

Stern, M., 103, 104
Stone, J. D., 215
Stone, W. J., 87, 91, 112
Stones, W. F., 40
Stormont, D. H., 244
Stout, C. M., 243
Stover, E. R., 97, 148
Straub, F. G., 22, 33, 53, 55
Streets, R. E., 128
Streicher, L., 154
Streicker, W., 104, 154, 161, 162
Stromberg, V. L., 200, 203
Stroud, E., 149
Stubblefield, E. M., 168
Stumm, W., 94, 95
Stutz, R. L., 114
Styrikovich, M. A., 26, 32
Sudbury, J. D., 58, 166, 176, 184, 185,
    186, 204, 211, 224, 237, 240, 274, 277,
    288, 296, 306
Sundberg, R. L., 203
Sushkov, B., 287
Sussman, S., 84, 85, 96, 104, 106, 117,
    118, 119
Sverepe, O., 84
Swerdloff, W., 253
Sympson, R. F., 107, 108
Szedaj, Z., 224, 237, 238
Szybalski, W., 103

T

Tait, E. J. M., 252
Tajc, J. A., 29
Takeuchi, K., 104, 111
Talboom, F. P., Jr., 157
Talbot, L. E., 76, 92, 93, 127
Tandy, E. H., 259, 260, 261, 286, 290, 291,
    292
Tanzola, W. A., 110, 112, 115
Tapp, P., 230
Tash, J. A., 19, 38
Tatarinov, B. P., 26
Tebenikhin, Z., 24
Tekht, V. P., 133
Tennyson, T. A., 131
Tester, M. E., 83
Thielcke, G. W., 302
Thompson, A. L., 134, 146
Thompson, P. F., 150
Thompson, R. B., 203, 275, 301, 302

Thompson, W. H., 279
Thornhill, R. S., 94
Thornley, J. L., 71
Titsworth, A. R., 200, 301
Tod, C. W., 104, 161
Toekelt, W. G., 168, 200, 245, 277
Torgeson, D. C., 239
Torman, P., 19
Torrey, P. D., 225, 226
Tourret, J., 252
Trautman, W. H., 27
Treseder, R. S., 209, 306
Triadis, D. N., 103, 104
Truit, J. K., 128, 136
Tseitlin, K. L., 28
Turner, T. H., 19
Tuttle, R. N., 224, 242
Twiss, S. B., 147

U

Uehara, I., 176, 179, 200
Uhl, W. C., 252
Uhlig, H. H., 19, 26, 27, 29, 31, 33, 34,
    38, 52, 53, 56, 57, 81, 103, 104, 147, 166
Ulanovskii, I. B., 233
Ulmer, R. C., 21, 23, 24, 25, 33, 47, 56,
    57, 61
Ulrich, J. A., 19
Updegraff, D. M., 76

V

Van der Vlugt, I. S., 154, 232
Van Wazer, J. R., 100
Varvel, C. W., 302
Verink, E. D., 117
Vernon, W. H., 148, 149
Villar, G. E., 26, 48, 53
Vincent, 160
Vincent-Genod, J., 286

W

Waber, J. T., 29
Wachter, A., 144, 145, 236, 263, 275
Wada, N., 277
Wainerdi, R. E., 242
Walker, C., 82
Walker, J. C., 192
Walling, I. W., 230, 239

Walston, K. R., 268, 269, 270
Warner, J. C., 142, 147
Watkins, F. M., 274, 288
Weir, C. D., 52
Welder, B. Q., 34, 61
Weltman, C. A., 149, 301
Welty, F., 156
Westlund, R. A., Jr., 202, 306
Wheelock, A., 298
Whirl, S. F., 29, 51, 52, 53
White, C. M., 152
White, D. E., 23
Whitefoot, T. B., 19, 38
Whitney, F. L., 114
Whitney, J. H., 47
Wickert, K., 25, 32
Wilcox, M. J., 274
Wilkes, J. F., 59, 131
Williams, A. E., 76, 90
Williams, E. P., 302
Williams, W. L., 30, 51
Willsey, W. B., 37
Winzig, W. J., 71
Wise, R. S., 94, 127
Wisherd, T. G., 210, 299
Wolf, P. A., 241
Wolfson, L. L., 224, 230, 231, 233

Wollerman, E., 47
Wood, J. W., 33, 47, 56, 57, 61, 105, 161, 162
Woodle, R. A., 150
Woods, W. W., 214
Woodward, E. R., 39, 40, 41
Wormwell, F., 81, 148, 151, 232
Wright, C. C., 224, 229, 246
Wukman, A. S., 128

Y

Yoder, D. M., 239
Young, G. W., 34

Z

Zaitseva, Z. I., 60
Zakharochkin, L. D., 252, 258
Zanchi, C., 39
Zapffe, C. A., 29
Zenkevich, Y. V., 23
Zhigalova, K. A., 35
Zimmerman, M., 39
Zisman, W. A., 59, 207
Zobachev, Y. E., 133
Zolotova, E. F., 101